SCHOLASTIC

ALPHA Mathematics

Develops mathematical thinking and problem-solving skills

Practice Book

3

Scholastic ALPHA™ Mathematics is adapted from the Primary Mathematics Project series (3rd Edition), originally developed by the Ministry of Education, Singapore. This edition contains new content developed by Scholastic Education International (Singapore) Private Limited, which is not attributable to the Ministry of Education, Singapore.

First edition 2014
Reprinted 2014 (twice), 2015 (twice), 2016, 2017 (thrice), 2018, 2019, 2020, 2022 (thrice), 2023, 2024, 2025, 2026

ISBN 978-93-5103-030-0

About ALPHA™ Mathematics

Welcome to **Scholastic ALPHA™ Mathematics.**

The programme covers four strands of mathematics across five grades: **Numbers and Operations, Measurement, Geometry** and **Data Analysis.**

Each Practice Book comprises chapters with several **Exercises**. Chapters end with **Problem Solving** exercises.

Exercises provide comprehensive practice for students to attain fluency and mastery of topics.

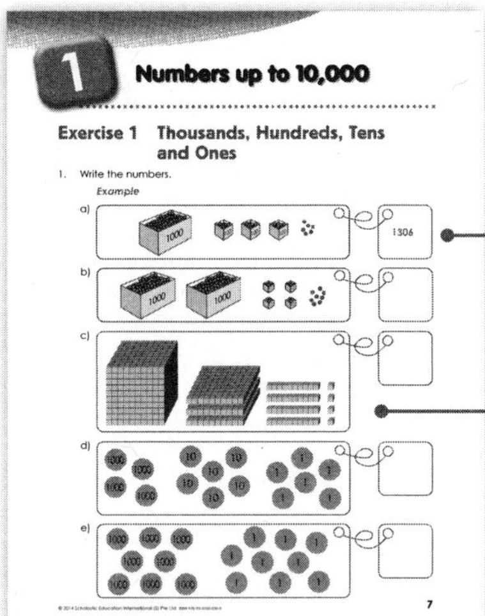

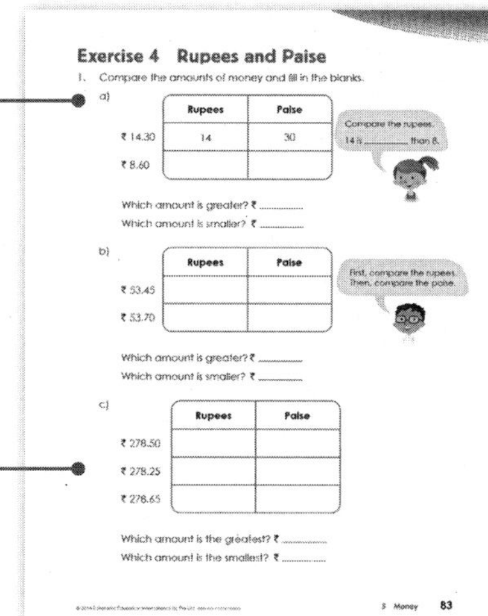

The first task is guided to help students.

Tasks in each exercise are systematically varied to provide comprehensive practice and formative assessment.

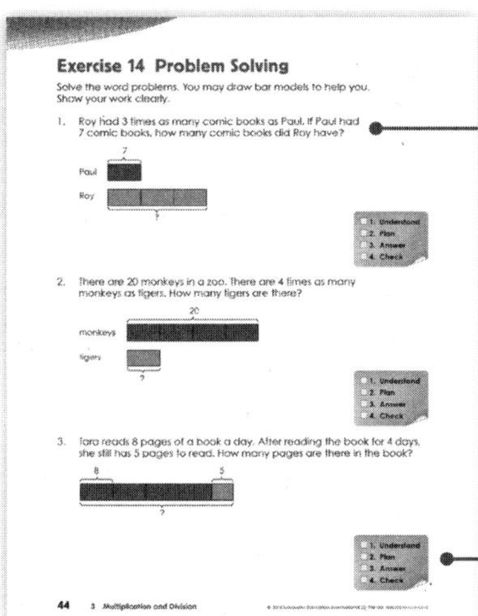

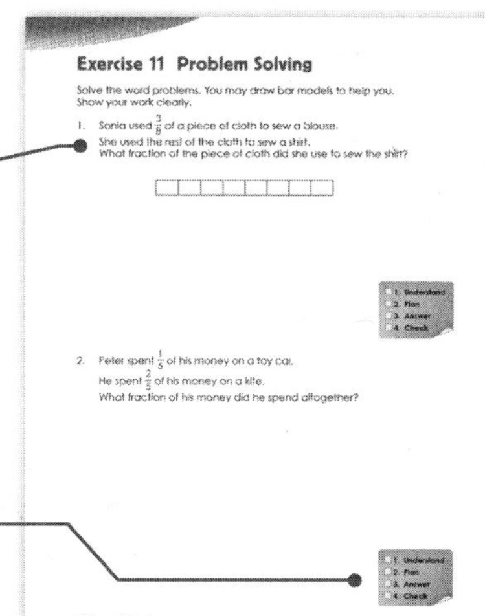

Word problems provide a meaningful context for students to apply mathematical knowledge.

A 4-step process checklist guides students to systematically solve word problems and to apply appropriate problem-solving strategies.

The **Answer Key** lists the correct response to tasks and provides worked solutions to word problems.

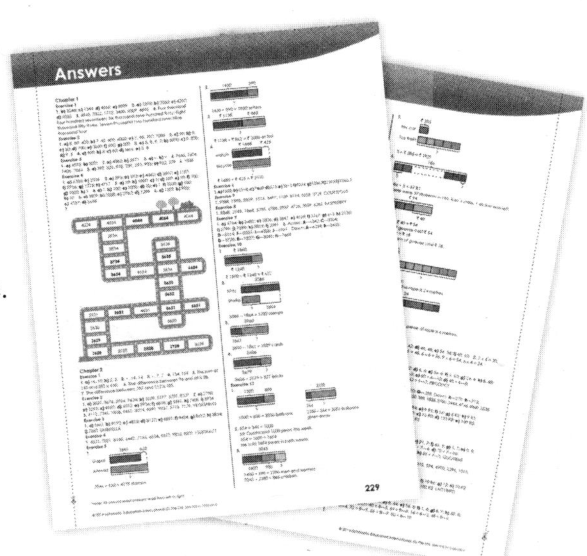

 ISBN 978-93-5103-030-0

Contents

 ISBN 978-93-5103-030-0

 ISBN 978-93-5103-030-0

 ISBN 978-93-5103-030-0

1 Numbers up to 10,000

Exercise 1 Thousands, Hundreds, Tens and Ones

1. Write the numbers.

Example

a)

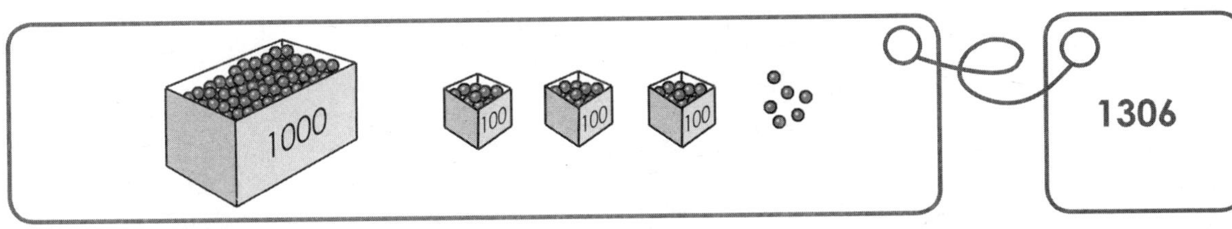

b)

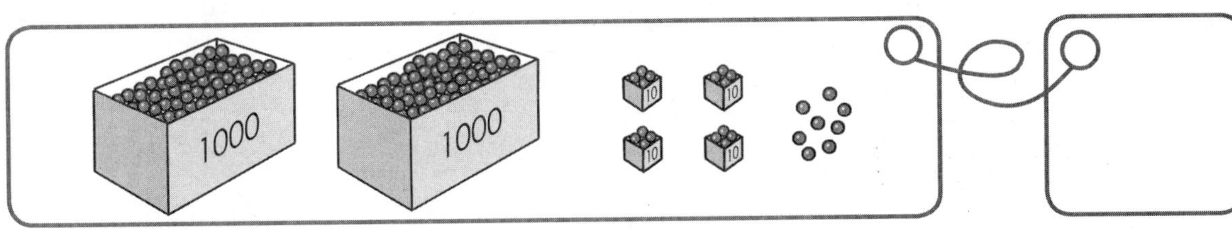

c)

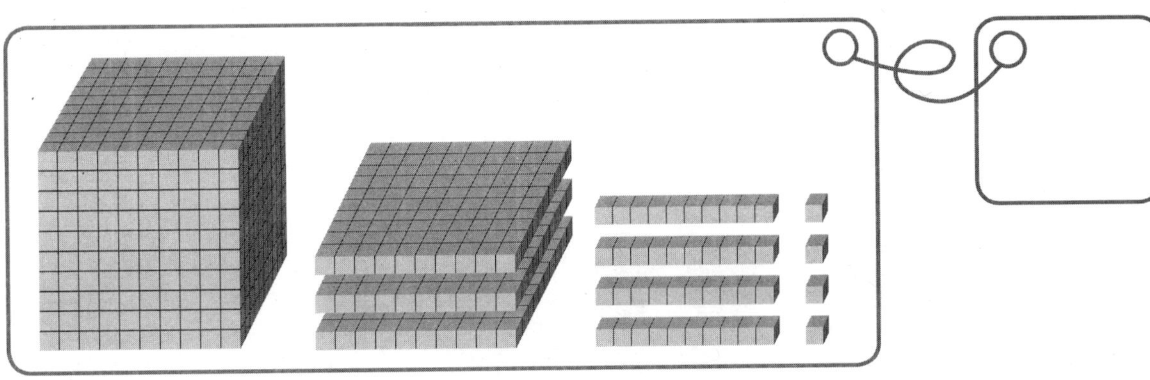

d)

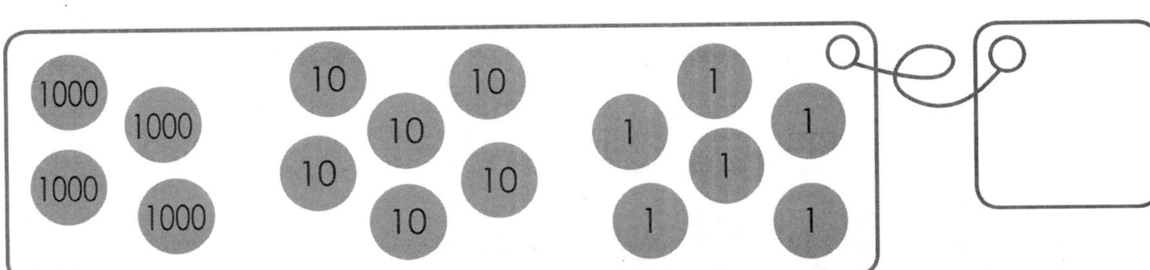

e)

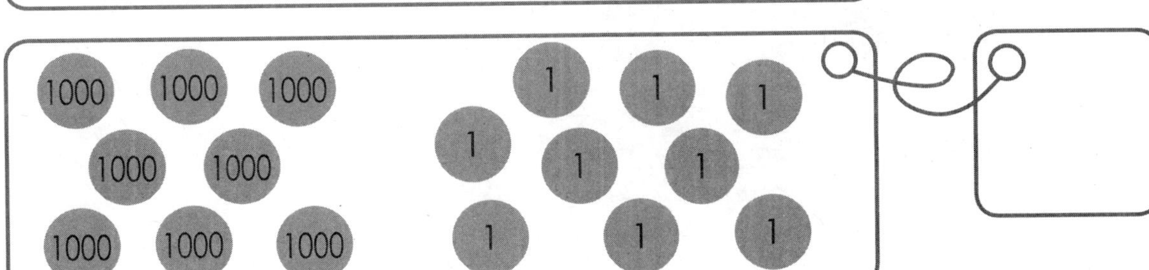

 ISBN 978-93-5103-030-0

2. Write the numbers.

a)

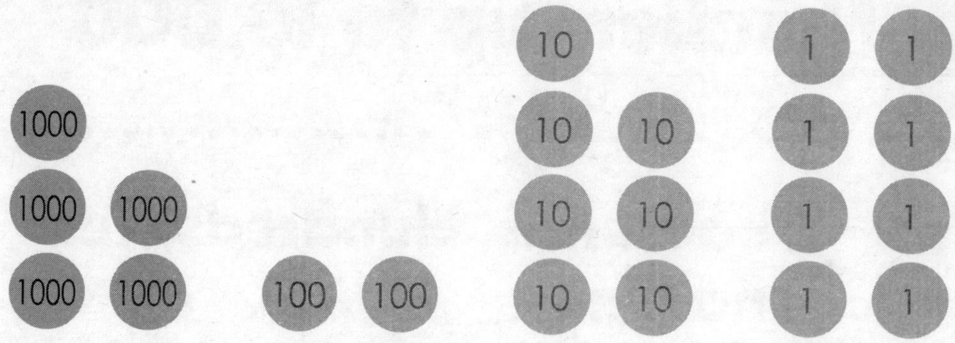

5000 + 200 + 70 + 8 = ________

b)

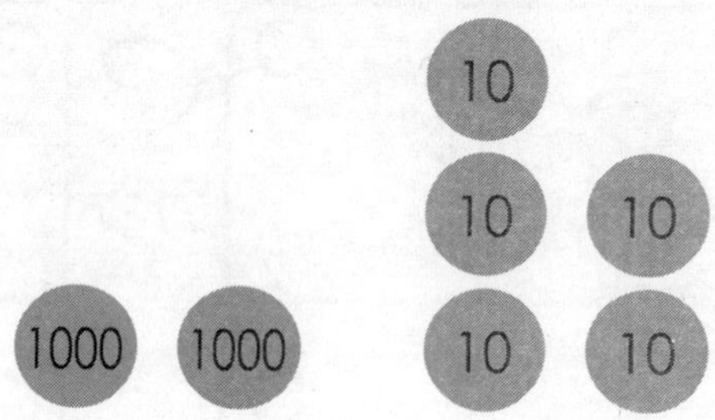

2000 + 50 = ________

c)

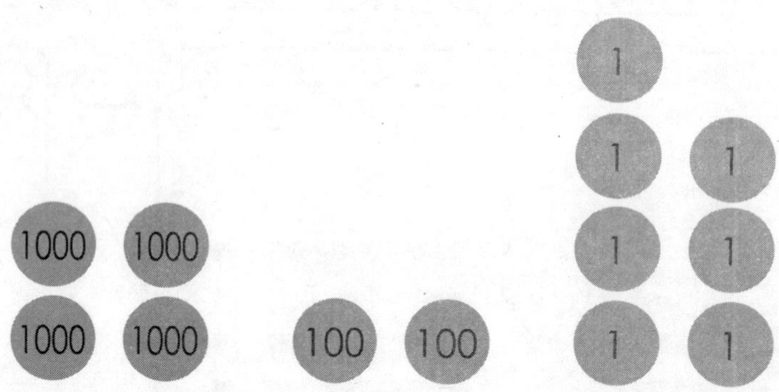

4000 + 200 + 7 = ________

d)

6000 + 30 + 5 = ________

 ISBN 978-93-5103-030-0

3. Write the numbers.

Example

two thousand one hundred fifty-one	**2151**
four thousand five hundred forty-eight	
three thousand three hundred two	
one thousand seven hundred twelve	
three thousand four hundred	
six thousand nine	
four thousand five hundred two	

4. Write the numbers in words.

5417	
6940	
8053	
7209	
9004	

 ISBN 978-93-5103-030-0

Exercise 2 Thousands, Hundreds, Tens and Ones

1. What does each digit stand for?

   a) 2488

   - 8 → ______
   - 8 → ______
   - 4 → ______
   - 2 → **2000**

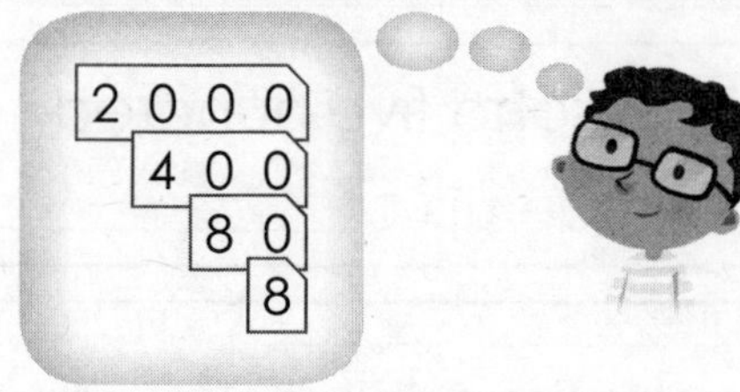

   b) 6447

   - 7 → ______
   - 4 → ______
   - 4 → ______
   - 6 → ______

   c) 7799

   - 9 → ______
   - 9 → ______
   - 7 → ______
   - 7 → ______

2. Write the missing numbers.

   a) 999 = 900 + ______ + 9

   b) 2658 = 2000 + 600 + 50 + ______

   c) 4955 = 4000 + 900 + ______ + 5

   d) 1773 = 1000 + ______ + 70 + 3

   e) 3332 = ______ + 300 + 30 + 2

   f) 5690 = 5000 + ______ + 90

   g) 6206 = 6000 + ______ + 6

 ISBN 978-93-5103-030-0

3. Look at the place value table below and fill in the blanks.

Th	H	T	O
5	8	9	7

a) 5897 is a 4-digit number.

It is made up of ________________ thousands,

________________ hundreds, ________________ tens and

________________ ones.

b) The digit 5 stands for ________________.

c) The digit ________________ is in the hundreds place.

The value of the digit is ________________.

d) The digit in the tens place is ________________ and

the digit in the thousands place is ________________.

4. Fill in the blanks.

a) In 3801, the digit 8 stands for ________________.

b) In 7604, the digit ________________ is in the hundreds place.

c) In 5263, the value of the digit 6 is ________________.

d) In 3507, the digit 0 is in the ________________ place.

e) In 3895, the digit in the ones place is ________________ and

the digit in the hundreds place is ________________.

 ISBN 978-93-5103-030-0

Exercise 3 Thousands, Hundreds, Tens and Ones

1. a) Which is greater, 4037 or 4073? ________

   b) Which is smaller, 5001 or 5010? ________

2. | 3747 | 4082 | 3761 | 3671 |
   |---|---|---|---|

   a) Which is the greatest number? ________

   b) Which is the smallest number? ________

3. Fill in the circles with **>** or **<**.

   a) 7685 ◯ 7865

   b) 5025 ◯ 5031

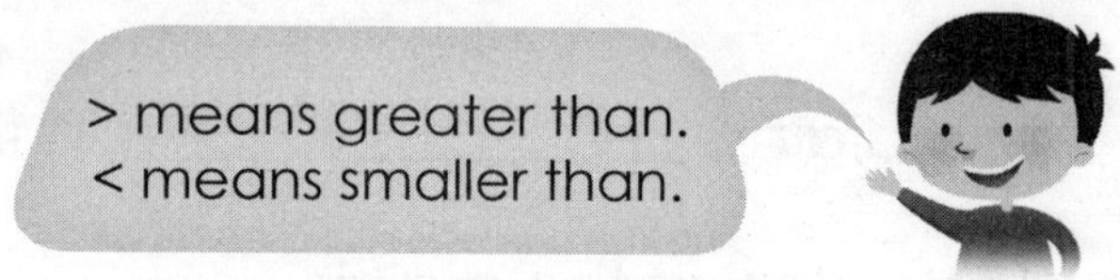

4. Arrange the numbers in order. Begin with the greatest.

   [ ] – [ ] – [ ] – [ ]

   (greatest)

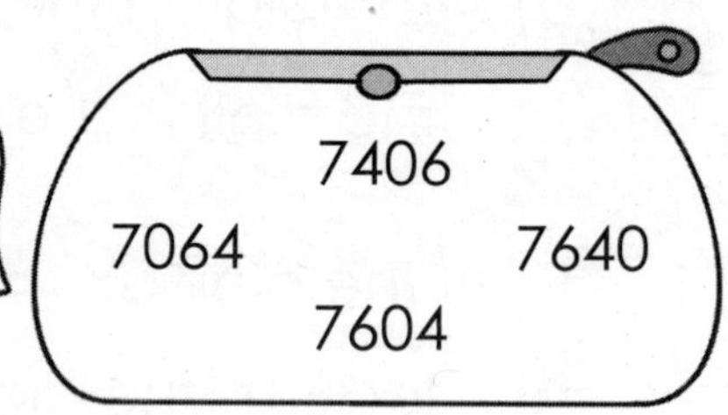

5. a) Use these cards to make different 3-digit numbers. Use each digit only once.

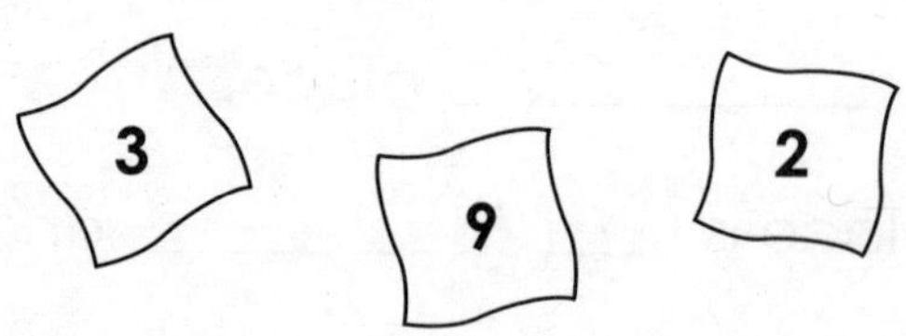

   The 3-digit numbers are:

   b) The greatest number is ________.

   The smallest number is ________.

6. What is the smallest 4-digit number you can make using the digits 1, 0, 3, 8? Use each digit only once. ________________

 ISBN 978-93-5103-030-0

Exercise 4 Number Patterns

1. Look at the place value charts and fill in the blanks.

a) 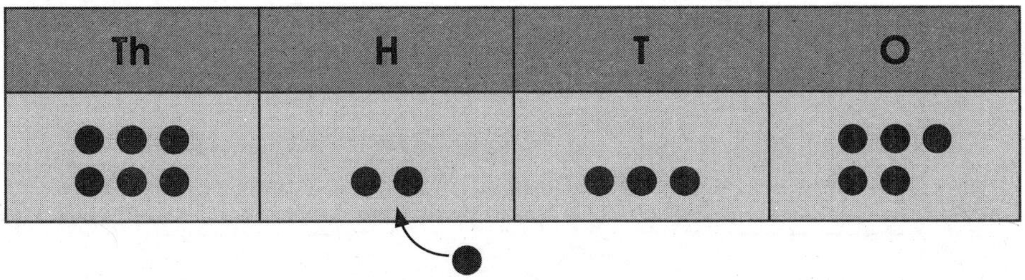

_________ is 100 more than 6235.

b) 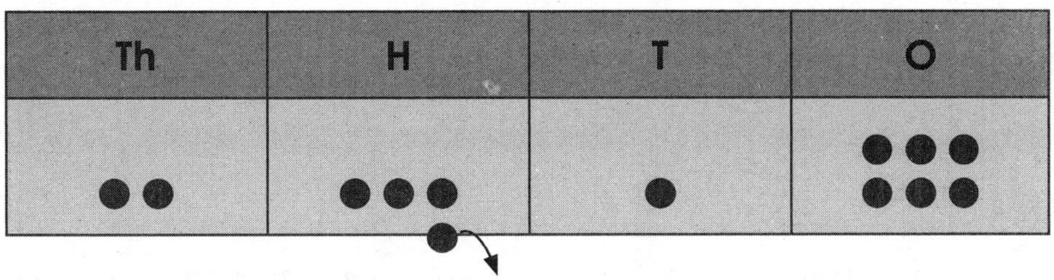

_________ is 100 less than 2416.

2. Fill in the blanks.

a) _________ is 10 more than 385.

b) _________ is 10 less than 600.

c) _________ is 100 more than 3942.

d) _________ is 1000 less than 4507.

e) 1083 + 100 = _________

f) 2316 + 400 = _________

g) 1325 – 100 = _________

h) 4917 – 200 = _________

3. Fill in the blanks.

a) 5409 + _________ = 5419

b) 5409 + _________ = 6409

c) 5409 + _________ = 5410

d) 5409 + _________ = 5509

e) 6998 + _________ = 7008

f) 6998 + _________ = 7098

g) 6998 + _________ = 7998

h) 6998 + _________ = 6999

4. Fill in the blanks.

a) 4864 – _________ = 4863

b) 4864 – _________ = 4764

c) 4864 – _________ = 3864

d) 4864 – _________ = 4854

e) 4050 – _________ = 4049

f) 4050 – _________ = 3050

g) 4050 – _________ = 3950

h) 4050 – _________ = 4040

 ISBN 978-93-5103-030-0

5. Complete the number patterns.

a) 3789, 3799, ________, 3819   b) 4738, 4838, 4938, ________

c) 987, 1987, ________, 3987   d) ________, 1300, 1301, 1302

6. Complete the number patterns.

a) ________, 1301, 1300, 1299   b) 3903, 2903, 1903, ________

c) 4737, 4637, ________, 4437   d) 3708, ________, 3688, 3678

7. Write the missing numbers.

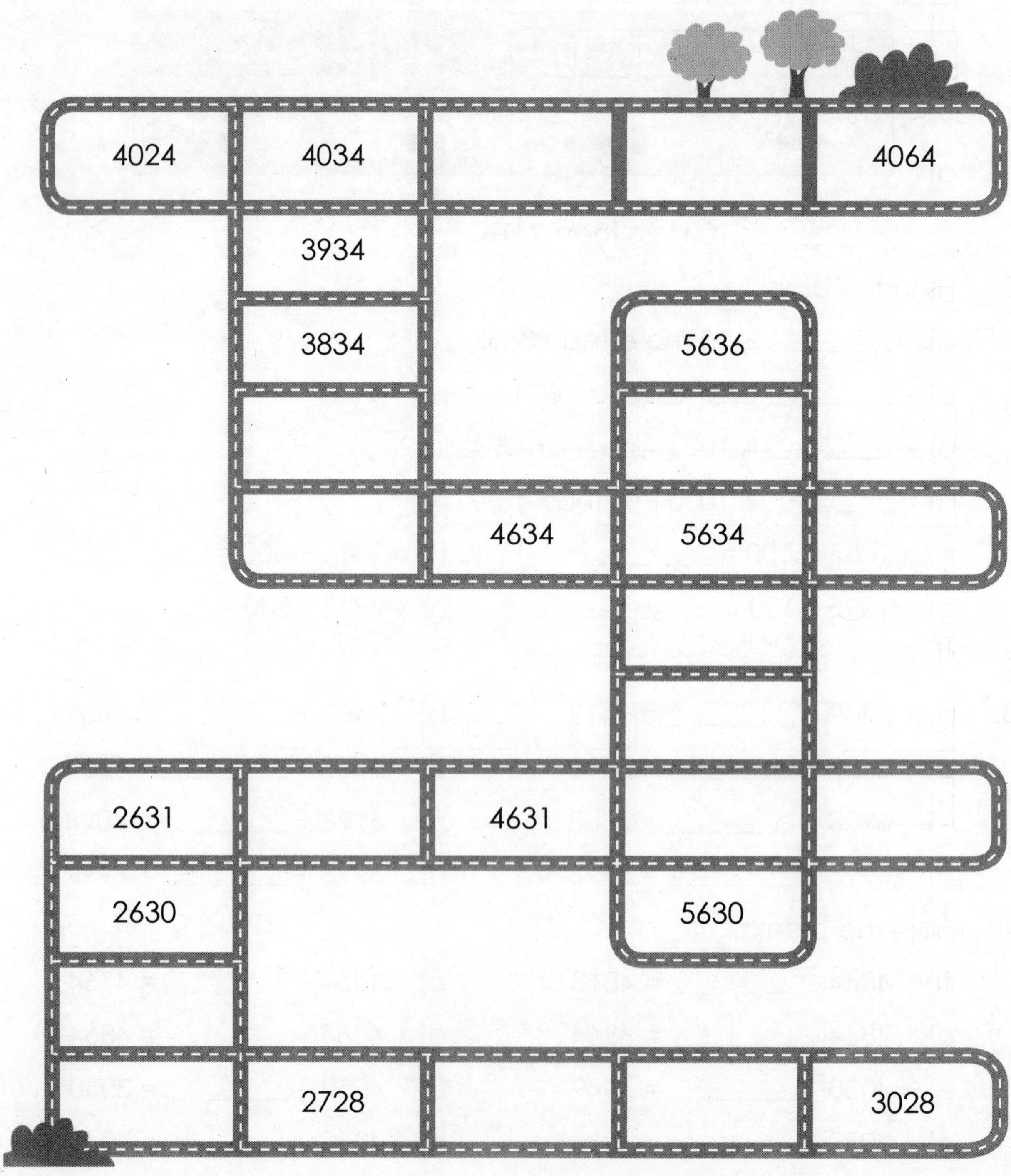

 ISBN 978-93-5103-030-0

2 Addition and Subtraction

Exercise 1 Sum and Difference

1. Fill in the blanks.

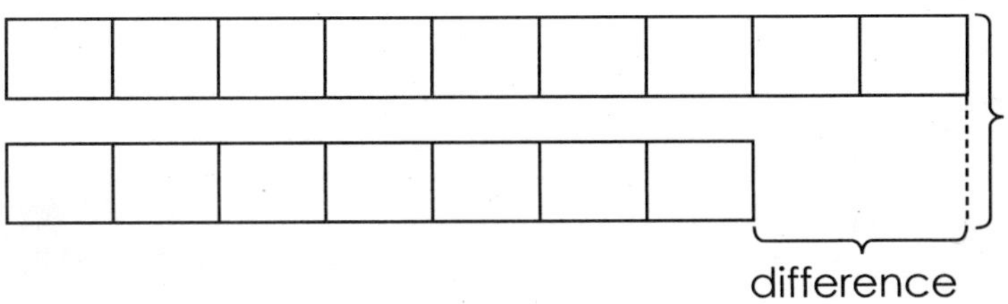

a) 9 + 7 = ________

The sum of 9 and 7 is ________.

b) 9 – 7 = ________

The difference between 9 and 7 is ________.

2. 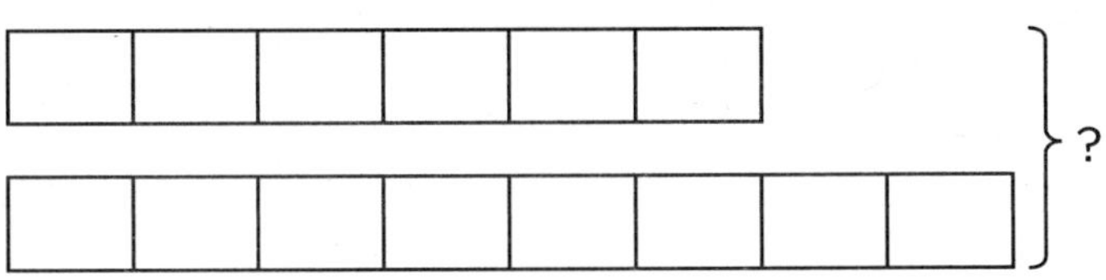

6 ◯ 8 = ________

The sum of 6 and 8 is ________.

3. 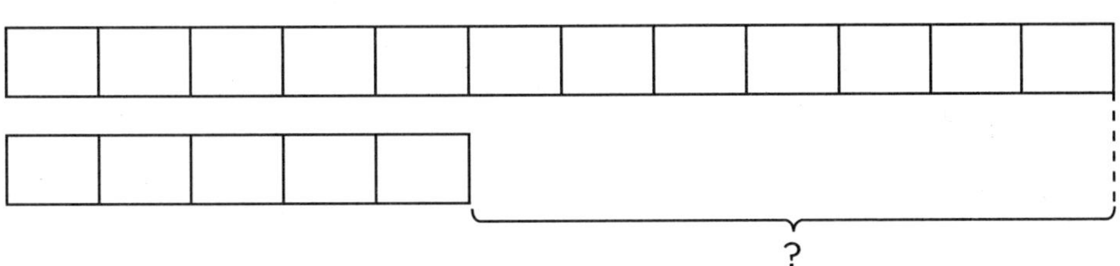

12 ◯ 5 = ________

The difference between 12 and 5 is ________.

 ISBN 978-93-5103-030-0

4. Find the sum of 65 and 89.

65 + 89 = ________

The sum of 65 and 89 is ________.

5. Find the sum of 145 and 285.

6. Find the difference between 96 and 68.

7. Find the difference between 387 and 512.

 ISBN 978-93-5103-030-0

Exercise 2 Adding Ones, Tens, Hundreds and Thousands

1. Add.

a)

3624 + 3 =

3624 + 50 =

3624 + 200 =

3624 + 4000 =

b)

5107 + 2 =

5107 + 70 =

5107 + 600 =

5107 + 3000 =

2. Add.

a) 2480 + 300	b) 5243 + 50	c) 4825 + 140
d) 2370 + 2500	e) 1934 + 4020	f) 6216 + 602
g) 5201 + 390	h) 3402 + 4006	i) 3614 + 5320

 ISBN 978-93-5103-030-0

3. Add.

4 1 0 7 + 5 ______ G	7 2 5 4 + 9 2 ______ V	1 0 8 2 + 7 3 6 ______ E
1 9 0 2 + 4 5 6 3 ______ T	3 0 5 8 + 1 6 ______ A	7 6 2 0 + 6 7 1 ______ L
5 1 0 8 + 4 8 2 9 ______ E	3 4 4 3 + 2 2 7 0 ______ S	6 3 5 5 + 8 2 4 ______ B

What tables do we eat?

Write the letters which match the answers above to find out.

7346	1818	4112	1818	6465	3074	7179	8291	9937	5713

 ISBN 978-93-5103-030-0

Exercise 3 Adding Ones, Tens, Hundreds and Thousands

1. Add.

a) $\begin{array}{r} 2067 \\ +\ 4594 \\ \hline \\ \hline \end{array}$	b) $\begin{array}{r} 2387 \\ +\ 6805 \\ \hline \\ \hline \end{array}$	c) $\begin{array}{r} 3247 \\ +\ 1568 \\ \hline \\ \hline \end{array}$
d) $\begin{array}{r} 2594 \\ +\ 533 \\ \hline \\ \hline \end{array}$	e) $\begin{array}{r} 4396 \\ +\ 2495 \\ \hline \\ \hline \end{array}$	f) $\begin{array}{r} 9076 \\ +\ 348 \\ \hline \\ \hline \end{array}$
g) $\begin{array}{r} 4828 \\ +\ 3864 \\ \hline \\ \hline \end{array}$	h) $\begin{array}{r} 3469 \\ +\ 385 \\ \hline \\ \hline \end{array}$	i) $\begin{array}{r} 1346 \\ +\ 5914 \\ \hline \\ \hline \end{array}$

Join the dots by following the order of the answers above.

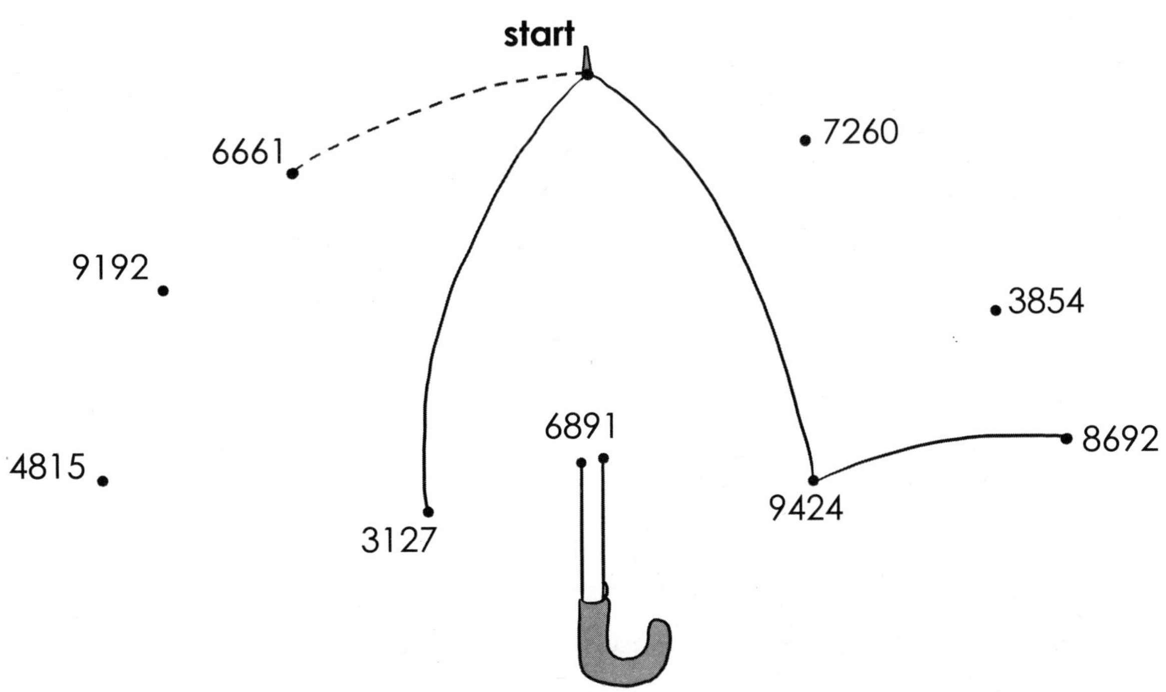

You will get a picture of an ______________.

Exercise 4 Adding Ones, Tens, Hundreds and Thousands

1. Add.

2464 + 1867 = ____ **S**	2935 + 2086 = ____ **R**	3176 + 4984 = ____ **T**
3683 + 2759 = ____ **B**	5297 + 1849 = ____ **I**	3978 + 2576 = ____ **T**
4586 + 3789 = ____ **A**	6935 + 2875 = ____ **U**	5409 + 2892 = ____ **C**

What do you do to find the difference between numbers?

Write the letters which match the answers above to find out.

7146

4331	9810	6442	8160	5021	8375	8301	6554

 ISBN 978-93-5103-030-0

Exercise 5 Adding Ones, Tens, Hundreds and Thousands

Solve the word problems. You may draw bar models to help you.
Show your work clearly.

1. Gopal collected 3546 stamps. Ahmad collected 632 more stamps than Gopal. How many stamps did Ahmad collect?

- [ ] 1. Understand
- [ ] 2. Plan
- [ ] 3. Answer
- [ ] 4. Check

2. After delivering 1430 letters, a postman still had 390 letters to deliver. How many letters were there altogether?

- [ ] 1. Understand
- [ ] 2. Plan
- [ ] 3. Answer
- [ ] 4. Check

3. After paying ₹ 1138 for a pair of shoes, Mr. Singh had ₹ 862 left. How much money did he have at first?

- [ ] 1. Understand
- [ ] 2. Plan
- [ ] 3. Answer
- [ ] 4. Check

4. A watch costs ₹ 1685. It is ₹ 425 cheaper than a bicycle. What is the cost of the bicycle?

- [ ] 1. Understand
- [ ] 2. Plan
- [ ] 3. Answer
- [ ] 4. Check

 ISBN 978-93-5103-030-0

Exercise 6 Subtracting Ones, Tens, Hundreds and Thousands

1. Subtract.

a)	b)	c)
9 3 2 4 – 2	6 5 4 7 – 2 9	7 6 4 7 – 2 4 7
d)	e)	f)
1 5 8 9 – 1 3 1 4	4 1 4 6 – 8 3 3	9 0 4 5 – 8 1 1
g)	h)	i)
5 6 9 1 – 4 5 5	4 3 9 3 – 1 8 0 0	2 7 5 2 – 1 4 9 2

Colour only the boxes which contain the answers.

What letter do you get? ________

2901	8234	1260	6518
313	7400	8324	4993
9084	5236	2593	3313
7800	275	9326	8526
4576	9322	5833	6558

 ISBN 978-93-5103-030-0

Exercise 7 Subtracting Ones, Tens, Hundreds and Thousands

1. Subtract.

(1)
```
  9474
-   86
------
```

(2)
```
  9835
-  246
------
```

(3)
```
  4066
- 1737
------
```

(4)
```
  2435
-  919
------
```

(5)
```
  3962
-  465
------
```

(6)
```
  2412
- 1283
------
```

(7)
```
  9731
- 1537
------
```

(8)
```
  8340
-   82
------
```

(9)
```
  6538
- 2809
------
```

Write the letters that match the answers. You will find the missing word.

C — 9388	E — 1129	R — 1516
U — 2329	S — 3729	O — 9589
T — 3497	O — 8194	U — 8258

ALWAYS BE

(1)	(2)	(3)	(4)	(5)	(6)	(7)	(8)	(9)

 ISBN 978-93-5103-030-0

Exercise 8 Subtracting Ones, Tens, Hundreds and Thousands

1. Subtract.

$\begin{array}{r} 9236 \\ -\ \ 968 \\ \hline \end{array}$ ①	$\begin{array}{r} 3533 \\ -\ \ 584 \\ \hline \end{array}$ ②	$\begin{array}{r} 6145 \\ -4277 \\ \hline \end{array}$ ③
$\begin{array}{r} 8260 \\ -2475 \\ \hline \end{array}$ ④	$\begin{array}{r} 7371 \\ -\ \ 585 \\ \hline \end{array}$ ⑤	$\begin{array}{r} 4216 \\ -1379 \\ \hline \end{array}$ ⑥
$\begin{array}{r} 7152 \\ -2426 \\ \hline \end{array}$ ⑦	$\begin{array}{r} 9542 \\ -5683 \\ \hline \end{array}$ ⑧	$\begin{array}{r} 7230 \\ -\ \ 947 \\ \hline \end{array}$ ⑨

Write the letters that match the answers. You will find the name of a fruit that can be either red, purple, black or yellow in colour.

A — 2949	P — 5785	R — 8268
E — 2837	Y — 6283	R — 4726
B — 6786	S — 1868	R — 3859

①	②	③	④	⑤	⑥	⑦	⑧	⑨

 ISBN 978-93-5103-030-0

Exercise 9 Subtracting Ones, Tens, Hundreds and Thousands

1. Subtract.

a)	b)	c)
5000 − 236 = ____	3000 − 518 = ____	7000 − 1694 = ____
d)	e)	f)
4004 − 157 = ____	6008 − 1379 = ____	9010 − 5243 = ____
g)	h)	i)
1300 − 687 = ____	3400 − 1265 = ____	5700 − 2901 = ____
j)	k)	l)
8054 − 456 = ____	7105 − 3286 = ____	9000 − 6919 = ____

 ISBN 978-93-5103-030-0

2. Subtract and write the answers in the boxes.

Example

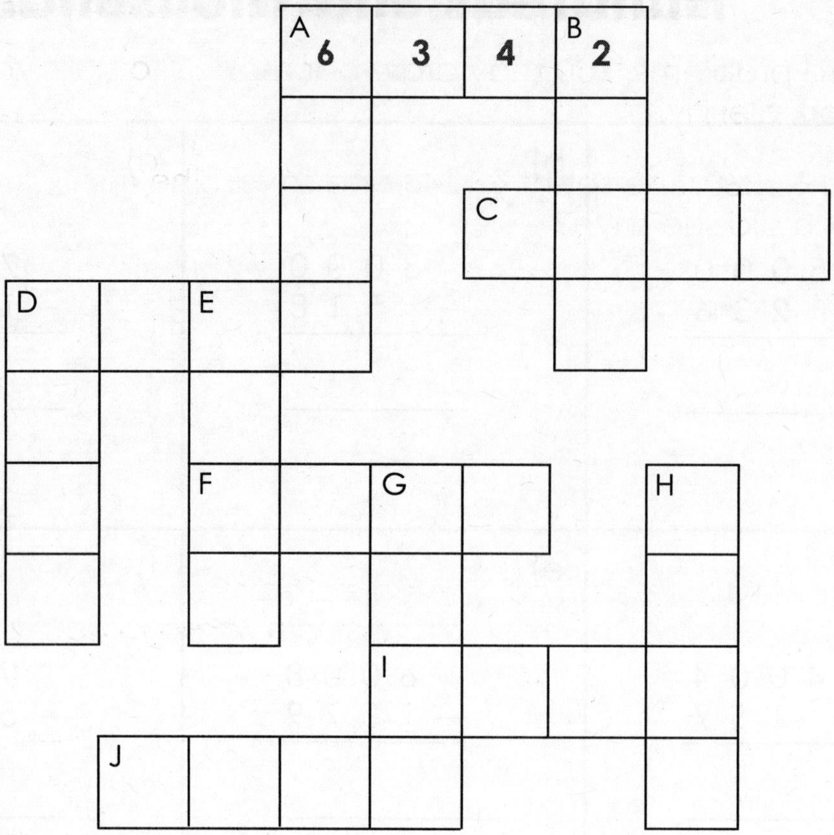

Across	**Down**
A. 9101 – 2759	A. 7032 – 778
C. 8290 – 4986	B. 8070 – 5635
D. 6000 – 486	D. 7968 – 2240
F. 9400 – 6869	E. 4005 – 2678
I. 5102 – 897	G. 7533 – 4492
J. 6400 – 4439	H. 8144 – 485

 ISBN 978-93-5103-030-0

Exercise 10 Subtracting Ones, Tens, Hundreds and Thousands

Solve the word problems. You may draw bar models to help you. Show your work clearly.

1. Amy had ₹ 1860. She spent ₹ 1248 and saved the rest. How much did she save?

- [ ] 1. Understand
- [ ] 2. Plan
- [ ] 3. Answer
- [ ] 4. Check

2. May collected 3586 stamps. She collected 1864 more stamps than Sheila. How many stamps did Sheila collect?

- [ ] 1. Understand
- [ ] 2. Plan
- [ ] 3. Answer
- [ ] 4. Check

3. A bookshop has 3690 cards for sale. 1861 of them are birthday cards. How many are not birthday cards?

- [ ] 1. Understand
- [ ] 2. Plan
- [ ] 3. Answer
- [ ] 4. Check

4. A worker needs 3606 bricks to build a house. He has 2679 bricks now. How many more bricks must he get?

- [ ] 1. Understand
- [ ] 2. Plan
- [ ] 3. Answer
- [ ] 4. Check

 ISBN 978-93-5103-030-0

Exercise 11 Problem Solving

Solve the word problems. You may draw bar models to help you.
Show your work clearly.

1. Atul ordered 1500 red balloons and 850 yellow balloons for a party. Some of the balloons were given away. 264 balloons were left after the party. How many balloons were given away at the party?

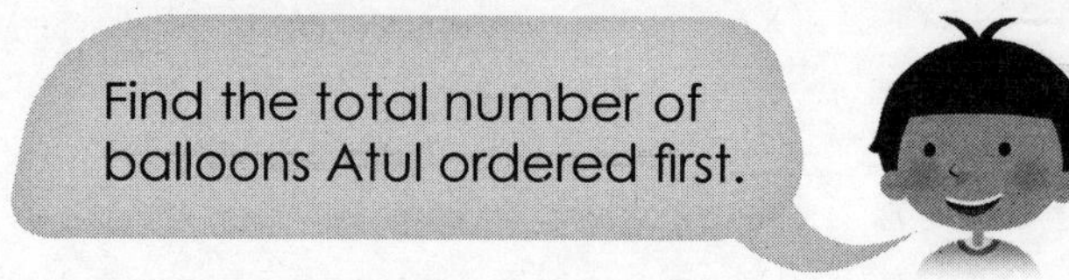

- ☐ 1. Understand
- ☐ 2. Plan
- ☐ 3. Answer
- ☐ 4. Check

2. Mr. Gupta sold 654 pears last week. He sold 346 more pears this week than last week. How many pears were sold in both weeks?

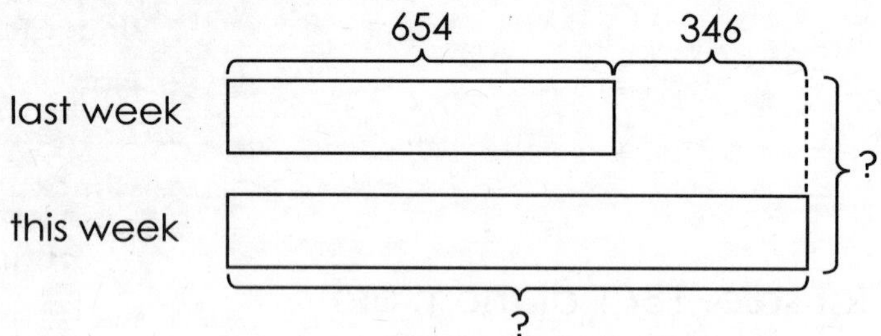

- ☐ 1. Understand
- ☐ 2. Plan
- ☐ 3. Answer
- ☐ 4. Check

3. There were 3245 people at a parade. 1400 of them were men and 980 were women. How many children were there?

- ☐ 1. Understand
- ☐ 2. Plan
- ☐ 3. Answer
- ☐ 4. Check

 ISBN 978-93-5103-030-0

4. Devi saved ₹ 1435. Mala saved ₹ 298 more than Devi. Alice saved ₹ 325 less than Mala. How much did Alice save?

- [ ] 1. Understand
- [ ] 2. Plan
- [ ] 3. Answer
- [ ] 4. Check

5. A factory has 2000 workers. 1340 of them are men. The rest are women. How many more men than women are there?

- [ ] 1. Understand
- [ ] 2. Plan
- [ ] 3. Answer
- [ ] 4. Check

6. The total cost of a shirt and a skirt is ₹ 2030. The shirt costs ₹ 695. Find the difference between the cost of the shirt and the cost of the skirt.

- [ ] 1. Understand
- [ ] 2. Plan
- [ ] 3. Answer
- [ ] 4. Check

 ISBN 978-93-5103-030-0

3 Multiplication and Division

Exercise 1 Multiplying Ones, Tens and Hundreds

1. Fill in the blanks.

a) 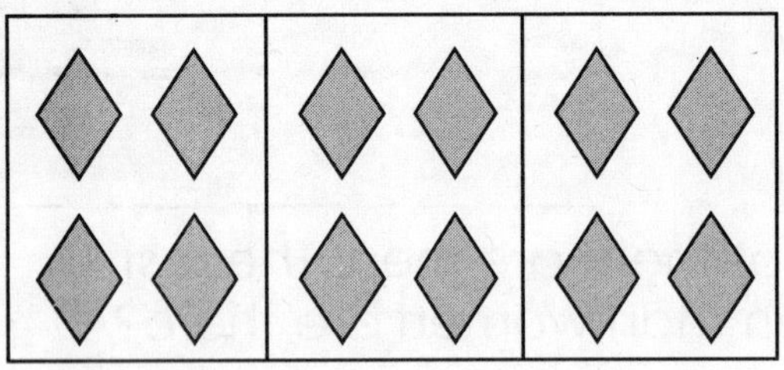

3 × 4 = ________

b) 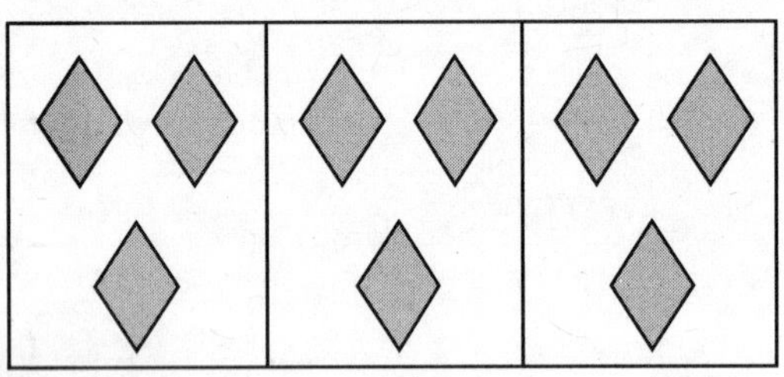

3 × 3 = ________

c) 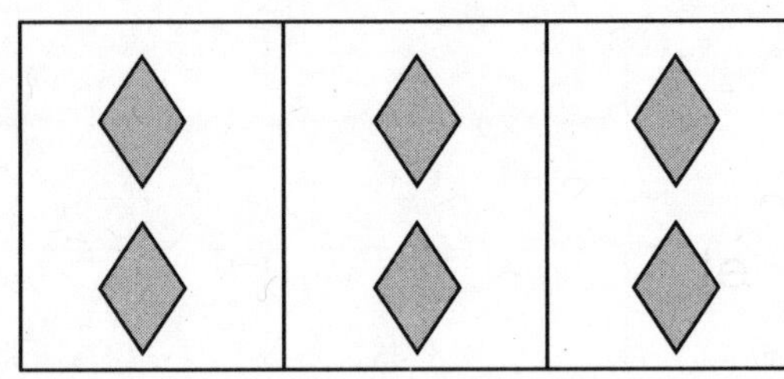

3 × 2 = ________

d) 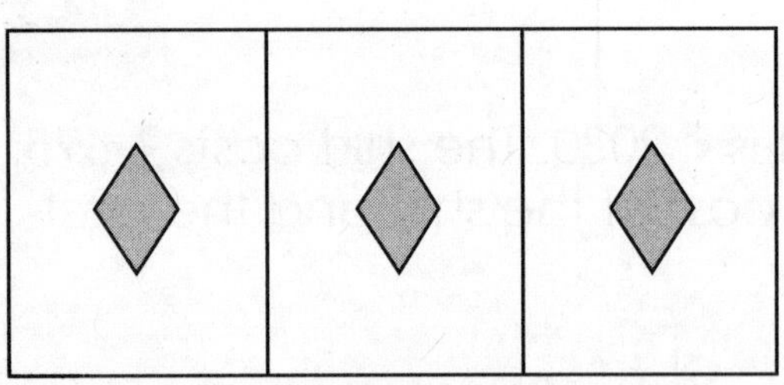

3 × 1 = ________

e) 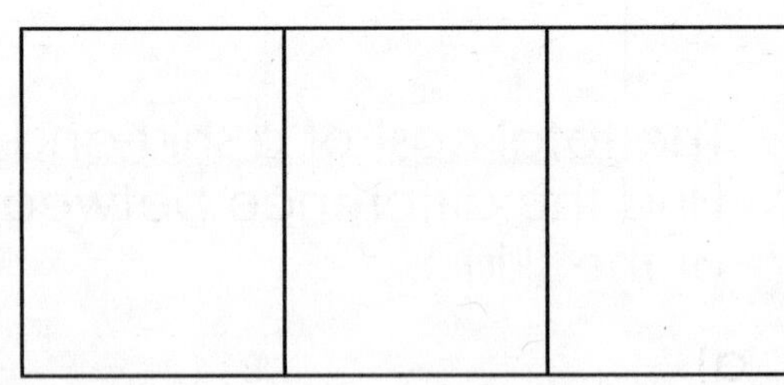

3 × 0 = ________

2. Multiply. Fill in the blanks.

a) 5 × 3 = ________

b) 5 × 0 = ________

c) 3 × 4 = ________

d) 4 × 8 = ________

e) 0 × 3 = ________

f) 3 × 9 = ________

 ISBN 978-93-5103-030-0

Exercise 2 Multiplying Ones, Tens and Hundreds

1. Multiply.

a)

$6 \times 2 =$ ____	$60 \times 2 =$ ____

b)

$7 \times 3 =$ ____	$70 \times 3 =$ ____

c)

$5 \times 4 =$ ____	$50 \times 4 =$ ____

d)

$9 \times 2 =$ ____	$900 \times 2 =$ ____

e)

$8 \times 3 =$ ____	$800 \times 3 =$ ____

f)

$7 \times 4 =$ ____	$700 \times 4 =$ ____

2. a) $90 \times 2 =$ ____ b) $80 \times 5 =$ ____ c) $200 \times 6 =$ ____ d) $300 \times 9 =$ ____

 ISBN 978-93-5103-030-0

Exercise 3 Multiplying Ones, Tens and Hundreds

1. Multiply.

a)
```
   1 1
×    4
------

------
```

b)
```
   2 3
×    2
------

------
```

c)
```
   1 2
×    2
------

------
```

d)
```
   2 1
×    3
------

------
```

e)
```
   1 3
×    3
------

------
```

f)
```
   3 1
×    2
------

------
```

2. Multiply. Fill in the missing numbers.

a) $23 \times 3 =$ ☐

b) $30 \times 2 =$ ☐

c) $42 \times 2 =$ ☐

d) $22 \times 4 =$ ☐

 ISBN 978-93-5103-030-0

Exercise 4 Multiplying Ones, Tens and Hundreds

1. Multiply.

$\begin{array}{r} 12 \\ \times \quad 4 \\ \hline \\ \hline \end{array}$	$\begin{array}{r} 21 \\ \times \quad 4 \\ \hline \\ \hline \end{array}$	$\begin{array}{r} 34 \\ \times \quad 2 \\ \hline \\ \hline \end{array}$	$\begin{array}{r} 52 \\ \times \quad 3 \\ \hline \\ \hline \end{array}$	$\begin{array}{r} 32 \\ \times \quad 4 \\ \hline \\ \hline \end{array}$
$\begin{array}{r} 51 \\ \times \quad 5 \\ \hline \\ \hline \end{array}$	$\begin{array}{r} 83 \\ \times \quad 3 \\ \hline \\ \hline \end{array}$	$\begin{array}{r} 92 \\ \times \quad 4 \\ \hline \\ \hline \end{array}$	$\begin{array}{r} 84 \\ \times \quad 2 \\ \hline \\ \hline \end{array}$	$\begin{array}{r} 72 \\ \times \quad 4 \\ \hline \\ \hline \end{array}$

2. Fill in the missing numbers.

a) The product of 3 and 43 is ________.

$$\begin{array}{r} 43 \\ \times \quad 3 \\ \hline \\ \hline \end{array}$$

b) The product of 62 and 4 is ________.

c) The product of 5 and 71 is ________.

d) The product of 81 and 2 is ________.

 ISBN 978-93-5103-030-0

Exercise 5 Multiplying One, Tens and Hundreds

1. Multiply.

a)
$$\begin{array}{r} 17 \\ \times \quad 3 \\ \hline \\ \hline \end{array}$$

b)
$$\begin{array}{r} 15 \\ \times \quad 4 \\ \hline \\ \hline \end{array}$$

c)
$$\begin{array}{r} 29 \\ \times \quad 2 \\ \hline \\ \hline \end{array}$$

d)
$$\begin{array}{r} 16 \\ \times \quad 5 \\ \hline \\ \hline \end{array}$$

e)
$$\begin{array}{r} 48 \\ \times \quad 2 \\ \hline \\ \hline \end{array}$$

f)
$$\begin{array}{r} 24 \\ \times \quad 3 \\ \hline \\ \hline \end{array}$$

2. Multiply. Fill in the missing numbers.

a) 14 × 5 = ______

b) 19 × 4 = ______

c) 25 × 3 = ______

d) 47 × 2 = ______

 ISBN 978-93-5103-030-0

Exercise 6 Multiplying Ones, Tens and Hundreds

1. Multiply.

a) 37×2	b) 45×3	c) 58×2	d) 86×4
e) 37×5	f) 23×5	g) 32×3	h) 57×4
i) 65×3	j) 43×2	k) 79×4	l) 98×5

2. Find each product.

a) 52×2	b) 27×2	c) 35×4	d) 48×3
e) 27×5	f) 34×4	g) 26×5	h) 59×3
i) 42×5	j) 56×5	k) 97×4	l) 56×4

 ISBN 978-93-5103-030-0

Exercise 7 Multiplying Ones, Tens and Hundreds

1. Multiply.

a)
```
    5 8 4
×       2
---------

---------
```

b)
```
    3 4 0
×       4
---------

---------
```

c)
```
    3 6 1
×       5
---------

---------
```

d)
```
    6 6 4
×       2
---------

---------
```

e)
```
    4 5 3
×       3
---------

---------
```

f)
```
    5 9 2
×       3
---------

---------
```

2. Multiply. Fill in the missing numbers.

a) $362 \times 4 =$ ☐

b) $391 \times 3 =$ ☐

c) $260 \times 5 =$ ☐

d) $794 \times 2 =$ ☐

 ISBN 978-93-5103-030-0

Exercise 8 Multiplying Ones, Tens and Hundreds

1. Multiply.

$124 \times 2 =$ ____	$148 \times 4 =$ ____	$227 \times 5 =$ ____
$256 \times 4 =$ ____	$302 \times 3 =$ ____	$374 \times 3 =$ ____
$361 \times 3 =$ ____	$184 \times 3 =$ ____	$217 \times 4 =$ ____

2. Multiply.

a) $155 \times 3 =$ ____	b) $388 \times 5 =$ ____	c) $264 \times 4 =$ ____	d) $495 \times 2 =$ ____
e) $500 \times 2 =$ ____	f) $280 \times 5 =$ ____	g) $163 \times 4 =$ ____	h) $700 \times 3 =$ ____
i) $224 \times 5 =$ ____	j) $837 \times 4 =$ ____	k) $177 \times 4 =$ ____	l) $369 \times 3 =$ ____

 ISBN 978-93-5103-030-0

Exercise 9 Quotient and Remainder

1. Fill in the missing numbers.

   a) 7 ÷ 2 = ____ R____
   Quotient = ____
   Remainder = ____

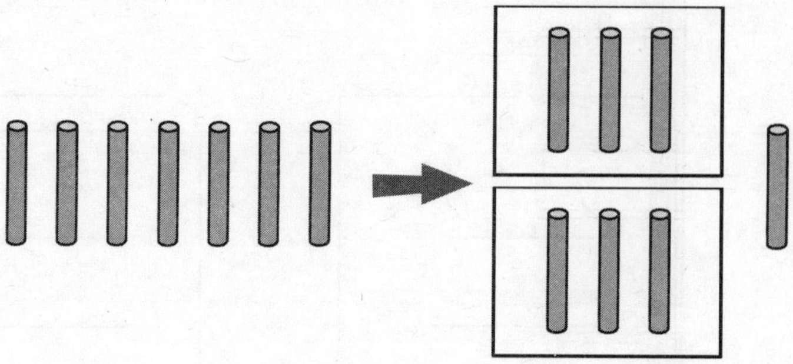

   b) 13 ÷ 2 = ____ R____
   Quotient = ____
   Remainder = ____

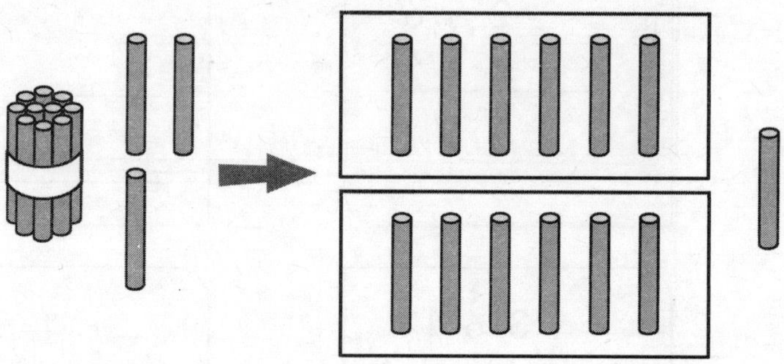

   c) 17 ÷ 2 = ____ R____
   Quotient = ____
   Remainder = ____

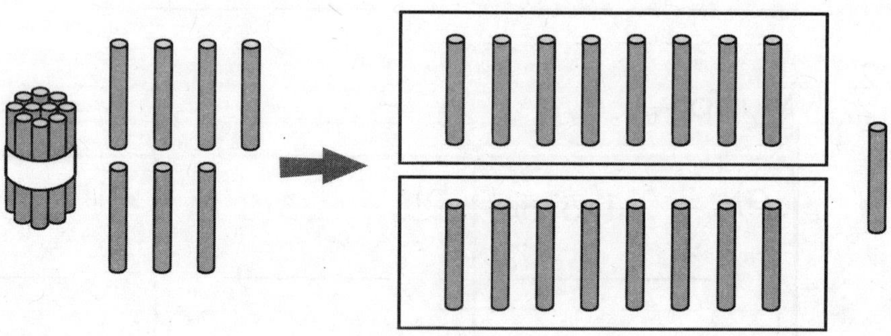

   d) 20 ÷ 2 = ____ R____
   Quotient = ____
   Remainder = ____

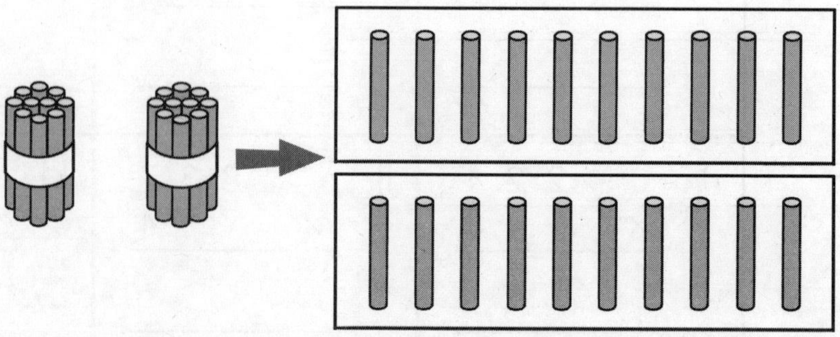

 ISBN 978-93-5103-030-0

Exercise 10 Quotient and Remainder

1. Divide.

$2\overline{)15}$	$5\overline{)40}$	$3\overline{)63}$
$4\overline{)33}$	$3\overline{)30}$	$5\overline{)86}$
$2\overline{)96}$	$5\overline{)83}$	$4\overline{)99}$

2. Colour the spaces that contain even numbers.

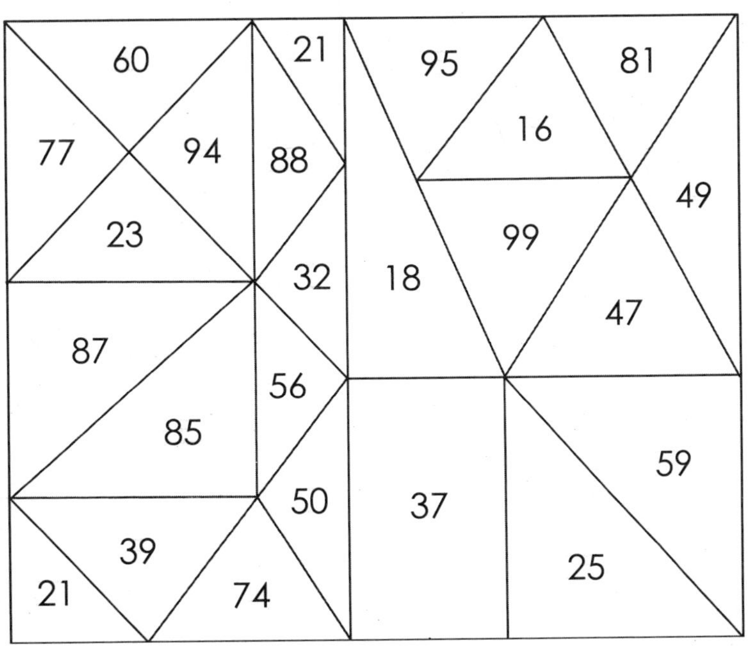

The ones digits in the odd numbers are ____________________.

The ones digits in the even numbers are ____________________.

 ISBN 978-93-5103-030-0

Exercise 11 Dividing Hundreds, Tens and Ones

1. Divide. Fill in the missing numbers.

a) 2) 4 0 0

b) 2) 3 0 0

c) 2) 5 4 0

d) 2) 9 3 0

e) 2) 8 8 0

f) 2) 6 5 0

 ISBN 978-93-5103-030-0

Exercise 12 Dividing Hundreds, Tens and Ones

1. Find the quotient and remainder.

a) $2\overline{)83}$

Quotient ☐
Remainder ☐

b) $4\overline{)65}$

Quotient ☐
Remainder ☐

c) $5\overline{)67}$

Quotient ☐
Remainder ☐

d) $3\overline{)96}$

Quotient ☐
Remainder ☐

e) $2\overline{)75}$

Quotient ☐
Remainder ☐

f) $4\overline{)78}$

Quotient ☐
Remainder ☐

g) $3\overline{)80}$

Quotient ☐
Remainder ☐

h) $5\overline{)95}$

Quotient ☐
Remainder ☐

 ISBN 978-93-5103-030-0

Exercise 13 Dividing Hundreds, Tens and Ones

1. Divide.

a) $2\overline{)473}$

b) $5\overline{)627}$

c) $4\overline{)980}$

d) $3\overline{)719}$

e) $2\overline{)506}$

f) $5\overline{)835}$

 ISBN 978-93-5103-030-0

2. Divide.

(C) $2\overline{)172}$

(E) $3\overline{)259}$

(H) $4\overline{)328}$

(O) $5\overline{)640}$

(P) $4\overline{)804}$

(R) $3\overline{)942}$

(I) $4\overline{)816}$

(T) $2\overline{)500}$

(L) $5\overline{)413}$

Which aircraft flies without wings?

Write the letters that match the answers to find out.

				C					
82	86 R1	82 R3	204	86	128	201	250	86 R1	314

 ISBN 978-93-5103-030-0

Exercise 14 Problem Solving

Solve the word problems. You may draw bar models to help you. Show your work clearly.

1. Roy had 3 times as many comic books as Paul. If Paul had 7 comic books, how many comic books did Roy have?

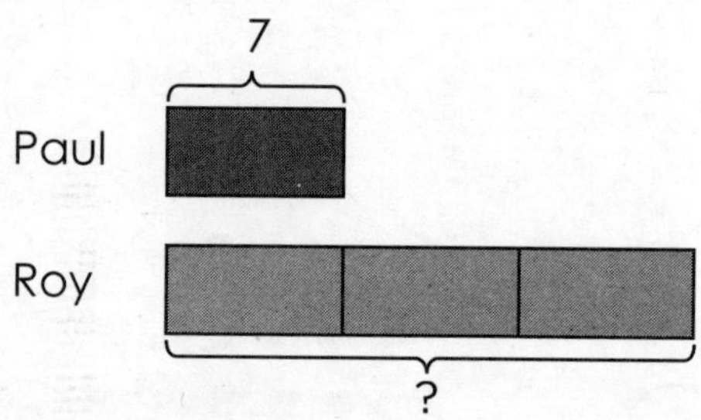

- [ ] 1. Understand
- [ ] 2. Plan
- [ ] 3. Answer
- [ ] 4. Check

2. There are 20 monkeys in a zoo. There are 4 times as many monkeys as tigers. How many tigers are there?

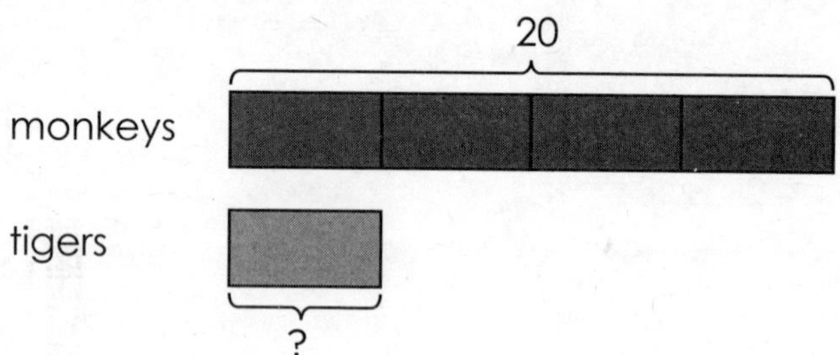

- [ ] 1. Understand
- [ ] 2. Plan
- [ ] 3. Answer
- [ ] 4. Check

3. Tara reads 8 pages of a book a day. After reading the book for 4 days, she still has 5 pages to read. How many pages are there in the book?

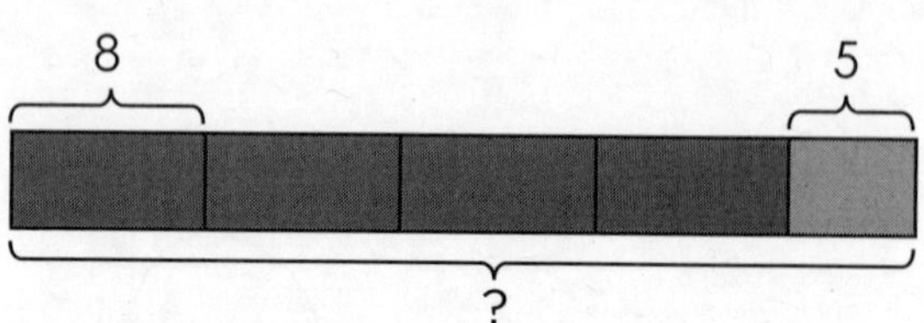

- [ ] 1. Understand
- [ ] 2. Plan
- [ ] 3. Answer
- [ ] 4. Check

 ISBN 978-93-5103-030-0

4. Maya bought 36 apples. She bought 4 times as many oranges as apples. How many more oranges than apples did she buy?

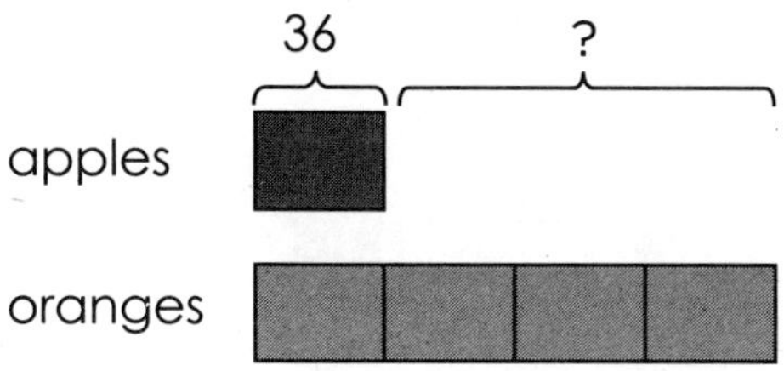

- ☐ 1. Understand
- ☐ 2. Plan
- ☐ 3. Answer
- ☐ 4. Check

5. A toy car costs ₹ 385. A toy train costs 5 times as much as the toy car. What is the cost of the toy train?

- ☐ 1. Understand
- ☐ 2. Plan
- ☐ 3. Answer
- ☐ 4. Check

6. Mrs. Rao had 186 stickers. She gave 5 stickers to each student in her class. How many students were there in her class? How many stickers were left?

- ☐ 1. Understand
- ☐ 2. Plan
- ☐ 3. Answer
- ☐ 4. Check

 ISBN 978-93-5103-030-0

7. Rani had ₹ 94. After paying for 3 kilograms of guavas, she had ₹ 40 left. Find the cost of 1 kilogram of guava.

- [ ] 1. Understand
- [ ] 2. Plan
- [ ] 3. Answer
- [ ] 4. Check

8. A pole is 3 metres long. A rope is 8 times as long as the pole. If the rope is divided equally into 4 pieces, what is the length of each piece of rope?

- [ ] 1. Understand
- [ ] 2. Plan
- [ ] 3. Answer
- [ ] 4. Check

 ISBN 978-93-5103-030-0

4 Multiplication Tables of 6, 7, 8 and 9

Exercise 1 Multiplying and Dividing by 6

1. Complete the multiplication sentences.

a) 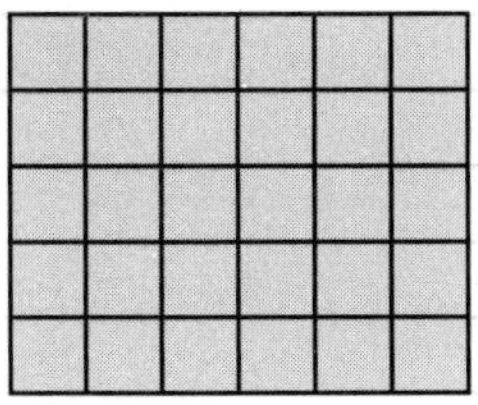

$5 \times 6 =$ ________

$6 \times 5 =$ ________

b) 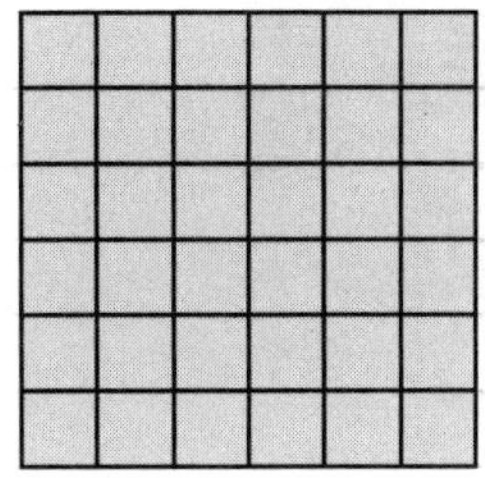

$6 \times 6 =$ ________

c) 

$7 \times 6 =$ ________

$6 \times 7 =$ ________

d) 

$8 \times 6 =$ ________

$6 \times 8 =$ ________

e) 

$9 \times 6 =$ ________

$6 \times 9 =$ ________

f) 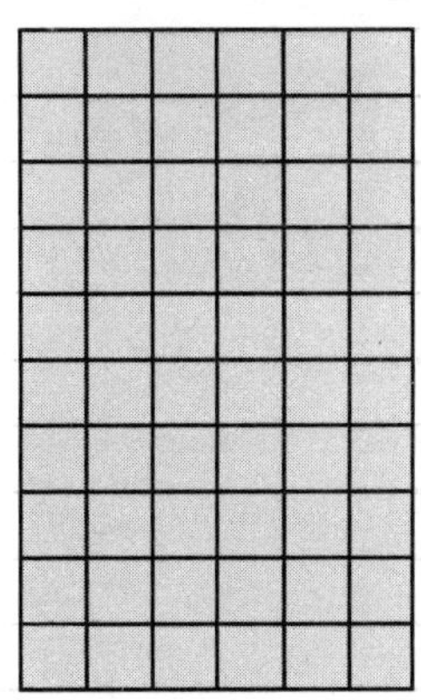

$10 \times 6 =$ ________

$6 \times 10 =$ ________

 ISBN 978-93-5103-030-0

2. Multiply and write the missing numbers.

  ISBN 978-93-5103-030-0

Exercise 2 Multiplying and Dividing by 6

1. Fill in the blanks.

a) ______ × 6 = 30 | ______ ÷ 6 = 5

b) 3 × 6 = ______ | 18 ÷ ______ = 3

c) 7 × 6 = ______ | ______ ÷ 6 = 7

d) 6 × ______ = 36 | 36 ÷ 6 = ______

e) 9 × 6 = ______ | 54 ÷ ______ = 9

f) 10 × ______ = 60 | ______ ÷ 6 = 10

g) 4 × 6 = ______ | 24 ÷ 6 = ______

h) ______ × 6 = 48 | ______ ÷ 6 = 8

i) ______ × 6 = 0 | 0 ÷ 6 = ______

 ISBN 978-93-5103-030-0

2. Join each pair of matching cards with a straight line. Each line will pass through a letter.

a)	12 ÷ 6	3
b)	18 ÷ 6	8
c)	60 ÷ 6	5
d)	48 ÷ 6	2
e)	30 ÷ 6	7
f)	54 ÷ 6	10
g)	42 ÷ 6	9

Letters: R, P, D, U, O, T, C

What is the answer to a multiplication question called?

Write the letters in order from a) to g) to find out.

P						
a)	b)	c)	d)	e)	f)	g)

 ISBN 978-93-5103-030-0

Exercise 3 Multiplying and Dividing by 6

1. Complete the cross-number puzzle.

Example

	A 2	2	8	
B			C	
		D		E
F				
		G		

ACROSS

A. 38×6
B. 5×6
D. 24×6
F. 6×35
G. 6×48

DOWN

A. 45×6
B. 52×6
C. 6×9
D. 6×17
E. 6×68

2. Find the product for each of the following.

$43 \times 6 =$ ______

$75 \times 6 =$ ______

$98 \times 6 =$ ______

$306 \times 6 =$ ______

$450 \times 6 =$ ______

$574 \times 6 =$ ______

$791 \times 6 =$ ______

$800 \times 6 =$ ______

$923 \times 6 =$ ______

 ISBN 978-93-5103-030-0

Exercise 4 Multiplying and Dividing by 6

1. Divide.

a) $6\overline{)53}$ (T)

b) $6\overline{)75}$ (N)

c) $6\overline{)84}$ (G)

d) $6\overline{)64}$ (P)

e) $6\overline{)49}$ (A)

f) $6\overline{)96}$ (O)

g) $6\overline{)38}$ (E)

h) $6\overline{)59}$ (N)

What do you call a figure that has 5 sides? 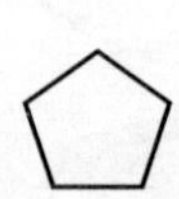

Write the letters that match the answers to find out.

			T				
10 R4	6 R2	12 R3	8 R5	8 R1	14	16	9 R5

 ISBN 978-93-5103-030-0

2. Find the quotient and remainder for each of the following.

a) $6\overline{)92}$

Quotient:
Remainder:

b) $6\overline{)84}$

Quotient:
Remainder:

c) $6\overline{)78}$

Quotient:
Remainder:

d) $6\overline{)800}$

Quotient:
Remainder:

e) $6\overline{)605}$

Quotient:
Remainder:

f) $6\overline{)546}$

Quotient:
Remainder:

g) $6\overline{)496}$

Quotient:
Remainder:

h) $6\overline{)719}$

Quotient:
Remainder:

i) $6\overline{)923}$

Quotient:
Remainder:

 ISBN 978-93-5103-030-0

Exercise 5 Multiplying and Dividing by 7

1. Multiply and write the missing numbers.

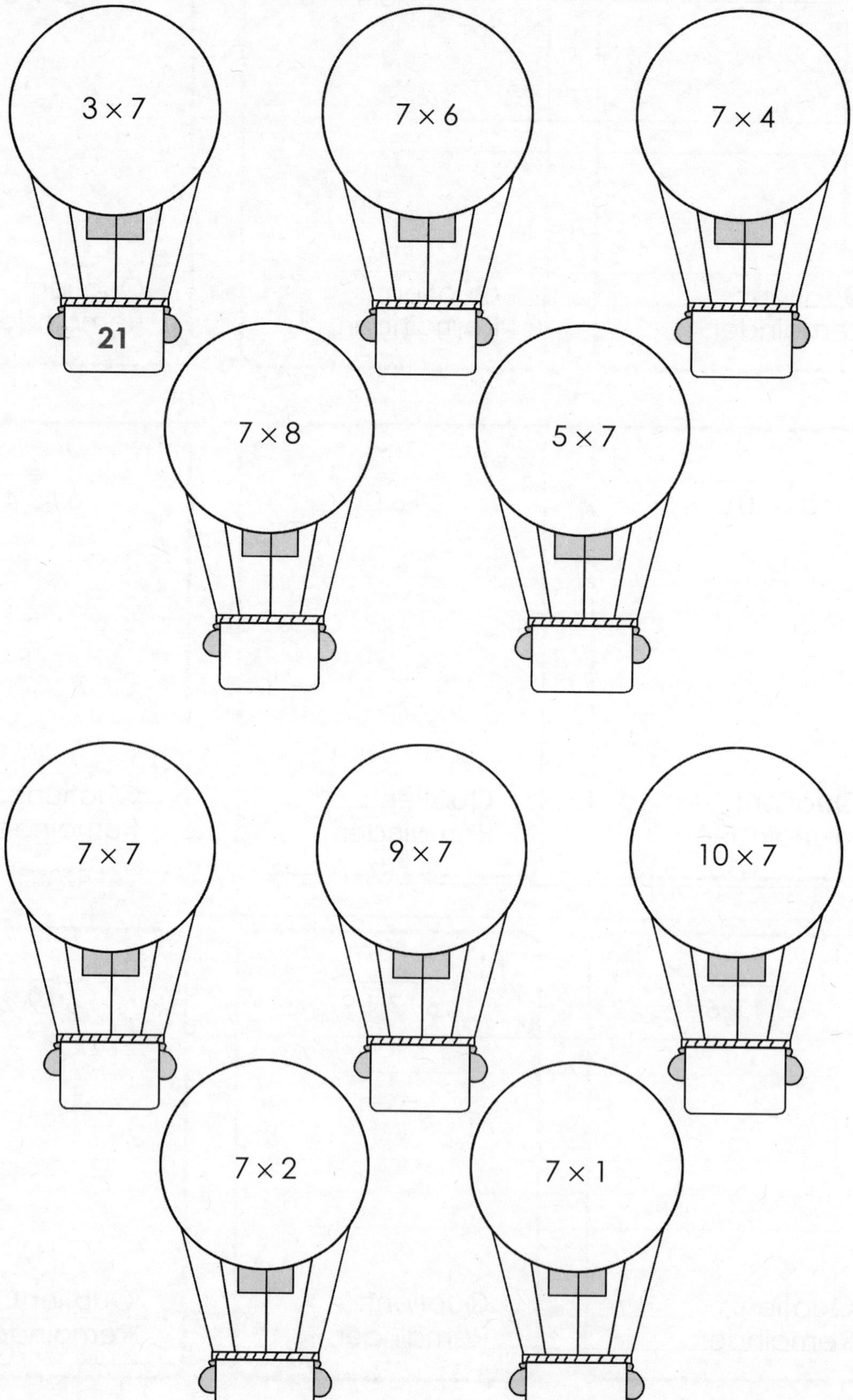

 ISBN 978-93-5103-030-0

Exercise 6 Multiplying and Dividing by 7

1. Write the missing numbers.

a) $6 \times 7 =$ ______ | $42 \div$ ______ $= 6$

b) ______ $\times 7 = 14$ | ______ $\div 7 = 2$

c) $8 \times$ ______ $= 56$ | $56 \div 7 =$ ______

d) $5 \times 7 =$ ______ | $35 \div$ ______ $= 5$

e) $3 \times 7 =$ ______ | $21 \div$ ______ $= 3$

f) $9 \times 7 =$ ______ | $63 \div 7 =$ ______

g) ______ $\times 7 = 7$ | ______ $\div 1 = 7$

h) $0 \times 7 =$ ______ | $0 \div 7 =$ ______

i) $7 \times$ ______ $= 49$ | ______ $\div 7 = 7$

 ISBN 978-93-5103-030-0

2. Join each pair of matching cards with a straight line.
Each line will pass through a letter.

		Letters		
a)	14 ÷ 7	Q	O	4
b)	49 ÷ 7			8
c)	28 ÷ 7	U		7
d)	70 ÷ 7	I	E	3
e)	56 ÷ 7			2
f)	21 ÷ 7	T		9
g)	63 ÷ 7	N		5
h)	35 ÷ 7	T		10

What is the answer to a division question called?

Write the letters in order from a) to h) to find out.

Q	___	___	___	___	___	___	___
a)	b)	c)	d)	e)	f)	g)	h)

 ISBN 978-93-5103-030-0

Exercise 7 Multiplying and Dividing by 7

1. Multiply.

80 × 7 = ____	54 × 7 = ____	39 × 7 = ____
71 × 7 = ____	62 × 7 = ____	43 × 7 = ____

2. Multiply.

(Y) 96 × 7 = ____	(N) 45 × 7 = ____	(A) 82 × 7 = ____
(T) 700 × 7 = ____	(G) 328 × 7 = ____	(S) 145 × 7 = ____
(R) 403 × 7 = ____	(M) 654 × 7 = ____	(I) 531 × 7 = ____

Which insect looks like it is praying?

Write the letters that match the answers to find out.

P ___ ___ ___ ___ N ___
2821 574 672 3717 2296

___ A ___ ___ I ___
4578 315 4900 1015

 ISBN 978-93-5103-030-0

Exercise 8 Multiplying and Dividing by 7

1. Divide.

a) $7\overline{)80}$	b) $7\overline{)55}$
c) $7\overline{)69}$	d) $7\overline{)43}$
e) $7\overline{)98}$	f) $7\overline{)76}$
g) $7\overline{)84}$	h) $7\overline{)72}$

 ISBN 978-93-5103-030-0

2. Divide.

(A) $7\overline{)91}$

(B) $7\overline{)135}$

(D) $7\overline{)455}$

(Y) $7\overline{)932}$

(L) $7\overline{)770}$

(I) $7\overline{)803}$

(R) $7\overline{)619}$

(D) $7\overline{)716}$

Which beetle is useful to farmers and has a colourful body?

Write the letters that match the quotients to find out.

	A						
110	13	65	133	19	114	88	102

 ISBN 978-93-5103-030-0

Exercise 9 Multiplying and Dividing by 8

1. Multiply and write the missing numbers.

Example

8×4 **32** D	8×7 O	8×3 L
8×5 S	8×8 G	8×6 F
9×8 A	2×8 I	10×8 H

What type of pet fish sleeps with its eyes open and has no stomach?
Write the letters that match the answers to find out.

___   ___ ___ ___ ___ ___ ___ ___ ___ !
72   64 56 24 32 48 16 40 80

 ISBN 978-93-5103-030-0

Exercise 10 Multiplying and Dividing by 8

1. Fill in the missing numbers.

a) $10 \times$ ________ $= 80$ | ________ $\div 8 = 10$

b) $0 \times 8 =$ ________ | ________ $\div 8 = 0$

c) ________ $\times 8 = 24$ | $24 \div 8 =$ ________

d) $8 \times$ ________ $= 64$ | ________ $\div 8 = 8$

e) $7 \times 8 =$ ________ | $56 \div$ ________ $= 7$

f) ________ $\times 8 = 8$ | ________ $\div 8 = 1$

g) $9 \times$ ________ $= 72$ | $72 \div 8 =$ ________

h) $4 \times 8 =$ ________ | $32 \div$ ________ $= 4$

i) ________ $\times 8 = 48$ | ________ $\div 8 = 6$

 ISBN 978-93-5103-030-0

2. Match each division sentence to the correct answer.

24 ÷ 8	5
40 ÷ 8	2
64 ÷ 8	3
16 ÷ 8	4
48 ÷ 8	8
32 ÷ 8	7
72 ÷ 8	10
56 ÷ 8	6
80 ÷ 8	9

 ISBN 978-93-5103-030-0

Exercise 11 Multiplying and Dividing by 8

1. Draw a straight line to match. Each line will pass through a letter.

a)	32 × 8	400
b)	54 × 8	704
c)	8 × 50	432
d)	8 × 63	256
e)	88 × 8	216
f)	27 × 8	736
g)	8 × 36	504
h)	8 × 14	288
i)	92 × 8	112

C E X L E L T E N

Write the letters in order from a) to i) to find out the message.

a)	b)	c)	d)	e)	f)	g)	h)	i)	
									WORK!

2. Multiply and use the products to complete the cross-number puzzle below.

ACROSS

A	D	F	H
$46 \times 8 =$ ______	$58 \times 8 =$ ______	$249 \times 8 =$ ______	$62 \times 8 =$ ______

I	J
$55 \times 8 =$ ______	$254 \times 8 =$ ______

DOWN

B	C	E	G
$803 \times 8 =$ ______	$649 \times 8 =$ ______	$784 \times 8 =$ ______	$120 \times 8 =$ ______

Example

A 3	B 6	8		C		D	E	
				F	G			
			H					
I				J				

 ISBN 978-93-5103-030-0

Exercise 12 Multiplying and Dividing by 8

1. Divide.

$8\overline{)850}$ (F)	$8\overline{)962}$ (O)	$8\overline{)372}$ (P)
$8\overline{)77}$ (K)	$8\overline{)528}$ (R)	$8\overline{)96}$ (T)
$8\overline{)103}$ (X)	$8\overline{)488}$ (S)	$8\overline{)748}$ (C)

Write the letters that match the answers to find out the message.

E ______ E ______ ______ I ______ E
12 R7 66 93 R4 61

T ______ ______ E E ______
120 R2 9 R5 46 R4

______ I ______ !
106 R2 12

 ISBN 978-93-5103-030-0

Exercise 13 Multiplying and Dividing by 9

1. Multiply.

9×3	27
9×5	
9×10	
9×4	
9×2	
9×7	
6×9	
9×9	
8×9	

 ISBN 978-93-5103-030-0

Exercise 14 Multiplying and Dividing by 9

1. Fill in the missing numbers.

a) | ______ × 9 = 63 | 63 ÷ 9 = ______ |
|---|---|

b) | 2 × 9 = ______ | 18 ÷ ______ = 2 |
|---|---|

c) | 3 × ______ = 27 | ______ ÷ 9 = 3 |
|---|---|

d) | ______ × 9 = 72 | 72 ÷ 9 = ______ |
|---|---|

e) | 9 × ______ = 81 | 81 ÷ ______ = 9 |
|---|---|

f) | 6 × 9 = ______ | ______ ÷ 9 = 6 |
|---|---|

g) | 5 × ______ = 45 | 45 ÷ 9 = ______ |
|---|---|

h) | 4 × 9 = ______ | 36 ÷ 9 = ______ |
|---|---|

 ISBN 978-93-5103-030-0

2. Match.

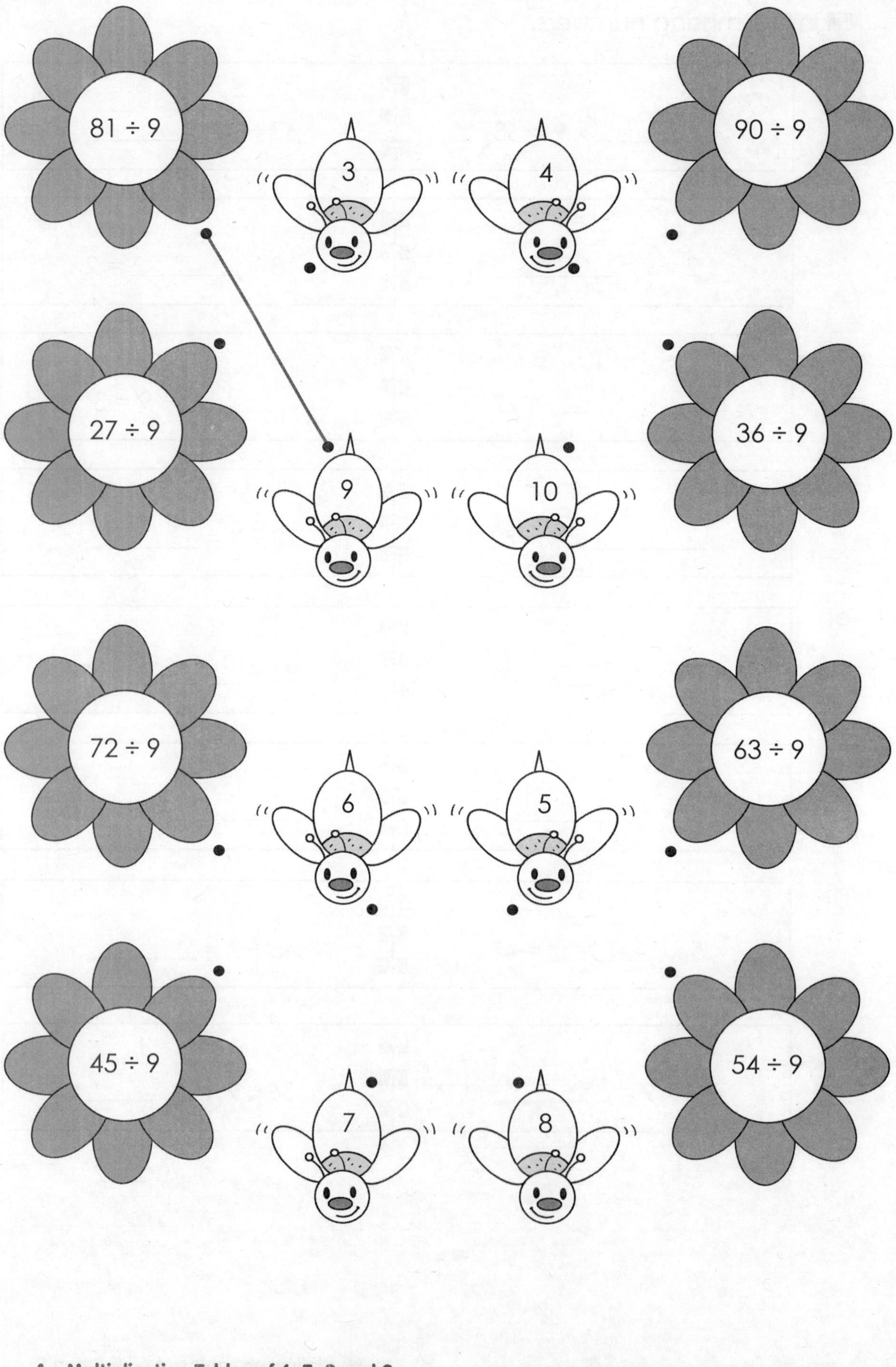

 ISBN 978-93-5103-030-0

Exercise 15 Multiplying and Dividing by 9

1. Multiply.

(J)
$$\begin{array}{r} 75 \\ \times\quad 9 \\ \hline \\ \hline \end{array}$$

(U)
$$\begin{array}{r} 106 \\ \times\quad 9 \\ \hline \\ \hline \end{array}$$

(O)
$$\begin{array}{r} 264 \\ \times\quad 9 \\ \hline \\ \hline \end{array}$$

(M)
$$\begin{array}{r} 99 \\ \times\quad 9 \\ \hline \\ \hline \end{array}$$

(T)
$$\begin{array}{r} 523 \\ \times\quad 9 \\ \hline \\ \hline \end{array}$$

(E)
$$\begin{array}{r} 612 \\ \times\quad 9 \\ \hline \\ \hline \end{array}$$

(A)
$$\begin{array}{r} 784 \\ \times\quad 9 \\ \hline \\ \hline \end{array}$$

(B)
$$\begin{array}{r} 80 \\ \times\quad 9 \\ \hline \\ \hline \end{array}$$

(J)
$$\begin{array}{r} 947 \\ \times\quad 9 \\ \hline \\ \hline \end{array}$$

What do you call an elephant with wings?

Write the letters that match the answers to find out.

___	J	___	___	___	___	J	___	___	!
7056	8523	954	891	720	2376	675	5508	4707	

 ISBN 978-93-5103-030-0

Exercise 16 Multiplying and Dividing by 9

1. Join each pair of matching shoes with a straight line.
   If you do it correctly, you will get 6 small triangles.

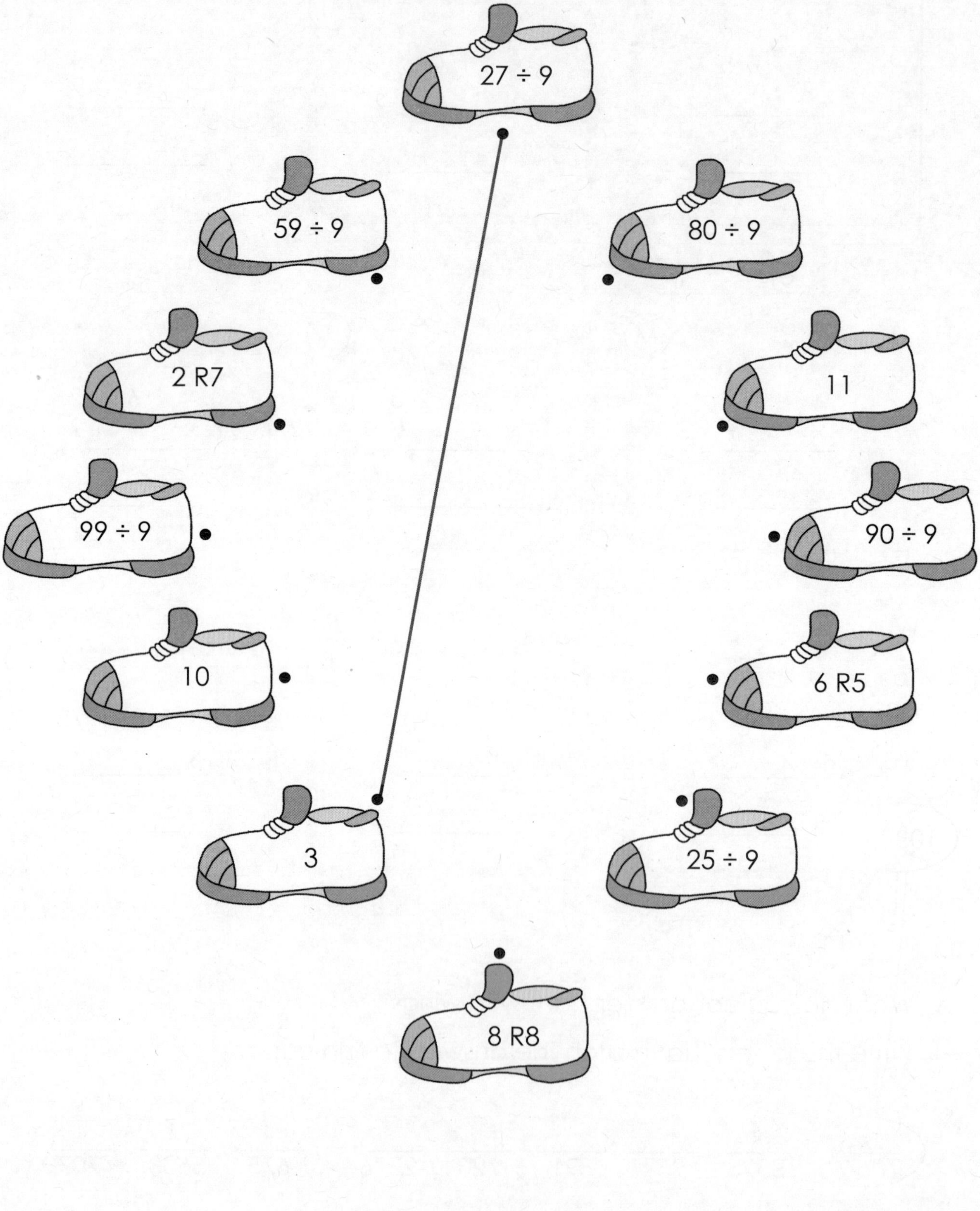

 ISBN 978-93-5103-030-0

2. Divide.

a) $9\overline{)929}$

b) $9\overline{)554}$

c) $9\overline{)657}$

d) $9\overline{)381}$

e) $9\overline{)852}$

f) $9\overline{)436}$

g) $9\overline{)207}$

Which bird has 2 toes on each foot? ________

To find out, trace the path by following the order of the answers above.

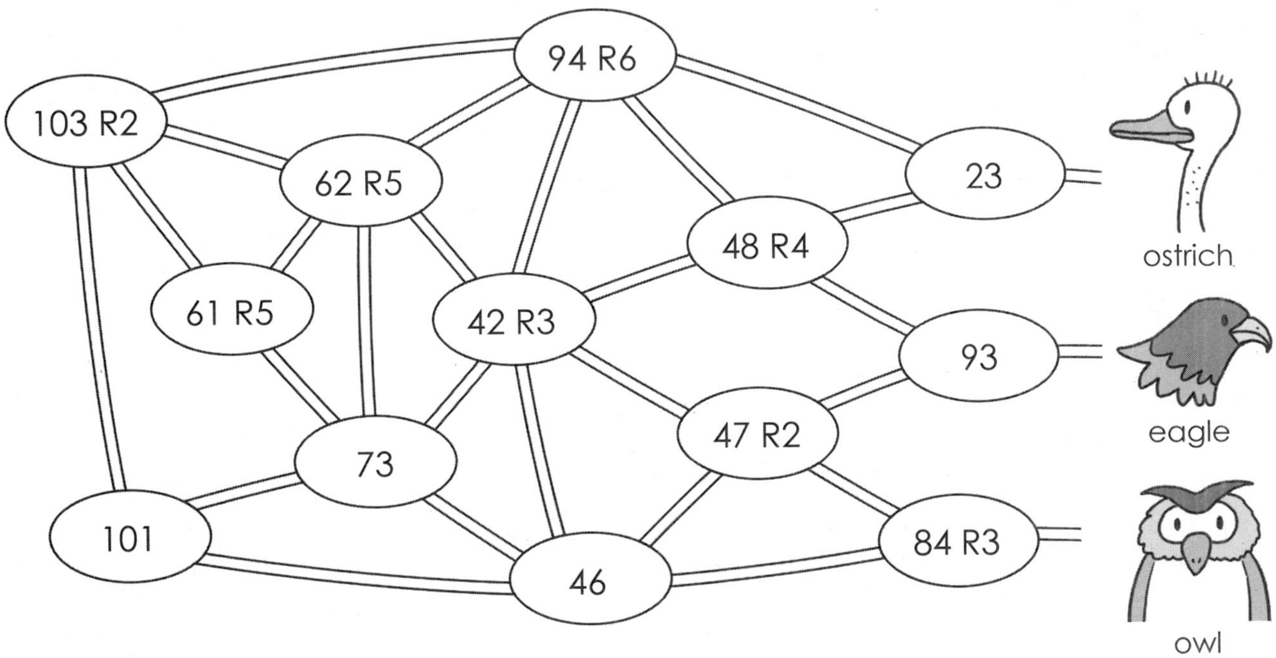

Exercise 17 Problem Solving

Solve the word problems. You may draw bar models to help you. Show your work clearly.

1. The human heart beats 72 times a minute. How many times does it beat in 6 minutes?

☐ 1. Understand
☐ 2. Plan
☐ 3. Answer
☐ 4. Check

2. Mohan worked for 7 hours. He was paid ₹ 36 an hour. How much money did he receive?

☐ 1. Understand
☐ 2. Plan
☐ 3. Answer
☐ 4. Check

3. There were 36 tables at a dinner party. 8 people sat at each table. How many people were there at the party?

☐ 1. Understand
☐ 2. Plan
☐ 3. Answer
☐ 4. Check

4. 25 boys went camping. Each boy brought 9 cans of food. How many cans did they bring altogether?

☐ 1. Understand
☐ 2. Plan
☐ 3. Answer
☐ 4. Check

 ISBN 978-93-5103-030-0

5. Meena has a rope 161 centimetres long. She cuts it into 7 equal pieces. What is the length of each piece?

- [ ] 1. Understand
- [ ] 2. Plan
- [ ] 3. Answer
- [ ] 4. Check

6. A vegetable seller packed 153 tomatoes into bags of 6 each. How many bags were there?

- [ ] 1. Understand
- [ ] 2. Plan
- [ ] 3. Answer
- [ ] 4. Check

7. Mr. Rao printed 904 diaries. He packed them equally into 8 boxes. How many diaries were there in each box?

- [ ] 1. Understand
- [ ] 2. Plan
- [ ] 3. Answer
- [ ] 4. Check

8. Kabir cut a length of wire measuring 918 metres into pieces. Each piece was 9 metres long. How many pieces did he get?

- [ ] 1. Understand
- [ ] 2. Plan
- [ ] 3. Answer
- [ ] 4. Check

 ISBN 978-93-5103-030-0

Exercise 18 Problem Solving

Solve the word problems. You may draw bar models to help you.
Show your work clearly.

1. Mrs. Kumar bought 35 metres of rope at ₹ 6 for 1 metre. She still had ₹ 25 left after paying for the rope. How much did she have at first?

- ☐ 1. Understand
- ☐ 2. Plan
- ☐ 3. Answer
- ☐ 4. Check

2. Mrs. Singh packed 112 pens into bags of 7 each. She sold all the pens at ₹ 3 a bag. How much money did she receive?

- ☐ 1. Understand
- ☐ 2. Plan
- ☐ 3. Answer
- ☐ 4. Check

3. A florist has 145 yellow roses. She has 8 times as many red roses as yellow roses. How many more red roses than yellow roses does she have?

- ☐ 1. Understand
- ☐ 2. Plan
- ☐ 3. Answer
- ☐ 4. Check

 ISBN 978-93-5103-030-0

4. Mr. Kumar had 194 magazines. 5 of them were torn. He tied the rest into bundles of 7 each. How many bundles of magazines did he get?

- [ ] 1. Understand
- [ ] 2. Plan
- [ ] 3. Answer
- [ ] 4. Check

5. 8 students sold 272 fair tickets at ₹ 3 each. Each student sold the same number of tickets. How much money did each student collect?

- [ ] 1. Understand
- [ ] 2. Plan
- [ ] 3. Answer
- [ ] 4. Check

6. There were 249 boys and 255 girls in a field. They lined up in 9 equal rows. How many children were there in each row?

- [ ] 1. Understand
- [ ] 2. Plan
- [ ] 3. Answer
- [ ] 4. Check

 ISBN 978-93-5103-030-0

5 Money

Exercise 1 Rupees and Paise

1. Match.

- ₹ 1.35

- ₹ 2.70

- ₹ 6.45

- ₹ 2.60

- ₹ 1.85

 ISBN 978-93-5103-030-0

2. Count and write the amounts of money.

a)

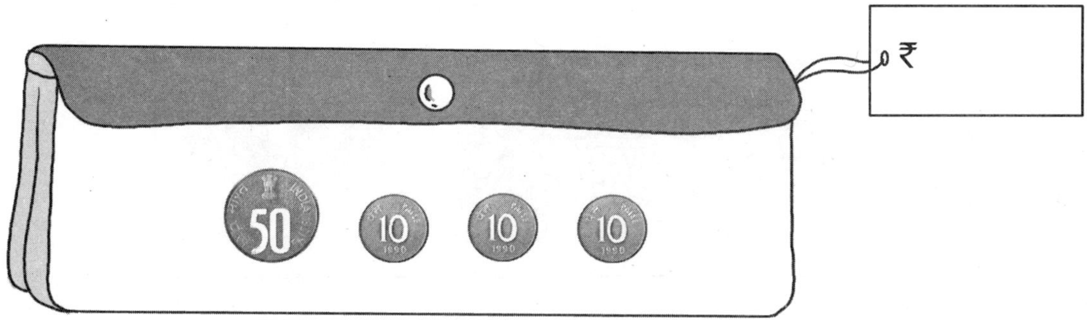

b)

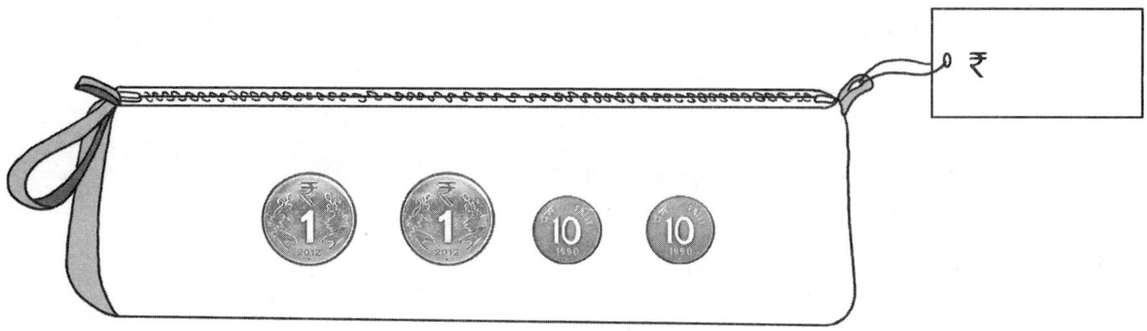

c)

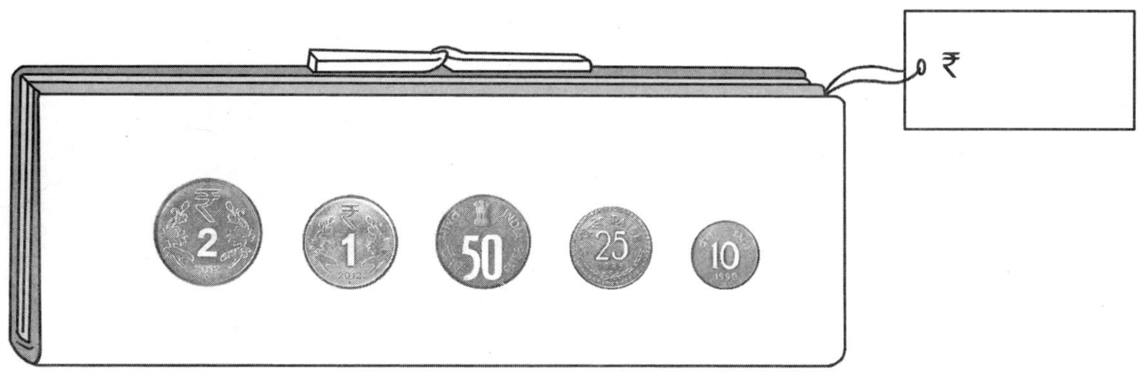

d)

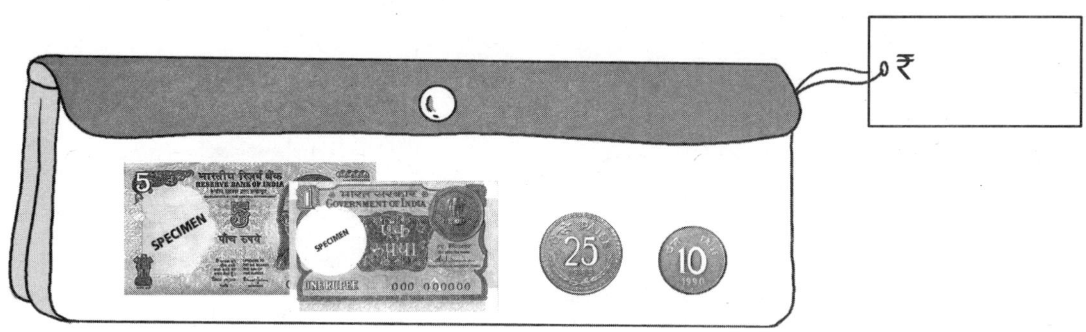

e)

 ISBN 978-93-5103-030-0

f)

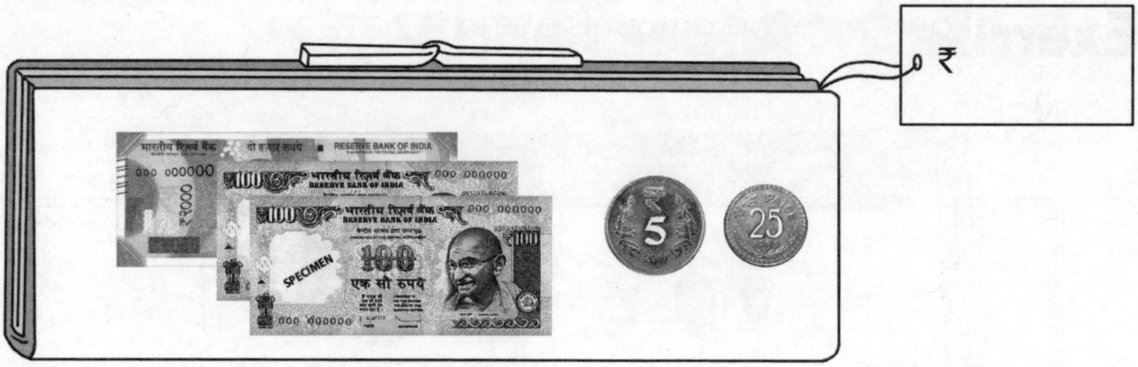

3. Count and write the amounts of money.

a)

b)

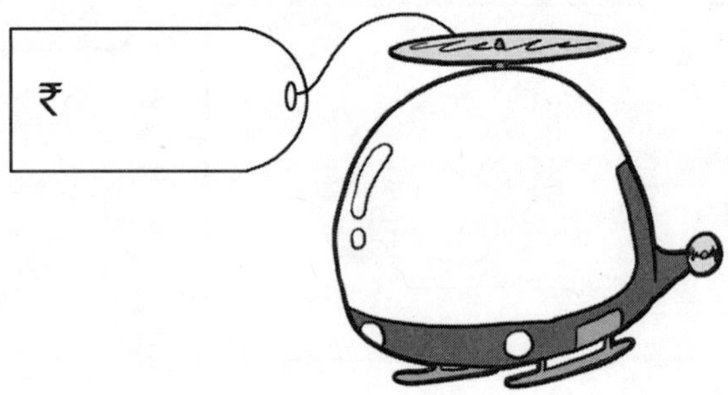

c)

 ISBN 978-93-5103-030-0

Exercise 2 Rupees and Paise

1. Match the amounts of money.

twenty-three rupees

four rupees

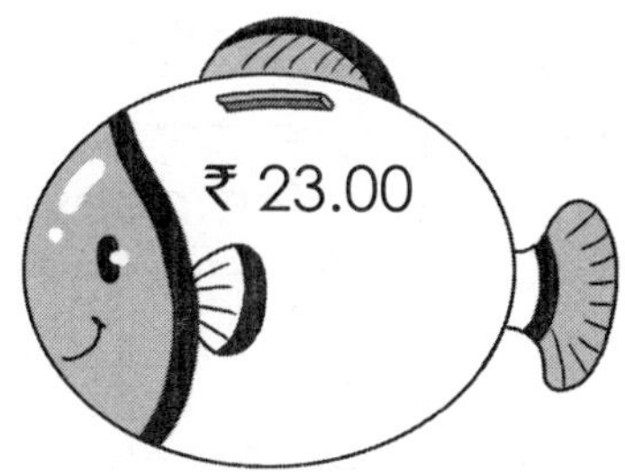

thirteen rupees and thirty paise

twenty paise

seven rupees and fifty paise

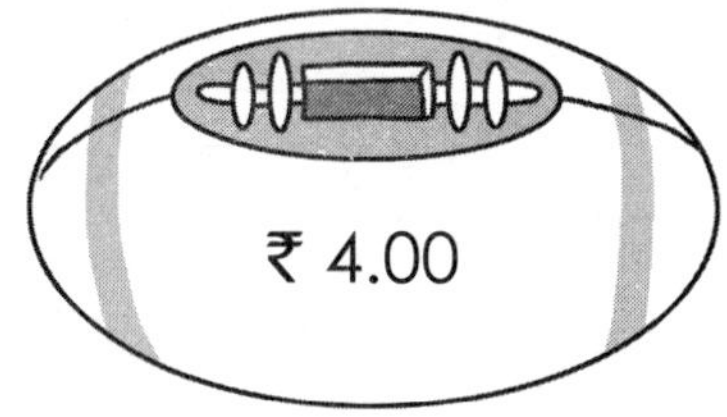

ninety-nine rupees and fifty-five paise

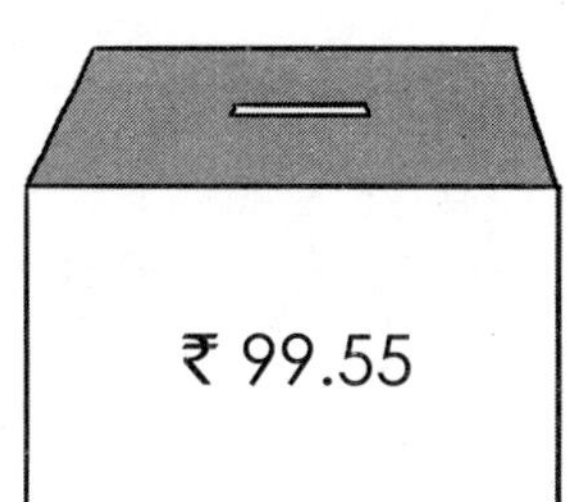

 ISBN 978-93-5103-030-0

2. Write each amount of money using the rupee symbol.

Example

3 rupees and 30 paise	**₹ 3.30**

a) 5 rupees

b) 9 rupees and 75 paise

c) 12 rupees and 90 paise

d) 154 rupees and 50 paise

3. Write the missing numbers.

Example

₹ 6.80	**6** rupees and **80** paise

a) ₹ 4.65 — rupees and paise

b) ₹ 0.70 — rupees and paise

c) ₹ 6.45 — rupees and paise

d) ₹ 15.00 — rupees and paise

e) ₹ 354.90 — rupees and paise

 ISBN 978-93-5103-030-0

4. Write each amount of money using the rupee or the paisa symbol.

Example fifteen paise	**15** p
a) twenty rupees	
b) forty-seven rupees	
c) seventy-four rupees and fifty paise	
d) thirty rupees and forty-five paise	
e) forty-seven rupees and fifteen paise	
f) ninety-five paise	
g) forty rupees and twenty-five paise	
h) five hundred sixty-five rupees and seventy-five paise	

 ISBN 978-93-5103-030-0

Exercise 3 Rupees and Paise

1. Match the same amounts.

₹ 1.80	270 p
₹ 2.70	345 p
₹ 3.45	180 p
10 p	₹ 0.35
35 p	₹ 3.00
300 p	₹ 0.10

2. Write in rupees.

a) 100 p = ₹ ________ b) 200 p = ₹ ________

c) 125 p = ₹ ________ d) 240 p = ₹ ________

e) 360 p = ₹ ________ f) 1900 p = ₹ ________

g) 85 p = ₹ ________ h) 70 p = ₹ ________

3. Write in paise.

a) ₹ 0.10 = ________ p b) ₹ 0.75 = ________ p

c) ₹ 2.50 = ________ p d) ₹ 7.80 = ________ p

e) ₹ 4.00 = ________ p f) ₹ 3.45 = ________ p

g) ₹ 10.00 = ________ p h) ₹ 28.95 = ________ p

 ISBN 978-93-5103-030-0

Exercise 4 Rupees and Paise

1. Compare the amounts of money and fill in the blanks.

a)

	Rupees	Paise
₹ 14.30	14	30
₹ 8.60		

Which amount is greater? ₹ ________

Which amount is smaller? ₹ ________

b)

	Rupees	Paise
₹ 53.45		
₹ 53.70		

Which amount is greater? ₹ ________

Which amount is smaller? ₹ ________

c)

	Rupees	Paise
₹ 278.50		
₹ 278.25		
₹ 279.65		

Which amount is the greatest? ₹ ________

Which amount is the smallest? ₹ ________

 ISBN 978-93-5103-030-0

2. Circle the greater amount.

a) ₹ 2.20, ₹ 4.55

b) ₹ 15.80, ₹ 15.90

c) ₹ 123.40, ₹ 133.40

3. Circle the smaller amount.

a) ₹ 5.00, ₹ 15.00

b) ₹ 46.70, ₹ 49.45

c) ₹ 371.05, ₹ 371.50

4. Circle the greatest amount.

a) ₹ 59.60, ₹ 61.30, ₹ 60.10

b) ₹ 38.35, ₹ 38.15, ₹ 38.25

c) ₹ 937.35, ₹ 938.15, ₹ 938.25

5. Circle the smallest amount.

a) ₹ 42.75, ₹ 43.05, ₹ 42.55

b) ₹ 85.95, ₹ 85.85, ₹ 85.65

c) ₹ 485.95, ₹ 484.85, ₹ 485.65

 ISBN 978-93-5103-030-0

Exercise 5 Adding Amounts of Money

1. How much more money is needed to make ₹ 1?

a)

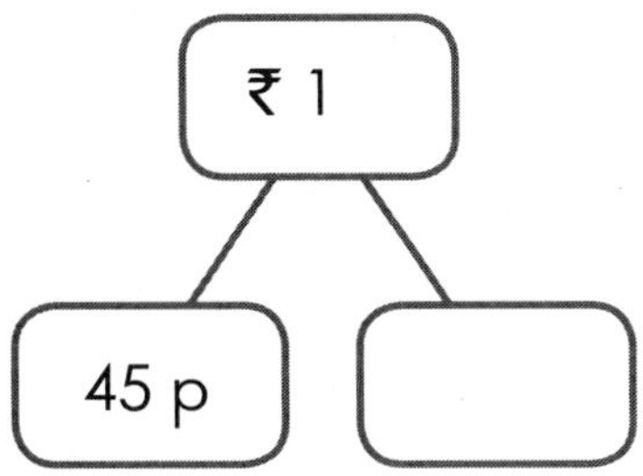

b)

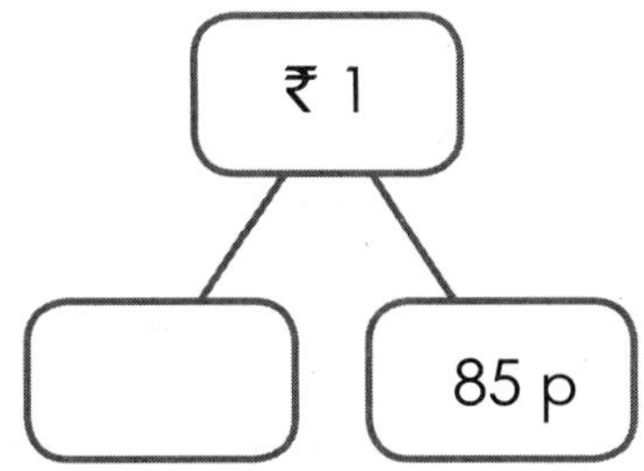

c)

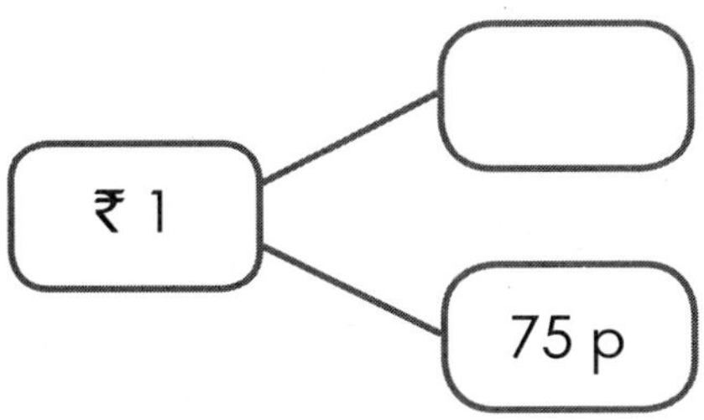

d)

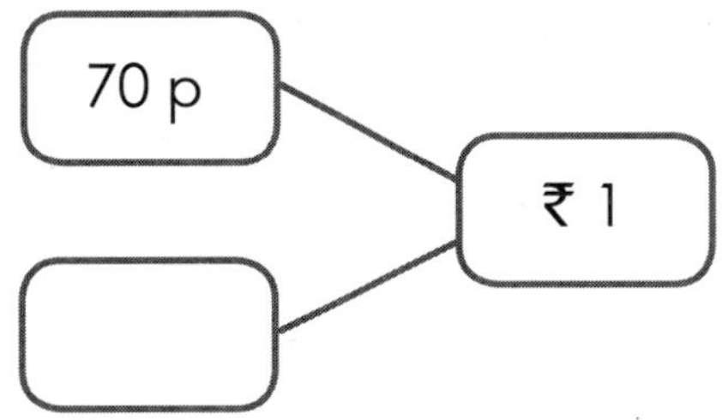

2. Write the missing amount of money on each arrow.

Example

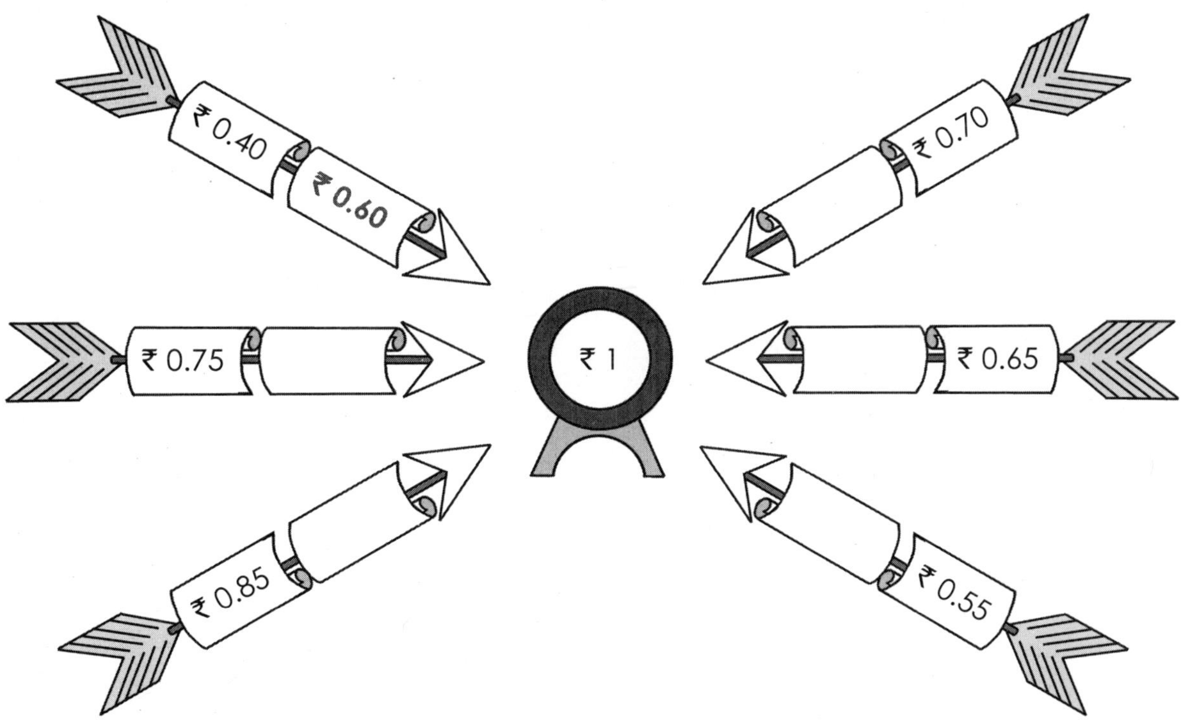

Exercise 6 Adding Amounts of Money

1. Add.

a) ₹ 0.85 $\xrightarrow{+₹\ 4}$ ₹ ________
b) ₹ 1.45 $\xrightarrow{+₹\ 3}$ ₹ ________
c) ₹ 2.05 $\xrightarrow{+₹\ 8}$ ₹ ________
d) ₹ 3.70 $\xrightarrow{+₹\ 10}$ ₹ ________
e) ₹ 2.35 $\xrightarrow{+\ 20\ p}$ ₹ ________
f) ₹ 1.25 $\xrightarrow{+\ 65\ p}$ ₹ ________
g) ₹ 2.60 $\xrightarrow{+\ 25\ p}$ ₹ ________
h) ₹ 5.05 $\xrightarrow{+\ 35\ p}$ ₹ ________

 ISBN 978-93-5103-030-0

2. Write the missing numbers.

a) ₹ 1.45 —(+ ₹ 2)→ ₹ ________ —(+ 30 p)→ ₹ ________

₹ 1.45 + ₹ 2.30 = ₹ ________

b) ₹ 2.60 —(+ ₹ 3)→ ₹ ________ —(+ 25 p)→ ₹ ________

₹ 2.60 + ₹ 3.25 = ₹ ________

c) ₹ 3.15 —(+ ₹ 2)→ ₹ ________ —(+ 65 p)→ ₹ ________

₹ 3.15 + ₹ 2.65 = ₹ ________

3. Add.

a) ₹ 2.40 + ₹ 1.20 =

b) ₹ 4.20 + ₹ 2.70 =

c) ₹ 2.50 + ₹ 2.35 =

d) ₹ 3.45 + ₹ 1.45 =

e) ₹ 2.25 + ₹ 3.25 =

f) ₹ 6.25 + ₹ 2.65 =

 ISBN 978-93-5103-030-0

Exercise 7 Adding Amounts of Money

1. Write the missing numbers.

a) 70 p + 30 p = ₹ ________
b) ₹ 1.70 + 30 p = ₹ ________
c) ₹ 2.25 + 75 p = ₹ ________
d) ₹ 4.45 + 55 p = ₹ ________
e) 35 p + ₹ 5.65 = ₹ ________
f) 85 p + ₹ 6.15 = ₹ ________

2. Write the missing numbers.

a) ₹ 1.30 + 80 p = ₹ ________
b) ₹ 3.55 + 70 p = ₹ ________
c) ₹ 4.65 + 85 p = ₹ ________
d) ₹ 16.45 + 60 p = ₹ ________
e) ₹ 28.45 + 75 p = ₹ ________
f) ₹ 43.55 + 65 p = ₹ ________

 ISBN 978-93-5103-030-0

Exercise 8 Adding Amounts of Money

1. Write the missing numbers.

a)

₹ ________

+ ₹ 8   + 25 p

₹ 3.70 —+ ₹ 8.25→ ₹ ________

b)

₹ ________

+ ₹ 4   + 40 p

₹ 5.85 —+ ₹ 4.40→ ₹ ________

c)

₹ ________

+ ₹ 6   + 75 p

₹ 28.35 —+ ₹ 6.75→ ₹ ________

d)

₹ ________

+ ₹ 20   + 85 p

₹ 46.35 —+ ₹ 20.85→ ₹ ________

2. Add.

a) ₹ 24.30 + ₹ 7.25 = ₹ ________

b) ₹ 30.60 + ₹ 4.50 = ₹ ________

c) ₹ 56.35 + ₹ 12.80 = ₹ ________

d) ₹ 12.85 + ₹ 40.55 = ₹ ________

e) ₹ 37.75 + ₹ 13.70 = ₹ ________

f) ₹ 63.25 + ₹ 29.95 = ₹ ________

 ISBN 978-93-5103-030-0

3. Write the missing numbers.

a)

₹ ________

+ ₹ 1 (arrow up) | − 5 p (arrow down)

₹ 3.80 —(+ ₹ 0.95)→ ₹ ________

b)

₹ ________

+ ₹ 1 (arrow up) | − 5 p (arrow down)

₹ 7.10 —(+ ₹ 0.95)→ ₹ ________

c)

₹ ________

+ ₹ 2 (arrow up) | − 5 p (arrow down)

₹ 14.55 —(+ ₹ 1.95)→ ₹ ________

d)

₹ ________

+ ₹ 15 (arrow up) | − 5 p (arrow down)

₹ 26.30 —(+ ₹ 14.95)→ ₹ ________

4. Add.

a) ₹ 13.40 + ₹ 2.95 = ₹ ________

b) ₹ 24.35 + ₹ 3.95 = ₹ ________

c) ₹ 35.55 + ₹ 4.95 = ₹ ________

d) ₹ 27.95 + ₹ 2.70 = ₹ ________

e) ₹ 40.95 + ₹ 5.60 = ₹ ________

f) ₹ 56.95 + ₹ 3.50 = ₹ ________

 ISBN 978-93-5103-030-0

Exercise 9 Adding Amounts of Money

1. Add.

₹0.85 + ₹2.20 = ____ R	₹3.60 + ₹1.85 = ____ E	₹2.75 + ₹0.80 = ____ B
₹7.75 + ₹0.60 = ____ U	₹4.25 + ₹3.95 = ____ E	₹5.35 + ₹3.95 = ____ Y
₹4.45 + ₹1.75 = ____ B	₹2.95 + ₹3.45 = ____ L	₹1.55 + ₹7.55 = ____ R

What is the name of this fruit?

Write the letters in the boxes below to find out.

₹ 6.20	₹ 6.40	₹ 8.35	₹ 5.45	₹ 3.55	₹ 8.20	₹ 9.10	₹ 3.05	₹ 9.30

 ISBN 978-93-5103-030-0

2. Add.

₹3.60 + ₹1.35 ______ ______ A	₹7.40 + ₹8.95 ______ ______ E	₹11.35 + ₹ 6.25 ______ ______ G
₹31.55 + ₹48.70 ______ ______ I	₹56.35 + ₹37.35 ______ ______ L	₹78.25 + ₹ 6.95 ______ ______ N
₹ 9.85 + ₹34.00 ______ ______ R	₹10.25 + ₹43.15 ______ ______ S	₹49.55 + ₹24.35 ______ ______ T

What can you get by dividing a square into halves?

Write the letters that match the answers to find out.

			A					
₹ 73.90	₹ 43.85	₹ 80.25	₹ 4.95	₹ 85.20	₹ 17.60	₹ 93.70	₹ 16.35	₹ 53.40

 ISBN 978-93-5103-030-0

Exercise 10 Adding Amounts of Money

Solve the word problems. You may draw bar models to help you.
Show your work clearly.

1. Abdul spent ₹ 22.60. His brother spent ₹ 0.95 more.
   How much did his brother spend?

☐ 1. Understand
☐ 2. Plan
☐ 3. Answer
☐ 4. Check

2. Leena bought a ball for ₹ 49.60. She also bought a toy for ₹ 50.20. How much did she spend altogether?

☐ 1. Understand
☐ 2. Plan
☐ 3. Answer
☐ 4. Check

3. Eva has ₹ 5.65. Her mother gives her ₹ 1.70 more.
   How much money does Eva have now?

☐ 1. Understand
☐ 2. Plan
☐ 3. Answer
☐ 4. Check

 ISBN 978-93-5103-030-0

4. Gopal has ₹ 92.65 in the bank. He deposits another ₹ 79.80. How much money does he have in the bank now?

- [ ] 1. Understand
- [ ] 2. Plan
- [ ] 3. Answer
- [ ] 4. Check

5. Jim has ₹ 62.25. He needs ₹ 98.65 more to buy a toy train. What is the cost of the toy train?

- [ ] 1. Understand
- [ ] 2. Plan
- [ ] 3. Answer
- [ ] 4. Check

6. A pack of 12 bangles costs ₹ 80.80. It costs ₹ 98.70 less than a pair of earrings. What is the cost of the pair of earrings?

- [ ] 1. Understand
- [ ] 2. Plan
- [ ] 3. Answer
- [ ] 4. Check

 ISBN 978-93-5103-030-0

Exercise 11 Subtracting Amounts of Money

1. Subtract.

a) ₹ 4.85 $\xrightarrow{-₹ 3}$ ₹ ________
b) ₹ 6.45 $\xrightarrow{-₹ 2}$ ₹ ________
c) ₹ 7.35 $\xrightarrow{-₹ 4}$ ₹ ________
d) ₹ 9.25 $\xrightarrow{-₹ 8}$ ₹ ________
e) ₹ 2.95 $\xrightarrow{-60\text{ p}}$ ₹ ________
f) ₹ 5.75 $\xrightarrow{-70\text{ p}}$ ₹ ________
g) ₹ 6.40 $\xrightarrow{-40\text{ p}}$ ₹ ________
h) ₹ 9.80 $\xrightarrow{-65\text{ p}}$ ₹ ________

 ISBN 978-93-5103-030-0

2. Write the missing numbers.

a) ₹ 6.80 —(– ₹ 2)→ ₹ ________ —(– 50 p)→ ₹ ________

₹ 6.80 – ₹ 2.50 = ₹ ________

b) ₹ 4.75 —(– ₹ 3)→ ₹ ________ —(– 35 p)→ ₹ ________

₹ 4.75 – ₹ 3.35 = ₹ ________

c) ₹ 5.90 —(– ₹ 3)→ ₹ ________ —(– 65 p)→ ₹ ________

₹ 5.90 – ₹ 3.65 = ₹ ________

3. Subtract.

a) ₹ 4.80 – ₹ 1.20 =

b) ₹ 5.85 – ₹ 2.60 =

c) ₹ 5.90 – ₹ 3.75 =

d) ₹ 6.70 – ₹ 2.35 =

e) ₹ 4.50 – ₹ 2.05 =

f) ₹ 7.70 – ₹ 3.45 =

 ISBN 978-93-5103-030-0

Exercise 12 Subtracting Amounts of Money

1. How much money is needed to make ₹ 10?

a)

₹ 10

₹ 9.20 | ______

b)

₹ 10

______ | ₹ 8.40

c)

______ | ₹ 2.60

₹ 10

d)

______ | ₹ 3.10

₹ 10

2. Write the missing numbers.

a) ₹ 6.50 —+ ______ p→ ₹ 7 —+ ₹ ______→ ₹ 10

₹ 6.50 + ₹ ______ = ₹ 10

b) ₹ 2.25 —+ ______ p→ ₹ 3 —+ ₹ ______→ ₹ 10

₹ 2.25 + ₹ ______ = ₹ 10

c) ₹ 4.70 + ₹ ______ = ₹ 10

d) ₹ ______ + ₹ 3.55 = ₹ 10

e) ₹ 1.75 + ₹ ______ = ₹ 10

 ISBN 978-93-5103-030-0

Exercise 13 Subtracting Amounts of Money

1. Write the missing numbers.

a) ₹ 4 —(− 80 p)→ ₹ ________

b) ₹ 5 —(− 70 p)→ ₹ ________

c) ₹ 3 —(− 55 p)→ ₹ ________

d) ₹ 6 —(− 75 p)→ ₹ ________

₹ 4 − 80 p
/ \
₹ 3 ₹ 1
Subtract 80 p from ₹ 1.

2. Subtract.

a) ₹ 1.40 − 60 p =
b) ₹ 2.55 − 50 p =
c) ₹ 4.35 − 85 p =
d) ₹ 13.30 − 75 p =
e) ₹ 27.45 − 55 p =
f) ₹ 49.25 − 80 p =

 ISBN 978-93-5103-030-0

Exercise 14 Subtracting Amounts of Money

1. Write the missing numbers.

a)

₹ ______

– ₹ 2 (arrow up) – 25 p (arrow down)

₹ 4.50 —(– ₹ 2.25)→ ₹ ______

b)

₹ ______

– ₹ 4 (arrow up) – 80 p (arrow down)

₹ 6.35 —(– ₹ 4.80)→ ₹ ______

c)

₹ ______

– ₹ 18 (arrow up) – 60 p (arrow down)

₹ 30 —(– ₹ 18.60)→ ₹ ______

d)

₹ ______

– ₹ 23 (arrow up) – 45 p (arrow down)

₹ 40.05 —(– ₹ 23.45)→ ₹ ______

2. Subtract.

a) ₹ 14.30 – ₹ 9.25 = ₹ ______
b) ₹ 7.40 – ₹ 3.35 = ₹ ______
c) ₹ 62.30 – ₹ 8.70 = ₹ ______
d) ₹ 80 – ₹ 26.45 = ₹ ______
e) ₹ 76.25 – ₹ 58.90 = ₹ ______
f) ₹ 90.30 – ₹ 19.95 = ₹ ______

 ISBN 978-93-5103-030-0

3. Write the missing numbers.

a) ₹ 2.20 —(– ₹ 0.95)→ ₹ ________

– ₹ 1 : ₹ 2.20 → ₹ ________ ; + 5 p → ₹ ________

b) ₹ 17.85 —(– ₹ 0.95)→ ₹ ________

– ₹ 1 : ₹ 17.85 → ₹ ________ ; + 5 p → ₹ ________

c) ₹ 25.50 —(– ₹ 3.95)→ ₹ ________

– ₹ 4 : ₹ 25.50 → ₹ ________ ; + 5 p → ₹ ________

d) ₹ 40.35 —(– ₹ 12.95)→ ₹ ________

– ₹ 13 : ₹ 40.35 → ₹ ________ ; + 5 p → ₹ ________

4. Subtract.

a) ₹ 4.10 – ₹ 3.95 = ₹ ________

b) ₹ 8.25 – ₹ 5.95 = ₹ ________

c) ₹ 26.45 – ₹ 4.95 = ₹ ________

d) ₹ 37.35 – ₹ 6.95 = ₹ ________

e) ₹ 49.75 – ₹ 7.95 = ₹ ________

f) ₹ 50.60 – ₹ 8.95 = ₹ ________

 ISBN 978-93-5103-030-0

Exercise 15 Subtracting Amounts of Money

1. Subtract.

₹2.25 − ₹0.60 ______ **R**	₹3.10 − ₹0.55 ______ **C**	₹5.00 − ₹0.25 ______ **I**
₹7.00 − ₹3.70 ______ **N**	₹6.35 − ₹3.50 ______ **O**	₹7.45 − ₹2.55 ______ **T**
₹8.50 − ₹5.90 ______ **A**	₹4.30 − ₹3.85 ______ **A**	₹9.20 − ₹7.65 ______ **N**

What is the name of this flower?

Write the letters in the boxes below to find out.

₹ 2.55	₹ 0.45	₹ 1.65	₹ 3.30	₹ 2.60	₹ 4.90	₹ 4.75	₹ 2.85	₹ 1.55

 ISBN 978-93-5103-030-0

2. Subtract.

₹64.60 − ₹27.40 ______ T	₹50.20 − ₹24.50 ______ L	₹60.35 − ₹43.90 ______ H
₹70.50 − ₹ 7.05 ______ E	₹20.45 − ₹ 3.50 ______ P	₹32.00 − ₹24.99 ______ E
₹41.30 − ₹ 5.35 ______ O	₹25.60 − ₹ 9.75 ______ E	₹27.80 − ₹17.90 ______ N

What has a ring but has no finger?
Write the letters in the spaces provided below to find out.

A ____ ____ ____ ____ ____ ____ ____ ____ ____
₹ 37.20 ₹ 63.45 ₹ 25.70 ₹ 7.01 ₹ 16.95 ₹ 16.45 ₹ 35.95 ₹ 9.90 ₹ 15.85

3. Subtract.

a)	5640 − 390 ______	₹56.40 − ₹ 3.90 ______
b)	4280 − 1755 ______	₹42.80 − ₹17.55 ______
c)	6025 − 1485 ______	₹60.25 − ₹14.85 ______
d)	5000 − 1485 ______	₹50.00 − ₹14.85 ______

  ISBN 978-93-5103-030-0

Exercise 16 Subtracting Amounts of Money

Solve the word problems. You may draw bar models to help you.
Show your work clearly.

1. Samy had ₹ 8. He bought a pencil for ₹ 5.35.
   How much money did he have left?

☐ 1. Understand
☐ 2. Plan
☐ 3. Answer
☐ 4. Check

2. A whistle costs ₹ 5.90. A balloon costs ₹ 3.85.
   How much cheaper is the balloon than the whistle?

☐ 1. Understand
☐ 2. Plan
☐ 3. Answer
☐ 4. Check

3. Lily saved ₹ 10. She saved ₹ 1.95 more than Alka.
   How much did Alka save?

☐ 1. Understand
☐ 2. Plan
☐ 3. Answer
☐ 4. Check

 ISBN 978-93-5103-030-0

4. Saba bought a pair of scissors and a pen for ₹ 60.25.
The pen cost ₹ 16.90. How much did the pair of scissors cost?

- [ ] 1. Understand
- [ ] 2. Plan
- [ ] 3. Answer
- [ ] 4. Check

5. Mrs. Gupta spent ₹ 97.60 at a supermarket. She spent ₹ 3.55 more than Mrs. Rao. How much did Mrs. Rao spend?

- [ ] 1. Understand
- [ ] 2. Plan
- [ ] 3. Answer
- [ ] 4. Check

6. The usual price of a diary is ₹ 70. At a sale, it is sold for ₹ 47.95.
How much cheaper is the diary at the sale?

- [ ] 1. Understand
- [ ] 2. Plan
- [ ] 3. Answer
- [ ] 4. Check

 ISBN 978-93-5103-030-0

Exercise 17 Problem Solving

Solve the word problems. You may draw bar models to help you. Show your work clearly.

1. Maya bought a pair of socks for ₹ 24.95. She also bought a handkerchief for ₹ 9.50. She gave the shopkeeper ₹ 50. How much change did she receive?

- ☐ 1. Understand
- ☐ 2. Plan
- ☐ 3. Answer
- ☐ 4. Check

2. Sarah bought a glue stick and a stapler. The glue stick cost ₹ 11.20. The stapler cost ₹ 52.60 more than the glue stick. How much did she spend altogether?

- ☐ 1. Understand
- ☐ 2. Plan
- ☐ 3. Answer
- ☐ 4. Check

 ISBN 978-93-5103-030-0

3. Atul spent ₹ 33.80 on breakfast. He spent ₹ 11.25 less on an afternoon snack than on breakfast. He had no money left. How much money did he have at first?

- [ ] 1. Understand
- [ ] 2. Plan
- [ ] 3. Answer
- [ ] 4. Check

4. Mary bought a pen and a notebook.
She gave the cashier ₹ 70 and received a change of ₹ 2.25.
The notebook cost ₹ 37.35. How much did the pen cost?

- [ ] 1. Understand
- [ ] 2. Plan
- [ ] 3. Answer
- [ ] 4. Check

 ISBN 978-93-5103-030-0

6 Mental Calculation

Exercise 1 Mental Addition

1. Add mentally.

   a) $42 \xrightarrow{+50}$ ________ b) $53 \xrightarrow{+30}$ ________

   c) $35 \xrightarrow{+60}$ ________ d) $86 \xrightarrow{+20}$ ________

2. Add mentally.

   a) 84 + 7 = ________ b) 48 + 9 = ________

   c) 18 + 80 = ________ d) 45 + 90 = ________

   e) 76 + 30 = ________ f) 54 + 50 = ________

3. Write the missing numbers.

   a)

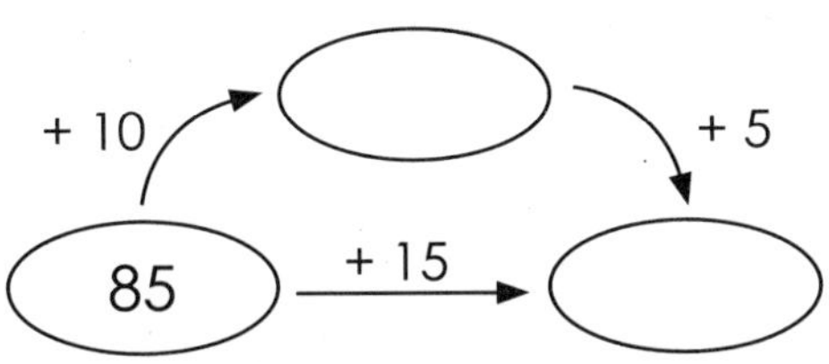

   b)

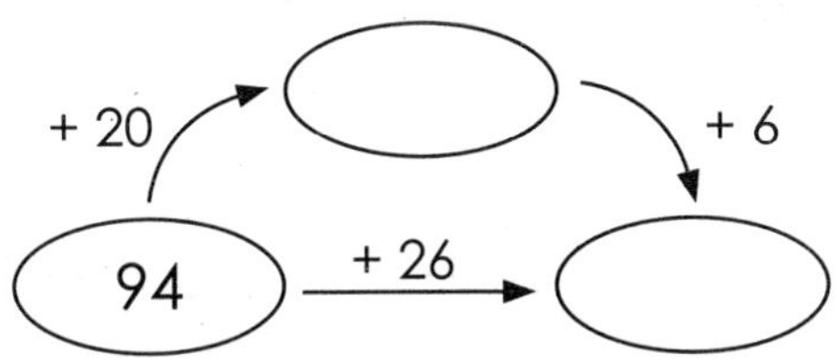

4. Add mentally.

   a) 58 + 34 = ________

   b) 46 + 24 = ________

   c) 24 + 68 = ________

   d) 47 + 62 = ________

 ISBN 978-93-5103-030-0

Exercise 2 Mental Addition

1. Add mentally.

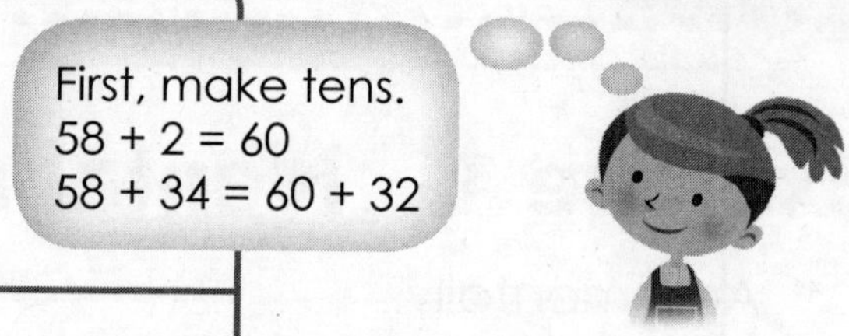

a) 58 + 34 = ________

34 → 2, 32

b) 37 + 49 = ________

37 → 36, 1

c) 87 + 43 = ________

43 → 3, 40

d) 69 + 54 = ________

e) 98 + 47 = ________

f) 45 + 95 = ________

g) 52 + 98 = ________

h) 49 + 36 = ________

 ISBN 978-93-5103-030-0

2. Add mentally.

a) 32 + 28 = ________	b) 45 + 55 = ________
c) 44 + 26 = ________	d) 59 + 31 = ________
e) 66 + 34 = ________	f) 59 + 41 = ________
g) 63 + 27 = ________	h) 18 + 82 = ________

3. Add mentally.

a) 99 + 6 = ________	b) 98 + 4 = ________
c) 98 + 43 = ________	d) 67 + 99 = ________
e) 83 + 99 = ________	f) 98 + 37 = ________
g) 98 + 92 = ________	h) 96 + 99 = ________
i) 99 + 98 = ________	j) 99 + 99 = ________

 ISBN 978-93-5103-030-0

Exercise 3 Mental Subtraction

1. Subtract mentally.

a) $42 \xrightarrow{-30}$ ________ b) $25 \xrightarrow{-20}$ ________

c) $97 \xrightarrow{-70}$ ________ d) $87 \xrightarrow{-60}$ ________

2. Subtract mentally.

a) $63 - 8 =$ ________ b) $34 - 5 =$ ________

c) $81 - 4 =$ ________ d) $57 - 9 =$ ________

3. Write the missing numbers.

a) $87 \xrightarrow{-40}$ ________ $\xrightarrow{-7}$ ________

$87 - 47 =$ ________

b) $93 \xrightarrow{-30}$ ________ $\xrightarrow{-4}$ ________

$93 - 34 =$ ________

4. Subtract.

a) $67 - 49 =$ ________

b) $84 - 78 =$ ________

c) $92 - 35 =$ ________

d) $46 - 27 =$ ________

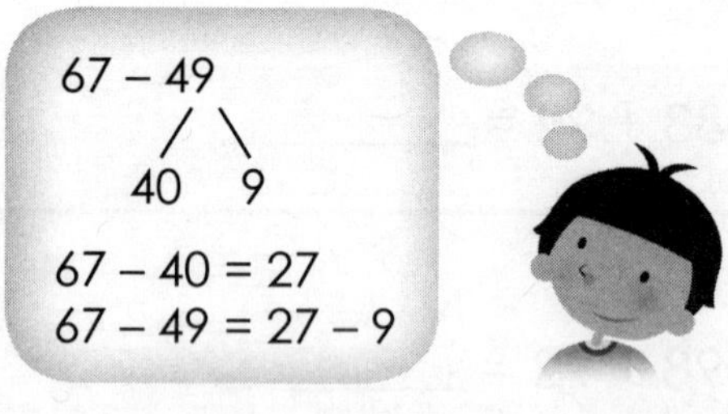

 ISBN 978-93-5103-030-0

Exercise 4 Mental Subtraction

1. Subtract mentally.

a) $80 - 58 =$ ________

20 60

b) $60 - 47 =$ ________

10 50

c) $70 - 29 =$ ________

d) $80 - 38 =$ ________

e) $90 - 67 =$ ________

f) $50 - 26 =$ ________

g) $70 - 45 =$ ________

h) $90 - 64 =$ ________

 ISBN 978-93-5103-030-0

Exercise 5 Mental Multiplication

1. Write the missing numbers.

Example

2 tens × 6 = **12** tens — 20 × 6 = **120**

a) 3 tens × 5 = ________ tens — 30 × 5 = ________

b) 4 tens × 5 = ________ tens — 40 × 5 = ________

c) 5 hundreds × 7 = ________ hundreds — 500 × 7 = ________

d) 6 hundreds × 4 = ________ hundreds — 600 × 4 = ________

2. Multiply.

2 × 8 = ________	20 × 8 = ________	200 × 8 = ________
3 × 7 = ________	30 × 7 = ________	300 × 7 = ________
4 × 6 = ________	40 × 6 = ________	400 × 6 = ________
5 × 8 = ________	50 × 8 = ________	500 × 8 = ________
6 × 6 = ________	60 × 6 = ________	600 × 6 = ________
7 × 8 = ________	70 × 8 = ________	700 × 8 = ________

 ISBN 978-93-5103-030-0

3. Multiply.

a)

2 tens × 4 = ________ tens

20 × 4 = ________

b)

4 hundreds × 2 = ________ hundreds

400 × 2 = ________

c) 80 × 5 = ________	d) 20 × 6 = ________
e) 20 × 7 = ________	f) 40 × 8 = ________
g) 50 × 4 = ________	h) 90 × 9 = ________
i) 60 × 3 = ________	j) 70 × 2 = ________
k) 300 × 8 = ________	l) 800 × 6 = ________
m) 400 × 9 = ________	n) 600 × 5 = ________
o) 700 × 4 = ________	p) 200 × 3 = ________
q) 900 × 2 = ________	r) 500 × 7 = ________

 ISBN 978-93-5103-030-0

Exercise 6 Mental Division

1. Write the missing numbers.

Example

8 tens ÷ 2 = **4** tens — 80 ÷ 2 = **40**

a) 9 tens ÷ 3 = ______ tens — 90 ÷ 3 = ______

b) 10 tens ÷ 5 = ______ tens — 100 ÷ 5 = ______

c) 9 hundreds ÷ 3 = ______ hundreds — 900 ÷ 3 = ______

d) 12 hundreds ÷ 3 = ______ hundreds — 1200 ÷ 3 = ______

2. Divide.

6 ÷ 2 = ______	60 ÷ 2 = ______	600 ÷ 2 = ______
8 ÷ 2 = ______	80 ÷ 2 = ______	800 ÷ 2 = ______
15 ÷ 3 = ______	150 ÷ 3 = ______	1500 ÷ 3 = ______
12 ÷ 4 = ______	120 ÷ 4 = ______	1200 ÷ 4 = ______
16 ÷ 4 = ______	160 ÷ 4 = ______	1600 ÷ 4 = ______
18 ÷ 6 = ______	180 ÷ 6 = ______	1800 ÷ 6 = ______

 ISBN 978-93-5103-030-0

3. Divide.

a) 

20 tens ÷ 4 = ________ tens

200 ÷ 4 = ________

b) 

10 hundreds ÷ 2 = ________ hundreds

1000 ÷ 2 = ________

c) 120 ÷ 6 = ________	d) 640 ÷ 8 = ________
e) 270 ÷ 3 = ________	f) 450 ÷ 9 = ________
g) 240 ÷ 4 = ________	h) 160 ÷ 2 = ________
i) 250 ÷ 5 = ________	j) 490 ÷ 7 = ________
k) 1800 ÷ 2 = ________	l) 2400 ÷ 3 = ________
m) 2000 ÷ 4 = ________	n) 3500 ÷ 5 = ________
o) 4000 ÷ 8 = ________	p) 4200 ÷ 7 = ________
q) 5400 ÷ 6 = ________	r) 3600 ÷ 9 = ________

 ISBN 978-93-5103-030-0

7 Graphs

Exercise 1 Block Graphs

1. The block graph shows the number of toy cars four brothers have.

Number of toy cars

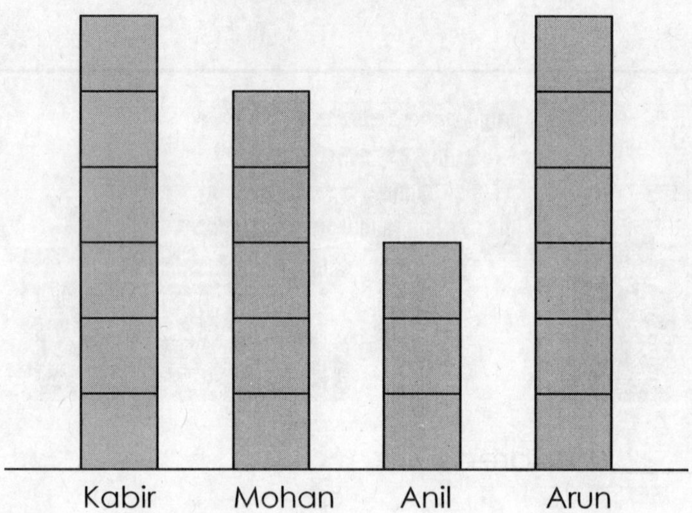

Fill in the blanks.

a) ________________ has the fewest toy cars.

b) ________________ and ________________ have the same number of toy cars.

c) Mohan has ________________ toy cars.

d) The brothers have ________________ toy cars altogether.

 ISBN 978-93-5103-030-0

2. The block graph shows the number of paper animals Rohit made in his art class.

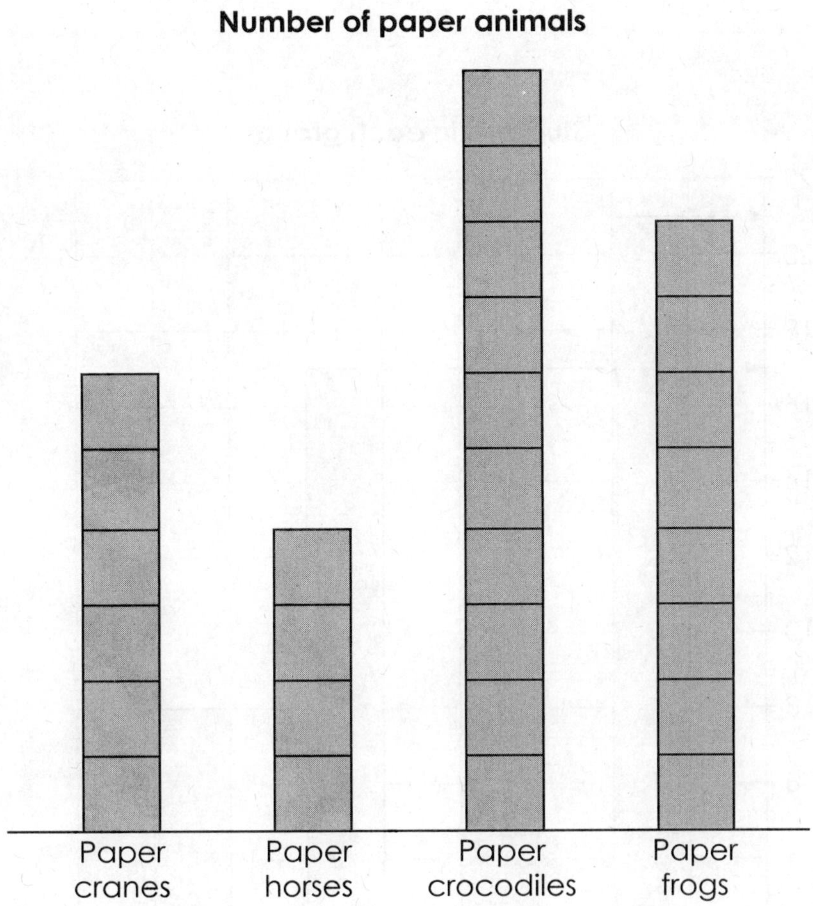

Fill in the blanks.

a) Rohit made the most number of ______________.

b) He made more paper cranes than paper ______________.

c) He made ______________ paper animals in all.

 ISBN 978-93-5103-030-0

Exercise 2 Bar Graphs

1. The bar graph shows the number of students in each study group.

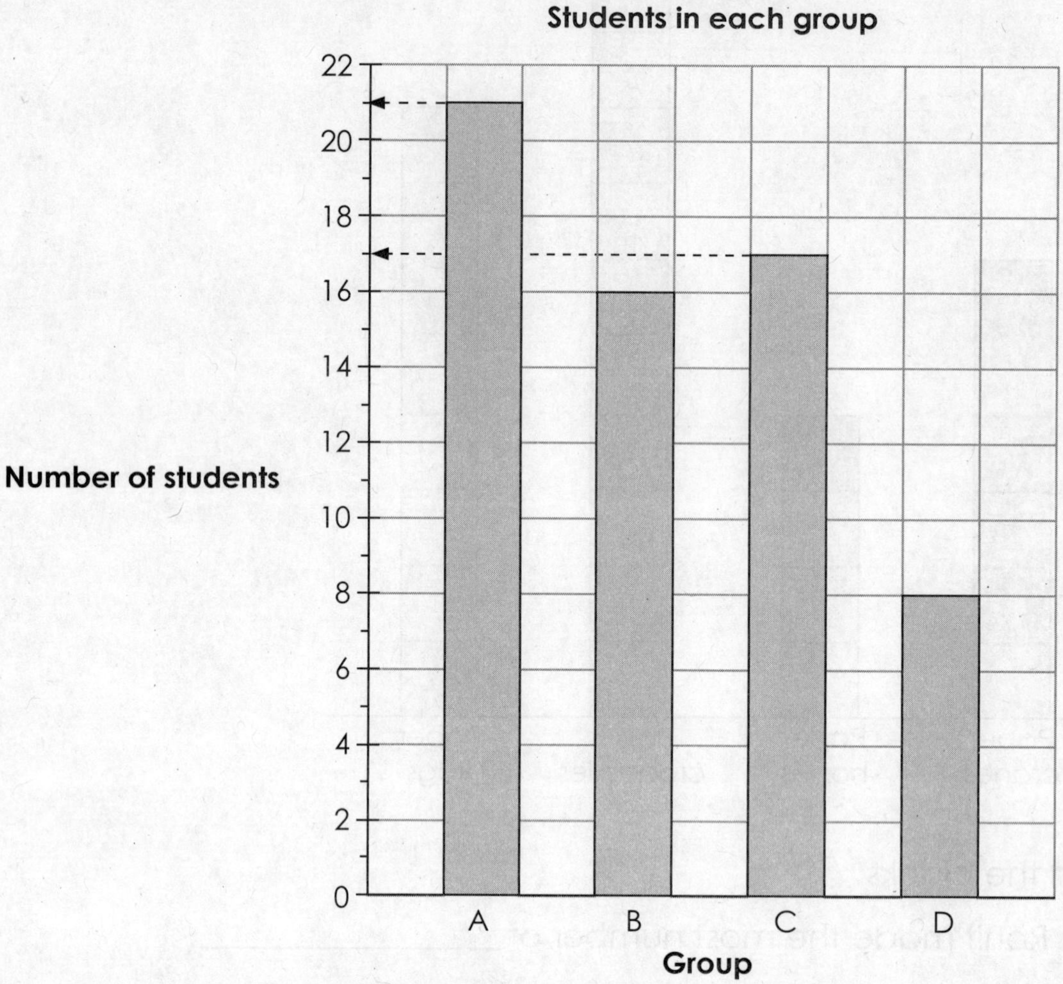

Fill in the blanks.

a) There are ________ more students in Group A than in Group C.

b) There are ________ times as many students in Group B than in Group D.

c) There are 9 girls and ________ boys in Group C.

d) There are ________ students altogether.

 ISBN 978-93-5103-030-0

2. The bar graph shows the number of museum tickets that were sold from Monday to Friday.

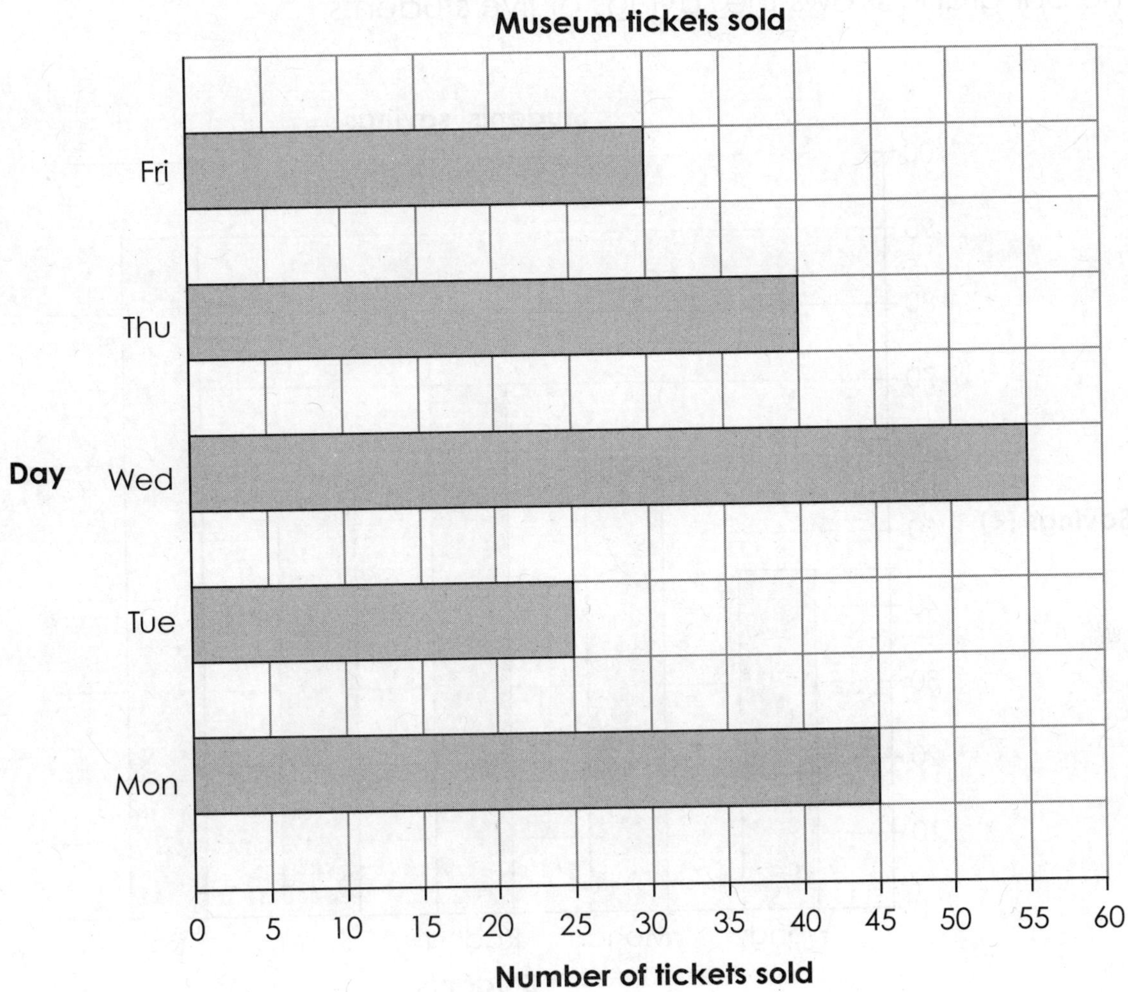

Answer the questions.

a) How many tickets were sold on Friday? ______________

b) How many more tickets were sold on Wednesday than on Thursday? ______________

c) On which day were the most number of tickets sold? ______________

d) What was the total number of tickets sold on Monday, Tuesday and Thursday? ______________

 ISBN 978-93-5103-030-0

Exercise 3 Bar Graphs

1. The bar graph shows the savings of five students.

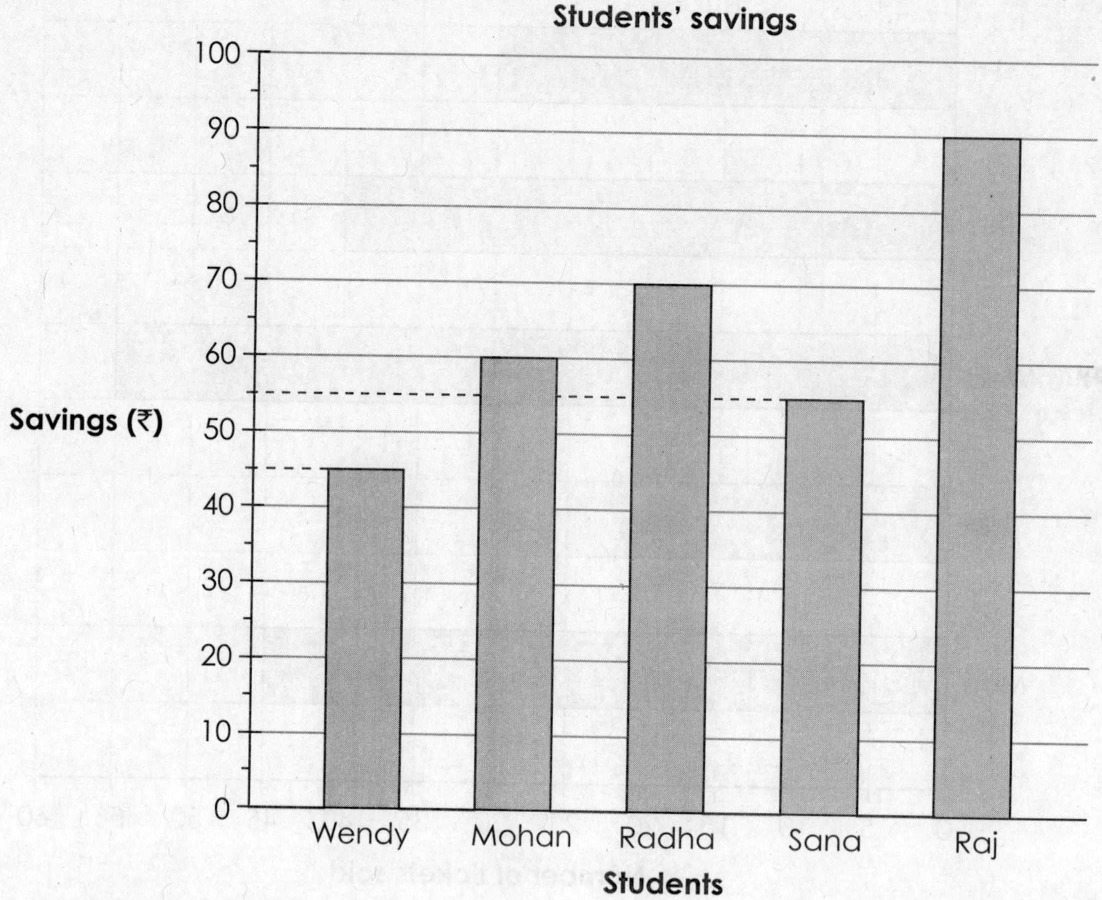

Fill in the blanks.

a) Wendy saved ₹ ________.

b) Radha saved ₹ ________ more than Mohan.

c) ________ saved twice as much as Wendy.

d) ________ saved the most.

e) Mohan, Radha and Sana saved ₹ ________ altogether.

 ISBN 978-93-5103-030-0

2. The bar graph shows the number of cricket cards collected by five boys.

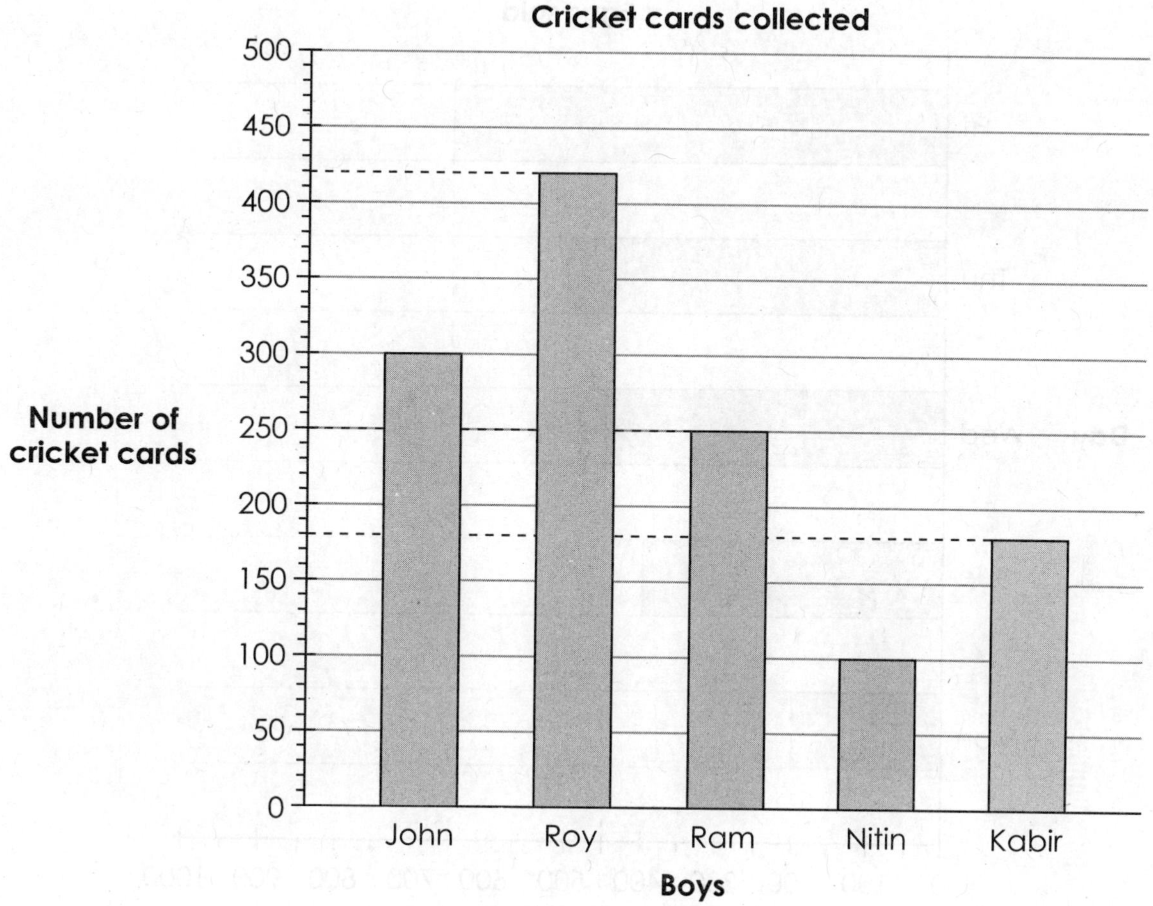

Fill in the blanks.

a) Kabir collected ________________ cricket cards.

b) John collected ________________ fewer cricket cards than Roy.

c) John collected 50 more cricket cards than ________________.

d) ________________ collected 3 times as many cricket cards as Nitin.

e) If Kabir gave Nitin ________________ cricket cards, they would each have an equal number of cricket cards.

 ISBN 978-93-5103-030-0

3. The bar graph shows the number of eggs Mrs. Pinto sold from Monday to Friday.

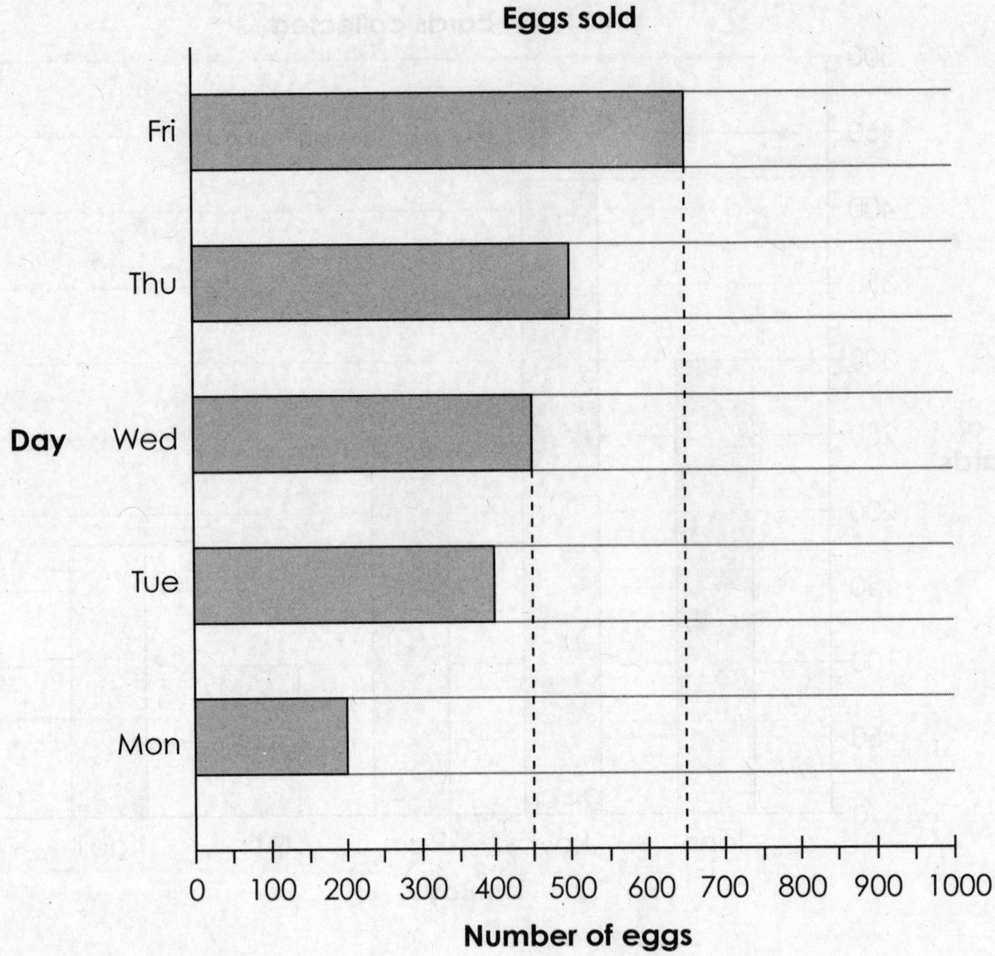

Fill in the blanks.

a) Mrs. Pinto sold ________________ eggs on Friday.

b) She sold ________________ more eggs on Friday than on Thursday.

c) She sold 450 eggs on ________________.

d) She sold twice as many eggs on Tuesday as on ________________.

e) She sold ________________ eggs altogether on the five days.

 ISBN 978-93-5103-030-0

8 Length

Exercise 1 Metres and Centimetres

1. Work with your friends.

   a) Estimate the length of your classroom.
   Then, measure the length with a measuring tape.

   b) Estimate how far you can walk in ten steps.
   Then, measure the distance with a measuring tape.

	My estimate	My measure
Length of classroom	about ________ m	about ________ m ________ cm
Distance in ten steps	about ________ m	about ________ m ________ cm

2. Express in centimetres.

   a) 2 m = ________ cm b) 3 m = ________ cm

   c) 5 m = ________ cm d) 9 m = ________ cm

3. Express in metres.

   a) 400 cm = ________ m b) 600 cm = ________ m

   c) 700 cm = ________ m d) 800 cm = ________ m

 ISBN 978-93-5103-030-0

4. Express in centimetres.

a) 1 m 50 cm = ________ cm

b) 3 m 28 cm = ________ cm

c) 5 m 9 cm = ________ cm

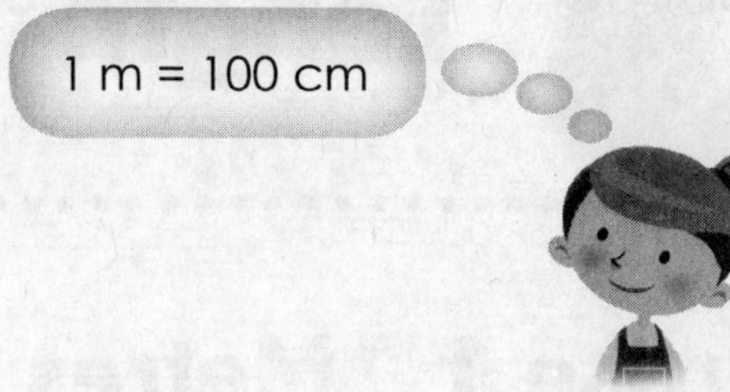

5. Express in metres and centimetres.

a) 210 cm = ________ m ________ cm

b) 275 cm = ________ m ________ cm

c) 306 cm = ________ m ________ cm

6. Circle the correct answer.

a) 135 cm is longer than / equal to / shorter than 1 m 40 cm.

b) 108 cm is longer than / equal to / shorter than 1 m 8 cm.

c) 230 cm is longer than / equal to / shorter than 2 m 3 cm.

7. Arrange the lengths in order. Begin with the shortest.

________, ________, ________, ________
(shortest)

8. Arrange the lengths in order. Begin with the longest.

________, ________, ________, ________
(longest)

 ISBN 978-93-5103-030-0

Exercise 2 Metres and Centimetres

1. Subtract.

   a) 1 m – 53 cm = ________ cm

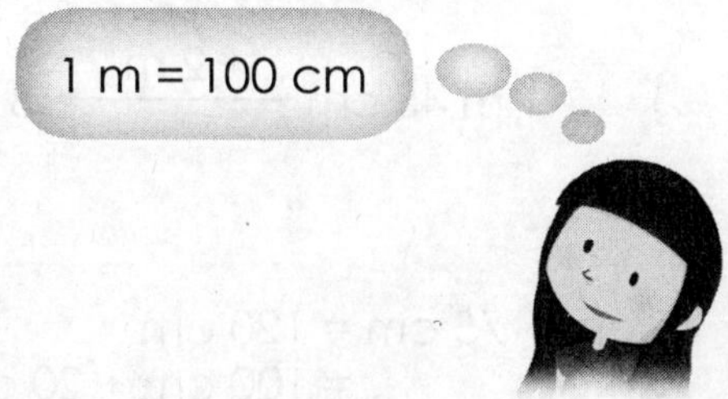

   b) 1 m – 85 cm = ________ cm

   c) 1 m – 74 cm = ________ cm

   d) 1 m – 78 cm = ________ cm

   e) 1 m – 97 cm = ________ cm

   f) 1 m – 62 cm = ________ cm

   g) 2 m – 190 cm = ________ cm

   h) 2 m – 1 m 65 cm = ________ cm

   i) 2 m – 1 m 5 cm = ________ cm

   j) 3 m – 2 m 30 cm = ________ cm

2. Add.

   a) 3 m 60 cm + 25 cm = ________ m ________ cm

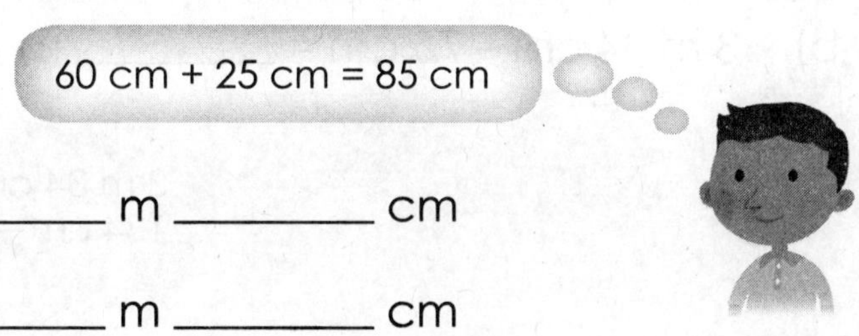

   b) 4 m 25 cm + 45 cm = ________ m ________ cm

   c) 5 m 74 cm + 36 cm = ________ m ________ cm

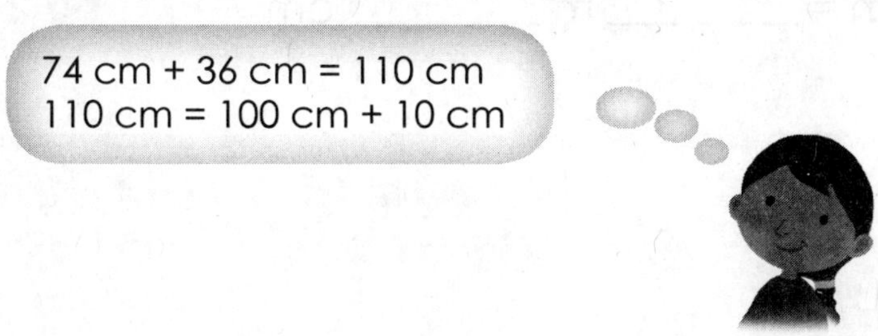

 ISBN 978-93-5103-030-0

3. Add.

a) 1 m 45 cm + 2 m 75 cm = ________ m ________ cm

1 m 45 cm $\xrightarrow{+2\text{ m}}$ 3 m 45 cm $\xrightarrow{+75\text{ cm}}$?

45 cm + 75 cm = 120 cm
= 100 cm + 20 cm

1 m 45 cm = 145 cm
2 m 75 cm = 275 cm
145 cm + 275 cm = ?

b) 2 m 55 cm + 3 m 30 cm = ________ m ________ cm

c) 3 m 28 cm + 4 m 40 cm = ________ m ________ cm

d) 1 m 90 cm + 2 m 36 cm = ________ m ________ cm

e) 4 m 48 cm + 2 m 70 cm = ________ m ________ cm

4. Subtract.

a) 1 m 85 cm – 75 cm = ________ m ________ cm

85 cm – 75 cm = 10 cm

b) 3 m 34 cm – 75 cm = ________ m ________ cm

3 m 34 cm = 2 m 134 cm
134 cm – 75 cm = ?

c) 7 m 25 cm – 86 cm = ________ m ________ cm

 ISBN 978-93-5103-030-0

5. Subtract.

a) 4 m 84 cm – 2 m 95 cm = ________ m ________ cm

4 m 84 cm $\xrightarrow{-2\text{ m}}$ 2 m 84 cm $\xrightarrow{-95\text{ cm}}$?

2 m 84 cm = 1 m 184 cm
184 cm – 95 cm = ?

4 m 84 cm = 484 cm
2 m 95 cm = 295 cm
484 cm – 295 cm = ?

b) 6 m 32 cm – 2 m 20 cm = ________ m ________ cm

c) 5 m 25 cm – 1 m 40 cm = ________ m ________ cm

d) 8 m 36 cm – 4 m 50 cm = ________ m ________ cm

6. Add or subtract. Match the ribbons of the same lengths.

a)	1 m 45 cm + 3 m 55 cm •	• 10 m 1 cm – 85 cm
b)	3 m 68 cm + 2 m 39 cm •	• 12 m – 12 cm
c)	4 m 4 cm + 5 m 12 cm •	• 8 m 90 cm – 3 m 90 cm
d)	6 m 40 cm + 6 m 7 cm •	• 10 m 37 cm – 4 m 30 cm
e)	10 m 8 cm + 1 m 80 cm •	• 13 m 50 cm – 1 m 3 cm

 ISBN 978-93-5103-030-0

Exercise 3 Kilometres

1. Fill in the blanks with **centimetre, metre** or **kilometre**.

   a) The distance from my home to my school is about 1 ______________.

   b) The length of my fingernail is about 1 ______________.

   c) My friend is about 1 ______________ tall.

2. Fill in the blanks.

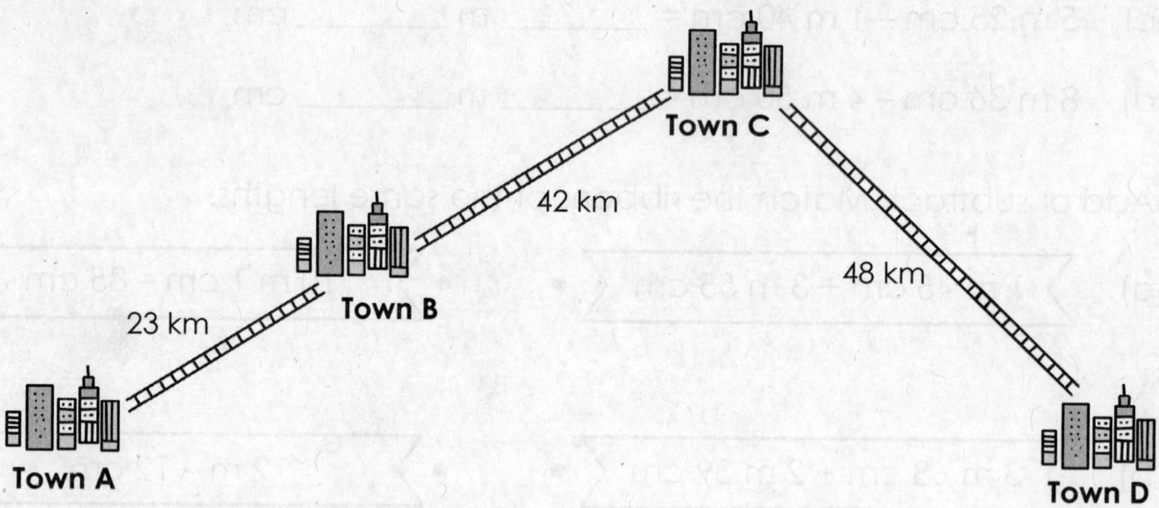

   a) The distance between Town A and Town B is ________ kilometres.

   b) The distance between Town B and Town D is ________ kilometres.

   c) The distance between Town C and Town A is ________ kilometres.

   d) Town B is ________ kilometres further from Town C than from Town A.

   e) Town C is ________ kilometres nearer to Town B than to Town D.

 ISBN 978-93-5103-030-0

Exercise 4 Kilometres

1. Express in metres.

   a) 2 km = ________ m b) 4 km = ________ m

   c) 5 km = ________ m d) 8 km = ________ m

2. Express in kilometres.

   a) 3000 m = ________ km b) 6000 m = ________ km

   c) 7000 m = ________ km d) 9000 m = ________ km

3. Express in metres.

   a) 1 km 145 m = ________ m b) 3 km 50 m = ________ m

   c) 2 km 580 m = ________ m d) 1 km 6 m = ________ m

4. Express in kilometres and metres.

   a) 1732 m = ________ km ________ m

   b) 1300 m = ________ km ________ m

   c) 3260 m = ________ km ________ m

   d) 3006 m = ________ km ________ m

   e) 2108 m = ________ km ________ m

5. Circle the correct answer.

   a) 1250 m is longer than / equal to / shorter than 1 km 25 m.

   b) 3300 m is longer than / equal to / shorter than 3 km 30 m.

   c) 3009 m is longer than / equal to / shorter than 3 km 900 m.

6. Arrange the lengths in order. Begin with the longest.

   7 km 10 m, 7090 m, 7 km 900 m, 7100 m

   ____________, ____________, ____________, ____________
   (longest)

7. Arrange the lengths in order. Begin with the shortest.

   8050 m, 8 km 500 m, 8 km 5 m, 8555 m

   ____________, ____________, ____________, ____________
   (shortest)

 ISBN 978-93-5103-030-0

Exercise 5 Kilometres

1. Match the lengths that add up to 1 kilometre.

950 m •	• 670 m
790 m •	• 820 m
140 m •	• 650 m
330 m •	• 480 m
350 m •	• 570 m
180 m •	• 210 m
520 m •	• 50 m
430 m •	• 860 m

2. Subtract.

a) 1 km – 980 m = ________ m   b) 1 km – 890 m = ________ m

c) 1 km – 790 m = ________ m   d) 1 km – 420 m = ________ m

e) 1 km – 920 m = ________ m   f) 1 km – 880 m = ________ m

3. Add.

a) 1 km 600 m + 250 m = ________ km ________ m

b) 2 km 760 m + 420 m = ________ km ________ m

c) 4 km 850 m + 380 m = ________ km ________ m

 ISBN 978-93-5103-030-0

4. Add.

a) 2 km 460 m + 3 km 650 m = ______ km ______ m

2 km 460 m $\xrightarrow{+\ 3\ \text{km}}$ 5 km 460 m $\xrightarrow{+\ 650\ \text{m}}$?

2 km 460 m = 2460 m
3 km 650 m = 3650 m
2460 m + 3650 m = ?

460 m + 650 m = 1100 m
= 1000 m + 100 m

b) 3 km 620 m + 4 km 350 m = ______ km ______ m

c) 4 km 550 m + 1 km 600 m = ______ km ______ m

d) 6 km 920 m + 2 km 280 m = ______ km ______ m

5. Subtract.

a) 2 km 720 m – 650 m = ______ km ______ m

b) 4 km 460 m – 520 m = ______ km ______ m

4 km 460 m = 3 km 1460 m
1460 m – 520 m = ?

4 km 460 m = 4000 m + 460 m
= 4460 m
4460 m – 520 m = ?

c) 6 km 50 m – 790 m = ______ km ______ m

6. Subtract.

a) 3 km 900 m – 1 km 250 m = ______ km ______ m

b) 8 km 440 m – 2 km 520 m = ______ km ______ m

8 km 440 m $\xrightarrow{-\ 2\ \text{km}}$ 6 km 440 m $\xrightarrow{-\ 520\ \text{m}}$?

8 km 440 m = 8440 m
2 km 520 m = 2520 m
8440 m – 2520 m = ?

8 km 440 m = 7 km 1440 m
1440 m – 520 m = ?

c) 5 km 30 m – 1 km 280 m = ______ km ______ m

d) 9 km 720 m – 2 km 800 m = ______ km ______ m

 ISBN 978-93-5103-030-0

7. Look at the map and answer the questions below.
Express your answers in kilometres and metres.

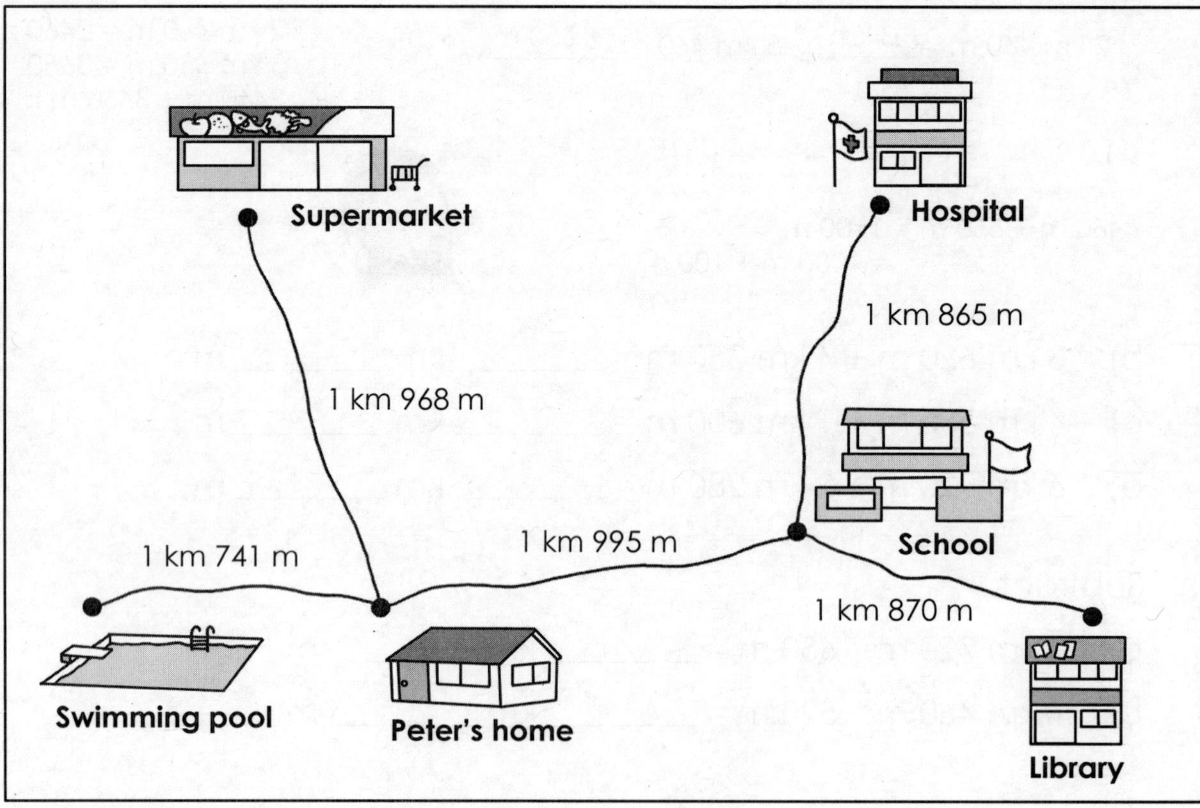

a) What is the distance from Peter's home to the swimming pool? ____________

b) What is the distance from Peter's home to the library? ____________

c) Which is further from Peter's home, the swimming pool or the library? ____________

How much further? ____________

d) Peter travelled from his home to the supermarket and back to his home. What is the total distance that Peter travelled? ____________

e) What is the distance from the hospital to the swimming pool? ____________

 ISBN 978-93-5103-030-0

Exercise 6 Millimetres

1. Fill in the blanks with **millimetres**, **centimetres**, **metres** and **kilometres**.

   a) The length of my book is about 30 ________________.

   b) The length of a railway track is about 20 ________________.

   c) The width of a notebook is about 10 ________________.

   d) The lamp post is about 3 ________________ tall.

2. Express in millimetres.

   a) 4 cm = ________ mm b) 5 cm = ________ mm

   c) 60 cm = ________ mm d) 70 cm = ________ mm

3. Express in centimetres.

   a) 10 mm = ________ cm b) 20 mm = ________ cm

   c) 100 mm = ________ cm d) 300 mm = ________ cm

4. Express in millimetres.

   a) 1 cm 5 mm = ________ mm b) 2 cm 4 mm = ________ mm

   c) 10 cm 1 mm = ________ mm

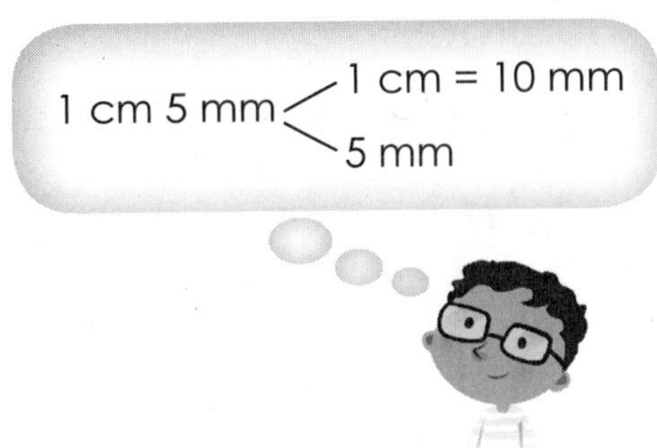

5. Express in centimetres and millimetres.

   a) 37 mm = ________ cm ________ mm

   b) 99 mm = ________ cm ________ mm

   c) 408 mm = ________ cm ________ mm

6. Circle the correct answer.

   a) 100 mm is longer than / as long as / shorter than 10 cm.

   b) 220 mm is longer than / as long as / shorter than 20 cm 2 mm.

   c) 505 mm is longer than / as long as / shorter than 55 cm.

 ISBN 978-93-5103-030-0

Exercise 7 Millimetres

1. Add.

   a) 1 cm 2 mm + 4 mm = ________ cm ________ mm

   b) 2 cm 9 mm + 3 mm = ________ cm ________ mm

   c) 9 cm 7 mm + 6 mm = ________ cm ________ mm

2. Add.

   a) 3 cm 2 mm + 4 cm 3 mm = ________ cm ________ mm

   3 cm 2 mm —+ 4 cm→ 7 cm 2 mm —+ 3 mm→ ?

   b) 5 cm 8 mm + 2 cm 4 mm = ________ cm ________ mm

   5 cm 8 mm —+ 2 cm→ 7 cm 8 mm —+ 4 mm→ 7 cm 12 mm = ?

   c) 8 cm 6 mm + 3 cm 5 mm = ________ cm ________ mm

   d) 10 cm 7 mm + 1 cm 7 mm = ________ cm ________ mm

3. Subtract.

   a) 3 cm 8 mm – 5 mm = ________ cm ________ mm

   8 – 5 = 3

   b) 10 cm 2 mm – 3 mm = ________ cm ________ mm

   10 cm 2 mm = 9 cm 12 mm

   c) 10 cm 1 mm – 4 cm 3 mm = ________ cm ________ mm

   d) 30 cm 3 mm – 3 cm 9 mm = ________ cm ________ mm

 ISBN 978-93-5103-030-0

Exercise 8 Problem Solving

Solve the word problems. You may draw bar models to help you. Show your work clearly.

1. Alka had to take a train and a bus to her grandmother's home. She travelled 5 kilometres 500 metres by train and 3 kilometres 5 metres by bus. How far did Alka travel altogether?

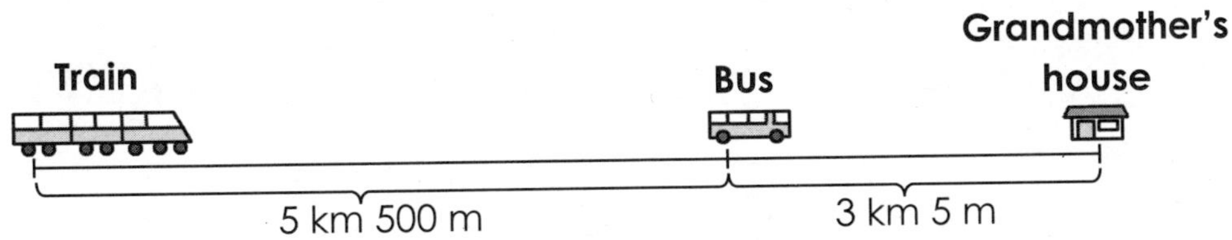

- ☐ 1. Understand
- ☐ 2. Plan
- ☐ 3. Answer
- ☐ 4. Check

2. Max's handkerchief was 13 centimetres 4 millimetres long at first. It shrunk by 9 millimetres after washing. What was the length of Max's handkerchief after washing?

- ☐ 1. Understand
- ☐ 2. Plan
- ☐ 3. Answer
- ☐ 4. Check

 ISBN 978-93-5103-030-0

3. Mr. Singh wants to build a fence on all 4 sides of a square plot of land. He needs 508 metres of fencing in total. How much fencing does Mr. Singh need for each side of the plot of land?

- [ ] 1. Understand
- [ ] 2. Plan
- [ ] 3. Answer
- [ ] 4. Check

4. Radha and her 5 friends took part in a marathon relay. They ran a total distance of 42 kilometres 195 metres. If each friend ran 7 kilometres, how far did Radha run?

- [ ] 1. Understand
- [ ] 2. Plan
- [ ] 3. Answer
- [ ] 4. Check

 ISBN 978-93-5103-030-0

5. The distance from Rohit's home to the library is 2 kilometres 1 metre. The distance from Maya's home to the library is 6 kilometres 210 metres.

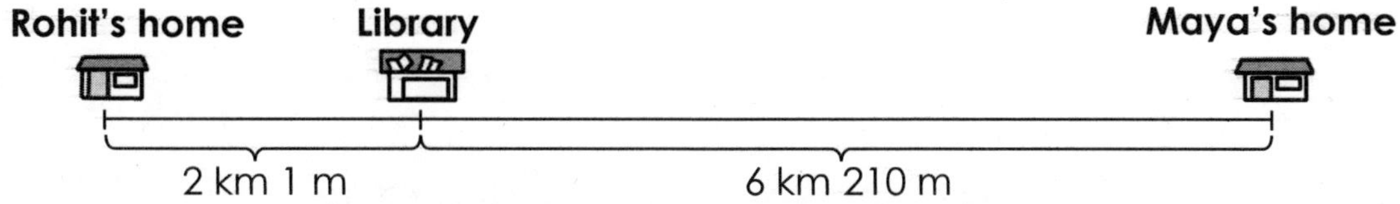

a) What is the distance between Rohit's home and Maya's home?

b) How much further from the library is Maya's home than Rohit's home?

☐ 1. Understand
☐ 2. Plan
☐ 3. Answer
☐ 4. Check

6. A truck is 14 metres 57 centimetres long. It is 9 metres 72 centimetres longer than a car. What is the total length of the truck and the car?

☐ 1. Understand
☐ 2. Plan
☐ 3. Answer
☐ 4. Check

 ISBN 978-93-5103-030-0

9 Weight

Exercise 1 Kilograms and Grams

1. Work with your friends.
Estimate the weight of each of the following.
Then, check the weight with a weighing scale.

Weight of	My estimate	My measure
five books	about ______ kg	about ______ kg ______ g
a school bag	about ______ kg	about ______ kg ______ g
a laptop	about ______ kg	about ______ kg ______ g

2. Fill in the blanks.

a)

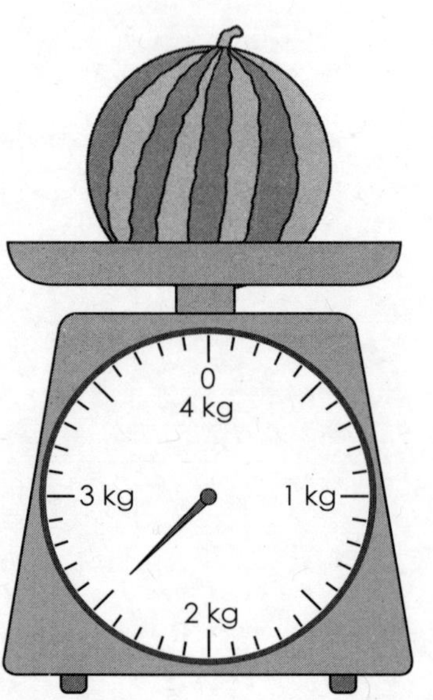

______ kg ______ g

b)

______ kg ______ g

 ISBN 978-93-5103-030-0

c)

_______ kg _______ g

d)

_______ kg _______ g

e)

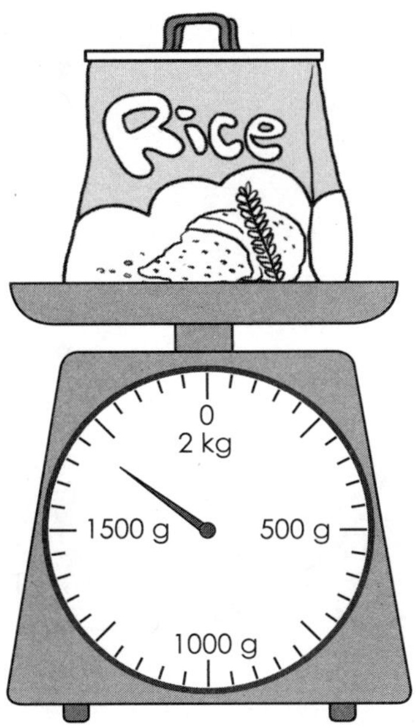

_______ kg _______ g

f)

_______ kg _______ g

 ISBN 978-93-5103-030-0

Exercise 2 Kilograms and Grams

1. Express in grams.

a) 1 kg 800 g = ________ g b) 6 kg 20 g = ________ g

c) 2 kg 300 g = ________ g d) 9 kg 2 g = ________ g

e) 4 kg 83 g = ________ g f) 8 kg 15 g = ________ g

2. Express in kilograms and grams.

a) 1280 g = ______ kg ______ g b) 4069 g = ______ kg ______ g

c) 2506 g = ______ kg ______ g d) 5108 g = ______ kg ______ g

e) 3009 g = ______ kg ______ g f) 6004 g = ______ kg ______ g

3. Match.

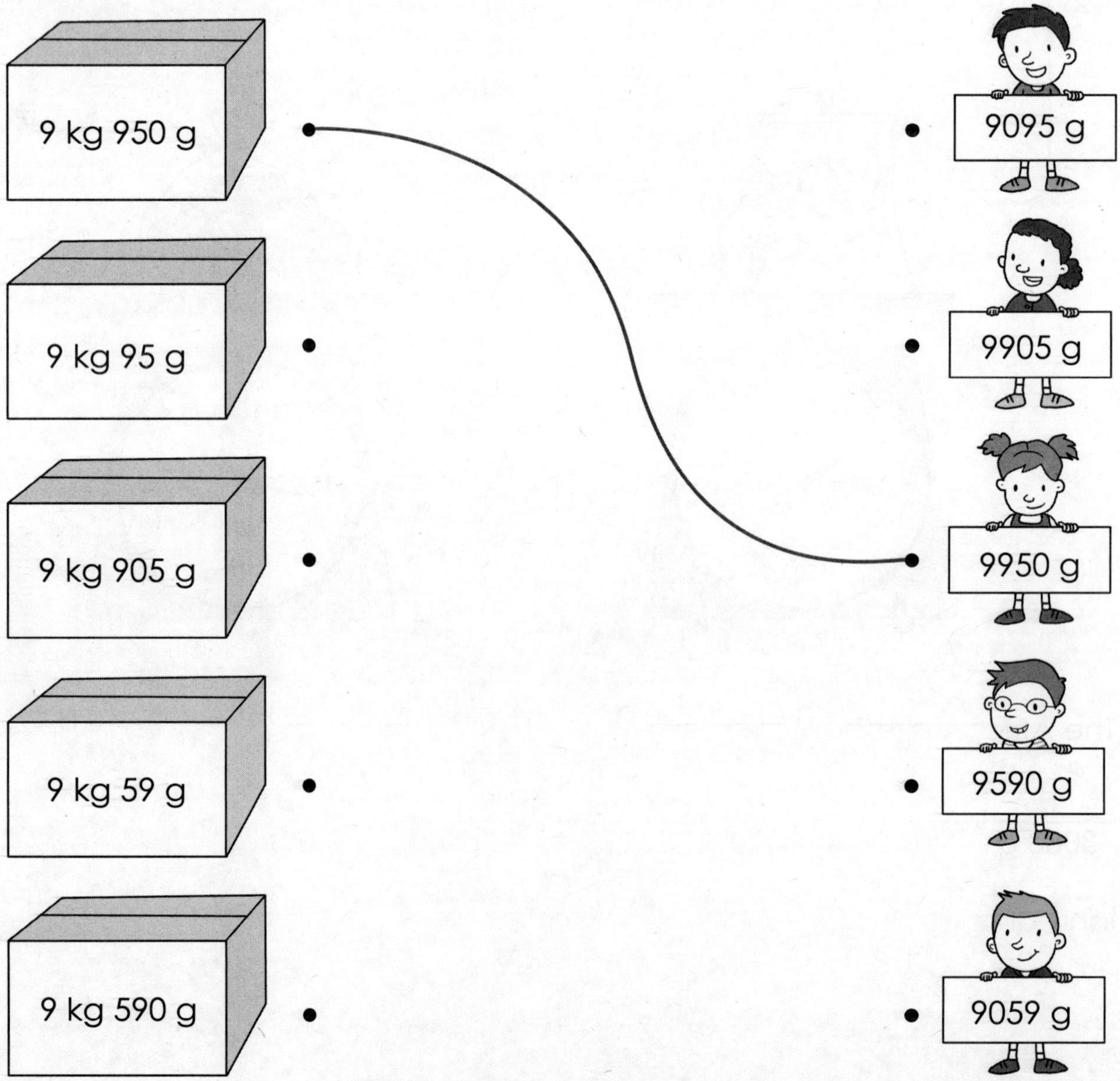

 ISBN 978-93-5103-030-0

4. Write the letters that match the weights and complete the sentence below. The first one is done for you.

1 kg 10 g	a
1 kg 100 g	e
1 kg 25 g	t
1 kg 250 g	v
2 kg 25 g	e
2 kg 50 g	s
3 kg 8 g	i
3 kg 80 g	h

The African elephant is the world's

h							
3080 g	2025 g	1010 g	1250 g	3008 g	1100 g	2050 g	1025 g

land animal.

 ISBN 978-93-5103-030-0

Exercise 3 Kilograms and Grams

1. a) Which is heavier?

1 kg 50 g

duck

1550 g

hen

The ________ is heavier than the ________.

b) Which is lighter?

2 kg 90 g

2780 g

Bag ________ is lighter than Bag ________.

2. Fill in the blanks.

A

1 kg 67 g

B

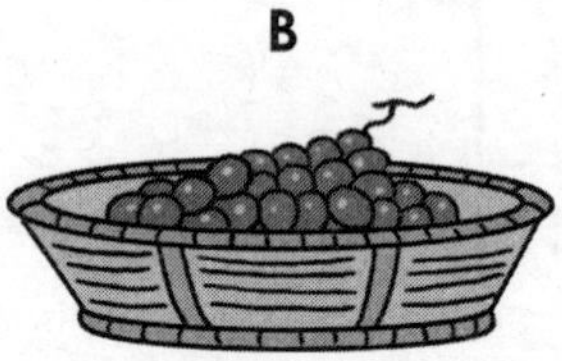

764 g

C

2670 g

D

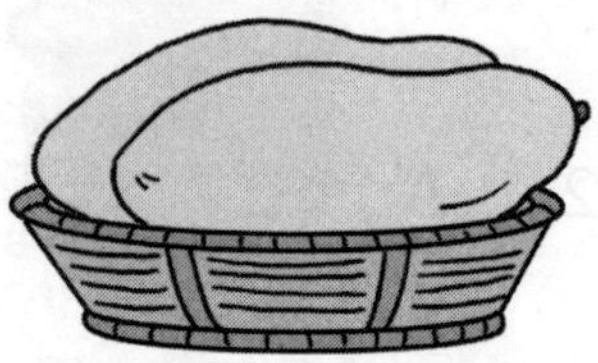

2 kg 700 g

a) Basket ________ is the heaviest.

b) Basket ________ is the lightest.

c) Basket A is heavier than Basket ________.

d) Basket C is lighter than Basket ________.

e) Arrange the baskets in order. Begin with the lightest.

________, ________, ________, ________
(lightest)

 ISBN 978-93-5103-030-0

Exercise 4 Kilograms and Grams

1. Fill in the missing numbers.

a)

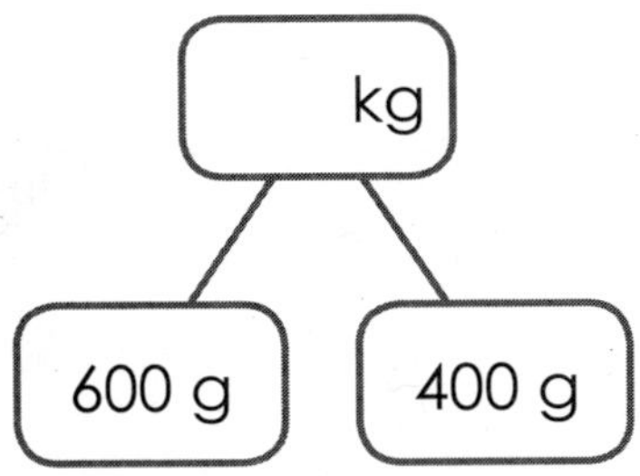

b)

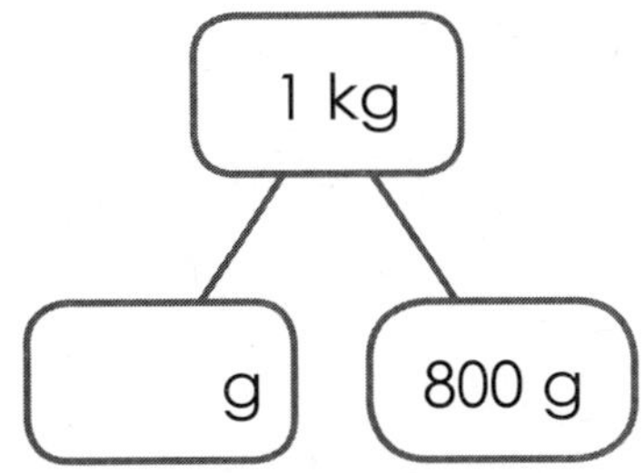

c)

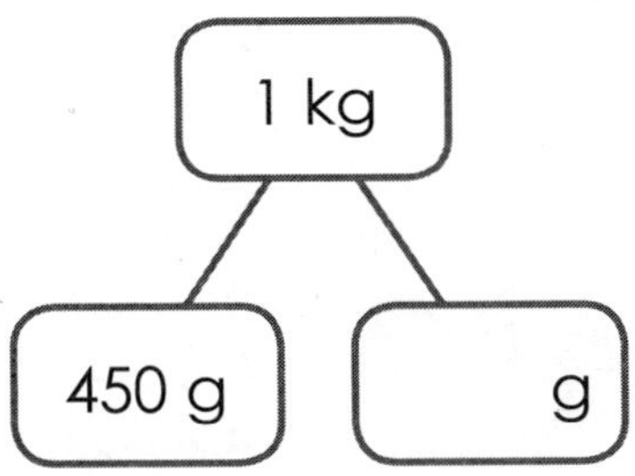

d)

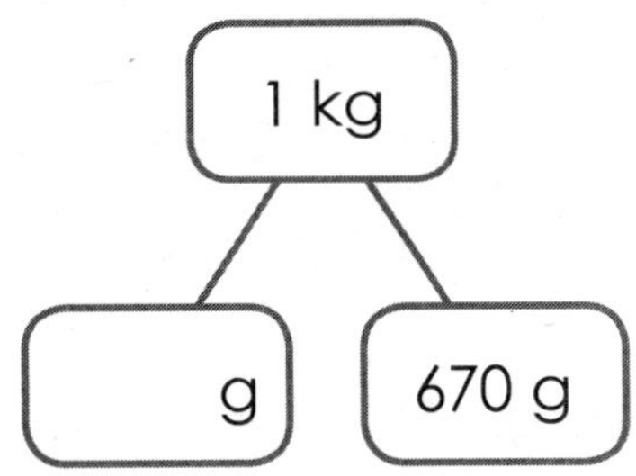

e) 1 kg – 750 g = ________ g

f) 1 kg – 390 g = ________ g

g) 1 kg – 150 g = ________ g

h) 1 kg – 220 g = ________ g

2. Add.

a) 1 kg 300 g + 550 g = ________ kg ________ g

b) 2 kg 650 g + 600 g = ________ kg ________ g

c) 3 kg 850 g + 430 g = ________ kg ________ g

 ISBN 978-93-5103-030-0

3. Add.

a) 2 kg 245 g + 1 kg 520 g = ________ kg ________ g

2 kg 245 g $\xrightarrow{+\,1\text{ kg}}$ 3 kg 245 g $\xrightarrow{+\,520\text{ g}}$?

b) 4 kg 680 g + 1 kg 570 g = ________ kg ________ g

4 kg 680 g $\xrightarrow{+\,1\text{ kg}}$ 5 kg 680 g $\xrightarrow{+\,570\text{ g}}$?

680 g + 570 g = 1250 g
= 1000 g + 250 g

4 kg 680 g = 4680 g
1 kg 570 g = 1570 g
4680 g + 1570 g = ?

c) 3 kg 95 g + 2 kg 960 g = ________ kg ________ g

d) 4 kg 804 g + 3 kg 205 g = ________ kg ________ g

4. Subtract.

a) 4 kg 850 g – 760 g = ________ kg ________ g

b) 5 kg 25 g – 480 g = ________ kg ________ g

c) 7 kg – 365 g = ________ kg ________ g

5. Subtract.

a) 2 kg 924 g – 1 kg 768 g = ________ kg ________ g

2 kg 924 g $\xrightarrow{-\,1\text{ kg}}$ 1 kg 924 g $\xrightarrow{-\,768\text{ g}}$?

 ISBN 978-93-5103-030-0

b) 4 kg 30 g – 1 kg 288 g = ________ kg ________ g

4 kg 30 g $\xrightarrow{-1\text{ kg}}$ 3 kg 30 g $\xrightarrow{-288\text{ g}}$?

3 kg 30 g = 2 kg 1030 g
1030 g – 288 g = ?

4 kg 30 g = 4030 g
1 kg 288 g = 1288 g
4030 g – 1288 g = ?

c) 3 kg 145 g – 2 kg 295 g = ________ kg ________ g

d) 10 kg 5 g – 3 kg 269 g = ________ kg ________ g

6. Fill in the blanks.

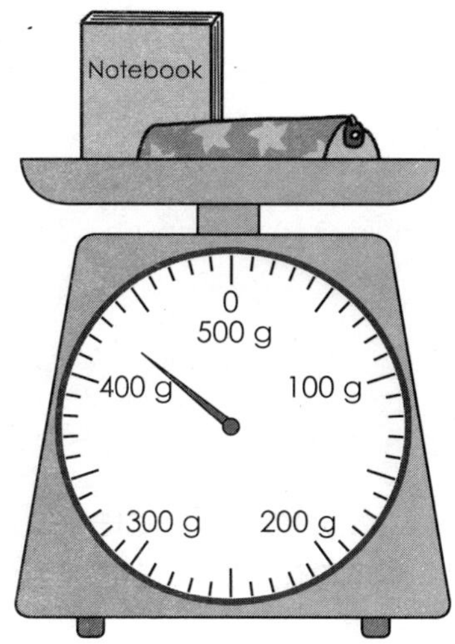

a) Total weight of the pencil case and the notebook = ________

b) The weight of the notebook is 100 grams.

Weight of the pencil case = ________

7. Fill in the blanks.

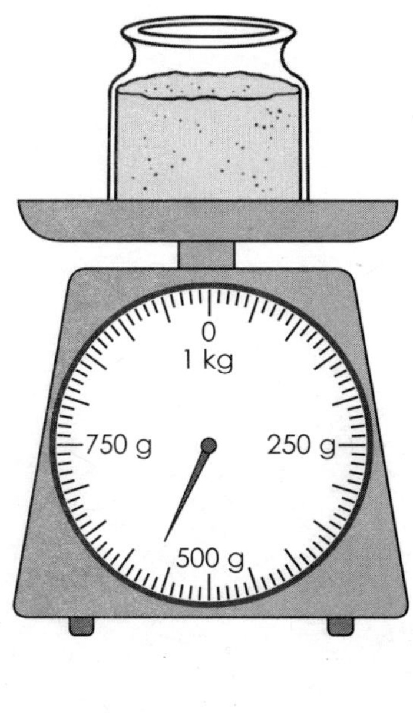

a) Weight of the bottle of sand = ________

b) The weight of the empty bottle is 250 grams.

Weight of the sand = ________

 ISBN 978-93-5103-030-0

Exercise 5 Problem Solving

Solve the word problems. You may draw bar models to help you.
Show your work clearly.

1. The weight of one dictionary is 950 grams. What is the total weight of 5 such dictionaries? Express your answer in kilograms and grams.

- [ ] 1. Understand
- [ ] 2. Plan
- [ ] 3. Answer
- [ ] 4. Check

2. A motorcycle is 8 times as heavy as a bicycle. If the weight of the motorcycle is 128 kilograms, what is the weight of the bicycle?

- [ ] 1. Understand
- [ ] 2. Plan
- [ ] 3. Answer
- [ ] 4. Check

 ISBN 978-93-5103-030-0

3. The total weight of Ali and Sam is 100 kilograms.
If Ali's weight is 46 kilograms 540 grams, what is Sam's weight?

- [ ] 1. Understand
- [ ] 2. Plan
- [ ] 3. Answer
- [ ] 4. Check

4. The weight of a goose is 3 kilograms 200 grams.
The weight of a duck is 1 kilogram 800 grams.
   a) What is the total weight of the goose and the duck?
   b) What is the difference in weight between the goose and the duck?

- [ ] 1. Understand
- [ ] 2. Plan
- [ ] 3. Answer
- [ ] 4. Check

 ISBN 978-93-5103-030-0

5. The total weight of 2 mangoes and a pineapple is 1 kilogram 370 grams. The weight of the pineapple is 930 grams.
   a) What is the weight of the 2 mangoes?
   b) If the weight of each mango is the same, what is the weight of one mango?

- [ ] 1. Understand
- [ ] 2. Plan
- [ ] 3. Answer
- [ ] 4. Check

6. The weight of a packet of flour is 2 kilograms 80 grams. A packet of rice is 2 kilograms 420 grams heavier than the packet of flour. What is the total weight of the packet of flour and the packet of rice?

- [ ] 1. Understand
- [ ] 2. Plan
- [ ] 3. Answer
- [ ] 4. Check

 ISBN 978-93-5103-030-0

7. The total weight of a school bag and 5 coursebooks is 2 kilograms 980 grams. If the weight of each coursebook is 425 grams, what is the weight of the school bag?

- [ ] 1. Understand
- [ ] 2. Plan
- [ ] 3. Answer
- [ ] 4. Check

8. Gaurav's weight is 54 kilograms. He is 3 times as heavy as Ashok. The weight of Gaurav's father is 4 times the weight of Ashok. What is Gaurav's father's weight?

- [ ] 1. Understand
- [ ] 2. Plan
- [ ] 3. Answer
- [ ] 4. Check

 ISBN 978-93-5103-030-0

10 Volume and Capacity

Exercise 1 Volume

1. Which bottle contains a greater volume of water?

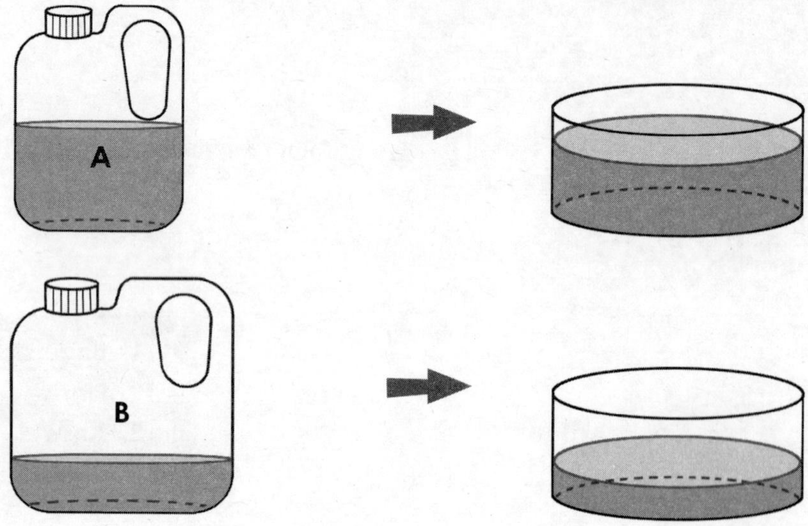

Bottle ________ contains a greater volume of water than Bottle ________.

2. Which pot contains a smaller volume of tea?

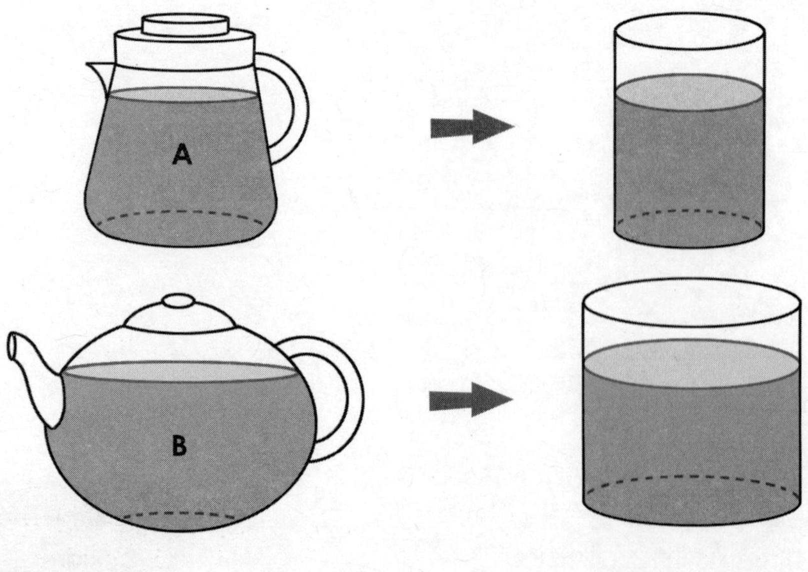

Pot ________ contains a smaller volume of tea than Pot ________.

 ISBN 978-93-5103-030-0

3.

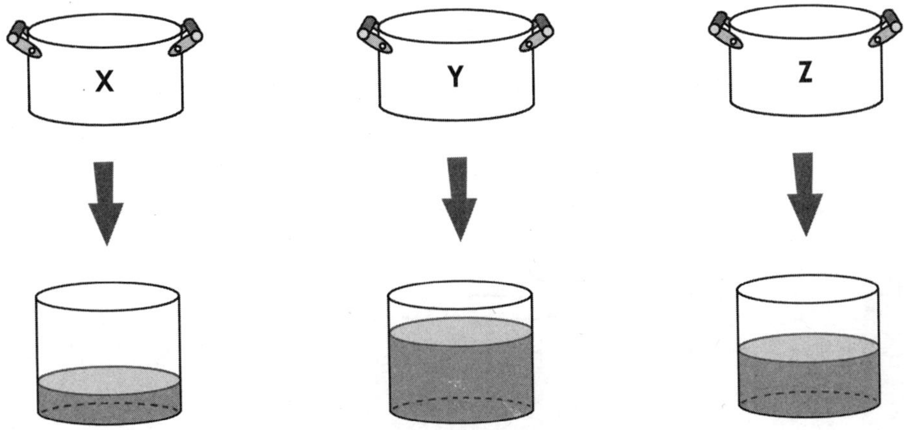

a) Which pot contains the smallest volume of soup? Pot ________.

b) Which pot contains the greatest volume of soup? Pot ________.

4. Fill in the blanks.

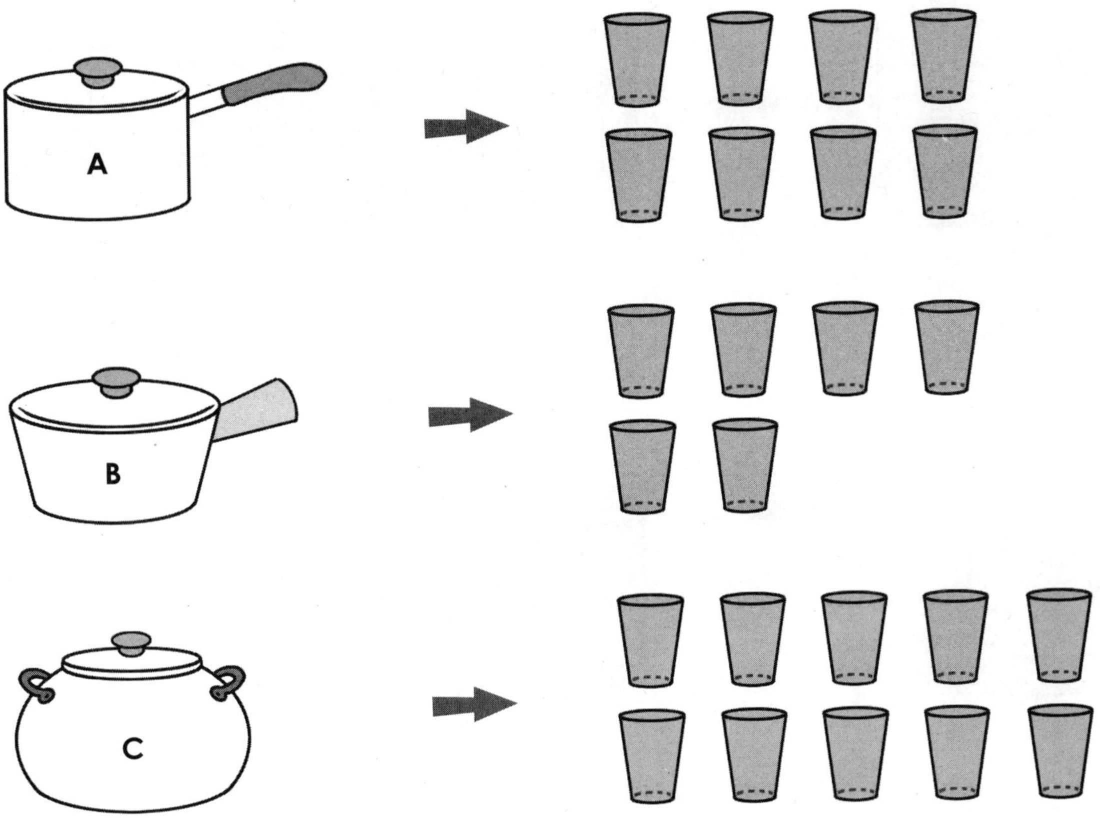

a) Pot A contains ________ more glasses of water than Pot B.

b) Pot A contains ________ fewer glasses of water than Pot C.

c) Pot ________ contains the greatest volume of water.

d) Pot ________ contains the smallest volume of water.

 ISBN 978-93-5103-030-0

Exercise 2 Litres

1. Fill in the blanks.

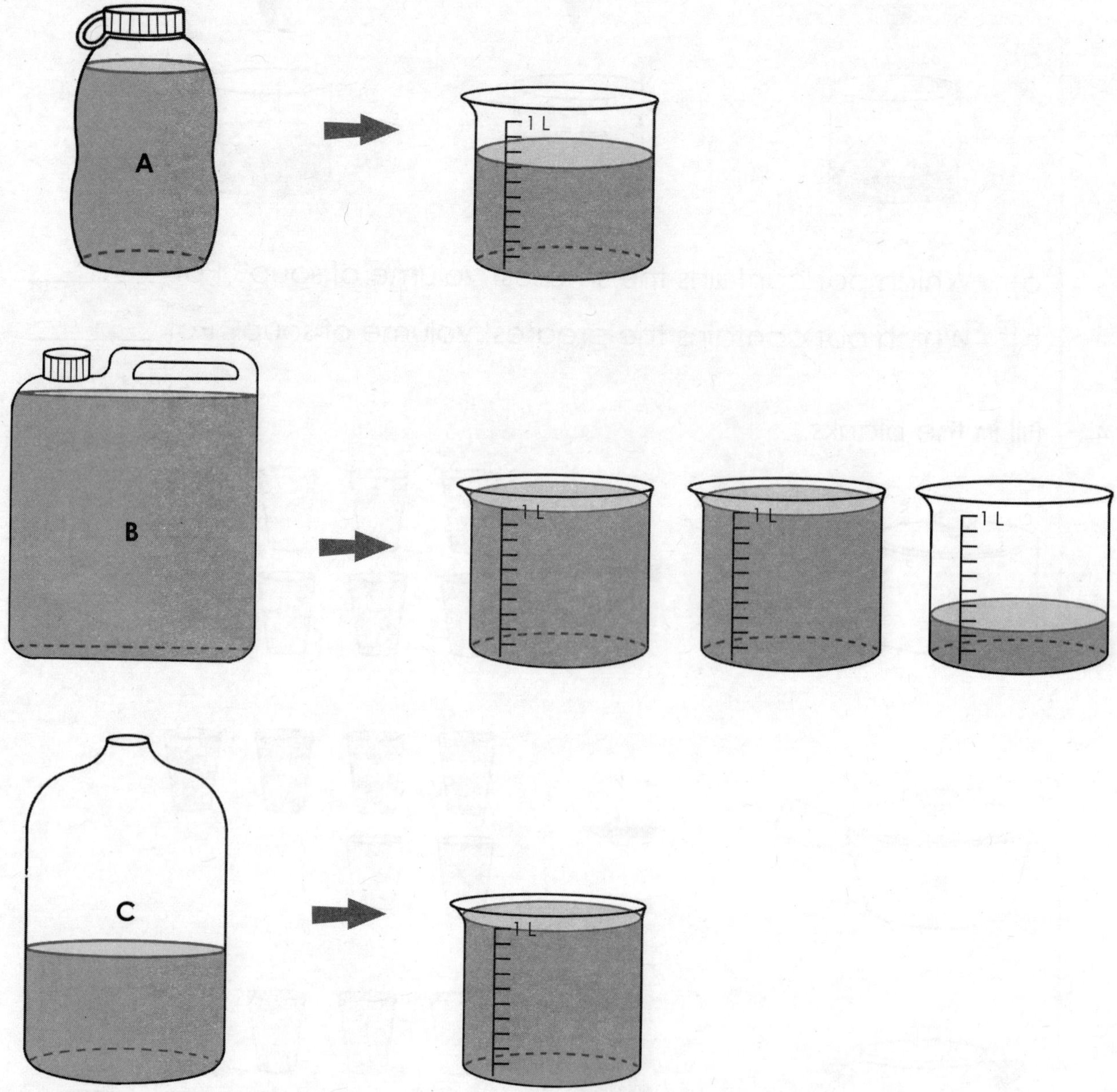

a) Bottle ________ contains a smaller volume of water than Bottle C.

b) Bottle ________ contains a greater volume of water than Bottle C.

c) Bottle ________ contains the smallest volume of water.

d) Bottle ________ contains the greatest volume of water.

 ISBN 978-93-5103-030-0

Exercise 3 Litres

1. Which container has a greater capacity?
   Circle it.

a)

b)

2. Circle the container that has the greatest capacity.
   Cross out the container that has the smallest capacity.

a)

b)

 ISBN 978-93-5103-030-0

3. Fill in the blanks.

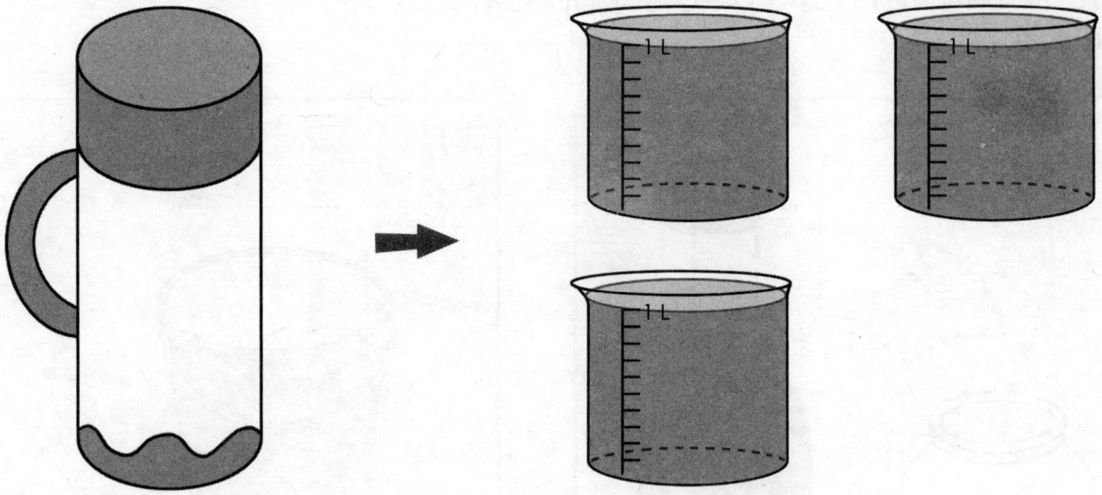

a) The flask can hold ________ litres of water.

b) The capacity of the flask is ________ litres.

4. Fill in the blanks with **volume** or **capacity**.

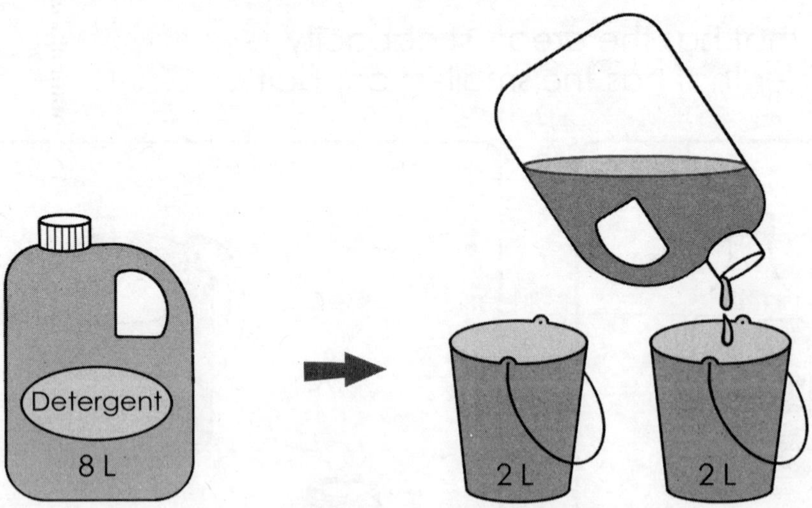

a) The ________________ of the bottle of detergent is 8 litres.

b) The ________________ of each bucket is 2 litres.

c) The ________________ of detergent left in the bottle after the buckets are filled is 4 litres.

 ISBN 978-93-5103-030-0

Exercise 4 Litres

1. All the water in the containers are poured into beakers.
   Fill in the blanks.

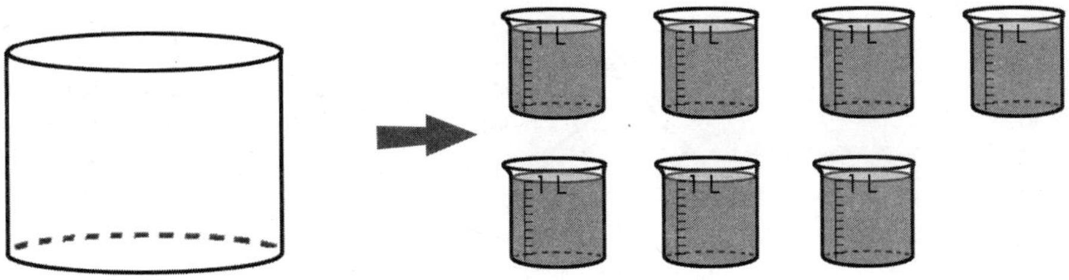

A

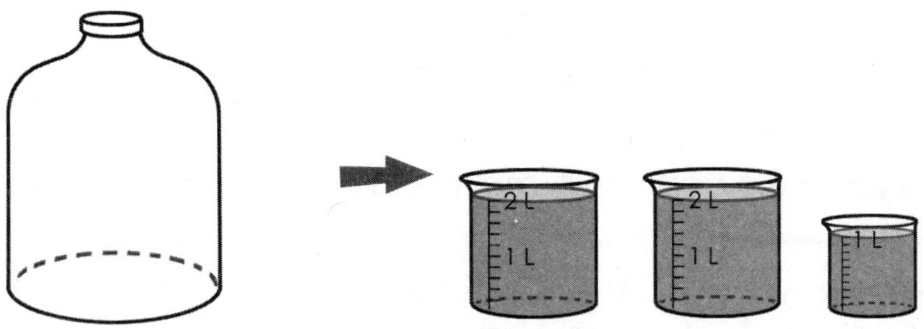

B

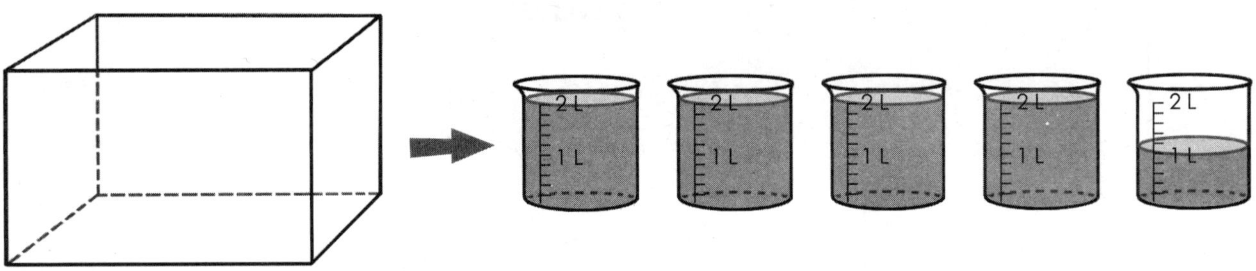

C

a) Container B can hold ________ litres of water.

b) Container A can hold ________ litres more water than Container B.

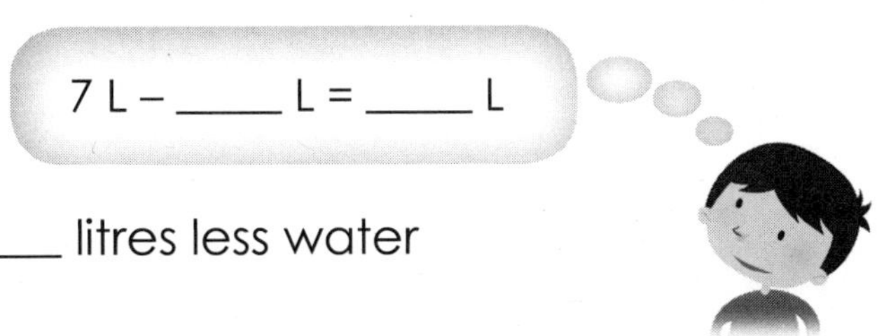

c) Container A can hold ________ litres less water than Container C.

d) Container ________ has the greatest capacity.

e) Container ________ has the smallest capacity.

 ISBN 978-93-5103-030-0

Exercise 5 Litres and Millilitres

1. Work with your friends.
   You need a 100-millilitre measuring cup.
   Get a plastic bottle which can hold 1 litre of water.

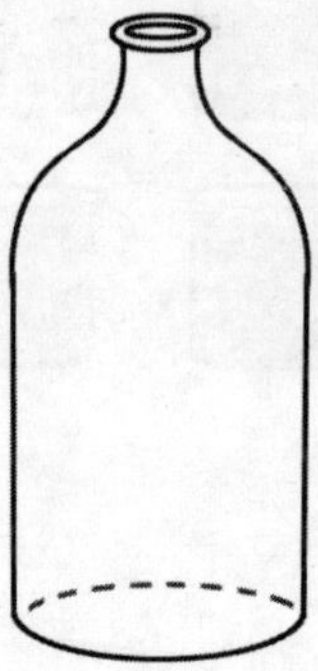

Use the bottle to make your own measuring container.

Pour 100 millilitres of water into the bottle. Mark the water level.	Pour another 100 millilitres of water into the bottle. Mark the water level.	And so on, ...

Your measuring container will look like this:

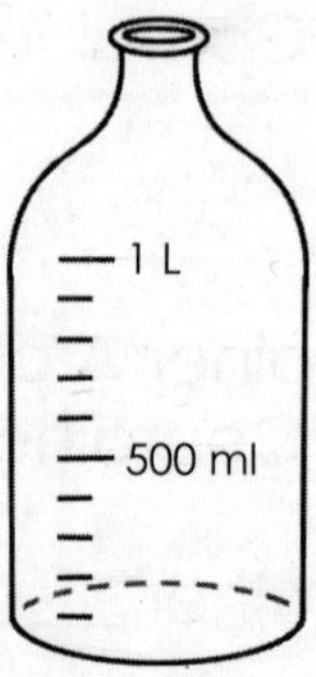

Use the measuring container you have made for the activities on the next page.

 ISBN 978-93-5103-030-0

2. Get three of your friends' water bottles.

Estimate and then measure the volume of water in each water bottle.

	Volume	
Water bottle	**My estimate**	**My measure**
A	about ________ ml	about ________ ml
B	about ________ ml	about ________ ml
C	about ________ ml	about ________ ml

3. Get a bucket, a basin and a big bottle.
Each container can hold more than 1 litre of water.
Estimate how many litres of water will fill each container.
Then, check by measuring the capacities of the containers.

	Capacity	
Container	**My estimate**	**My measure**
a bucket	about ________ L	about ________ L
a basin	about ________ L	about ________ L
a big bottle	about ________ L	about ________ L

 ISBN 978-93-5103-030-0

Exercise 6 Litres and Millilitres

1. Match.

1 L

100 ml

300 ml

600 ml

800 ml

200 ml

400 ml

900 ml

500 ml

700 ml

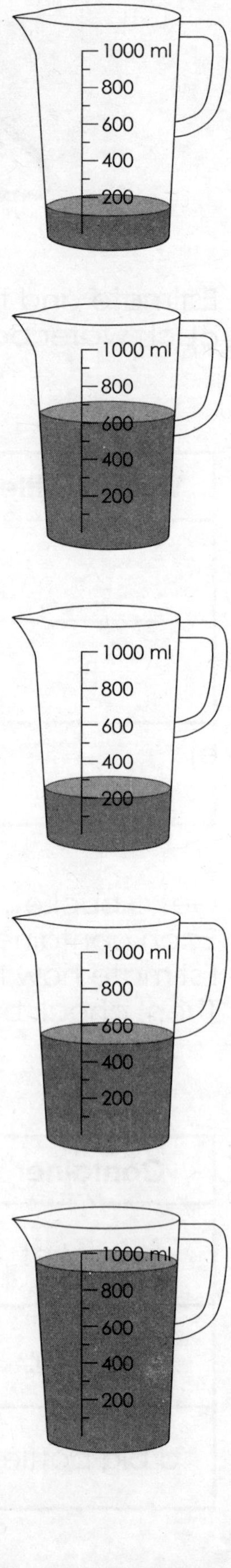

 ISBN 978-93-5103-030-0

2. Write the volume of water for each container.

a)

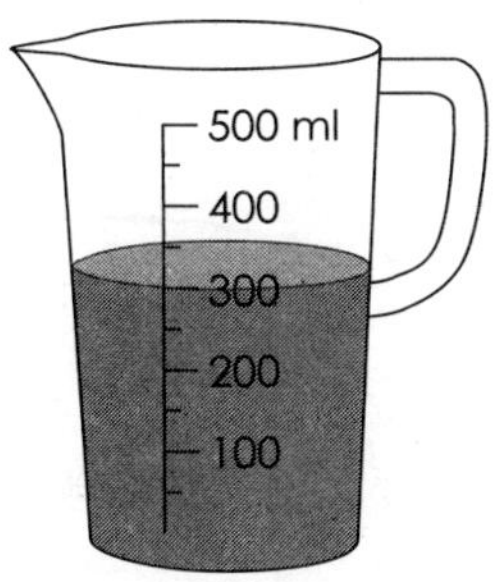

_______ ml

b)

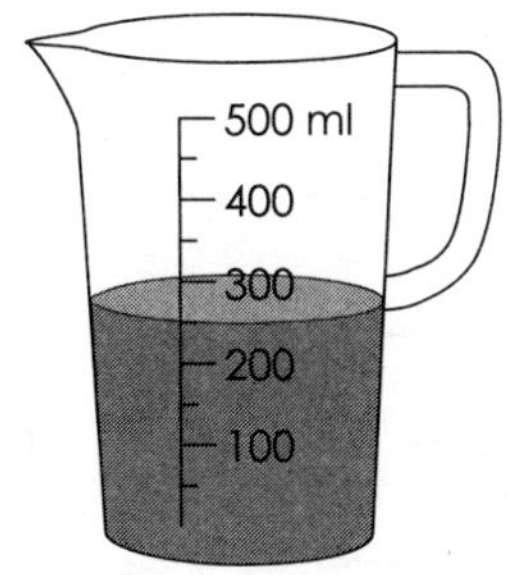

_______ ml

c)

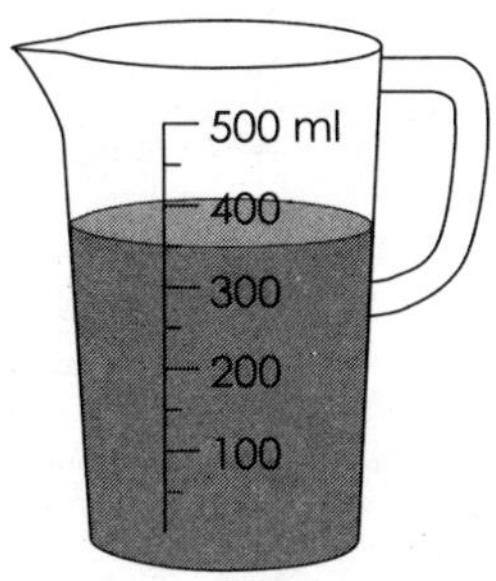

_______ ml

d)

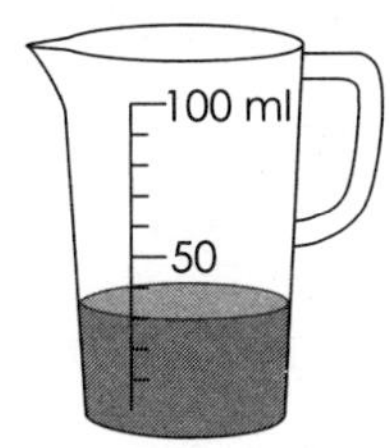

_______ ml

e)

_______ ml

f)

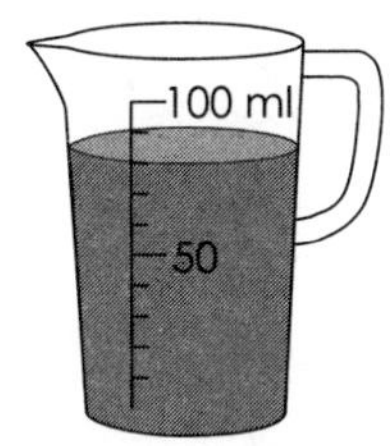

_______ ml

 ISBN 978-93-5103-030-0

Exercise 7 Litres and Millilitres

1. Match.

2 L	1120 ml
1 L 120 ml	2000 ml
1 L 35 ml	1350 ml
1 L 350 ml	2500 ml
2 L 500 ml	2050 ml
2 L 50 ml	1035 ml

 ISBN 978-93-5103-030-0

2. Express in millilitres.

a) 1 L 100 ml = ________ ml

b) 1 L 725 ml = ________ ml

c) 1 L 640 ml = ________ ml

d) 2 L 855 ml = ________ ml

e) 2 L 25 ml = ________ ml

f) 3 L 5 ml = ________ ml

3. Express in litres and millilitres.

a) 1300 ml = ________ L ________ ml

b) 1450 ml = ________ L ________ ml

c) 2090 ml = ________ L ________ ml

d) 2105 ml = ________ L ________ ml

e) 3075 ml = ________ L ________ ml

f) 4005 ml = ________ L ________ ml

4. Circle the correct answer.

a) 1 L 650 ml is more than / equal to / less than 1065 ml.

b) 2 L 75 ml is more than / equal to / less than 2750 ml.

c) 3 L 30 ml is more than / equal to / less than 3030 ml.

d) 3 L 90 ml is more than / equal to / less than 3900 ml.

e) 4 L 10 ml is more than / equal to / less than 4100 ml.

5. Arrange in order. Begin with the greatest.

5 L 9 ml, 5800 ml, 5090 ml, 5 L 900 ml

________________, ________________, ________________, ________________
(greatest)

 ISBN 978-93-5103-030-0

Exercise 8 Litres and Millilitres

1. Match the volumes that make up 1 litre.

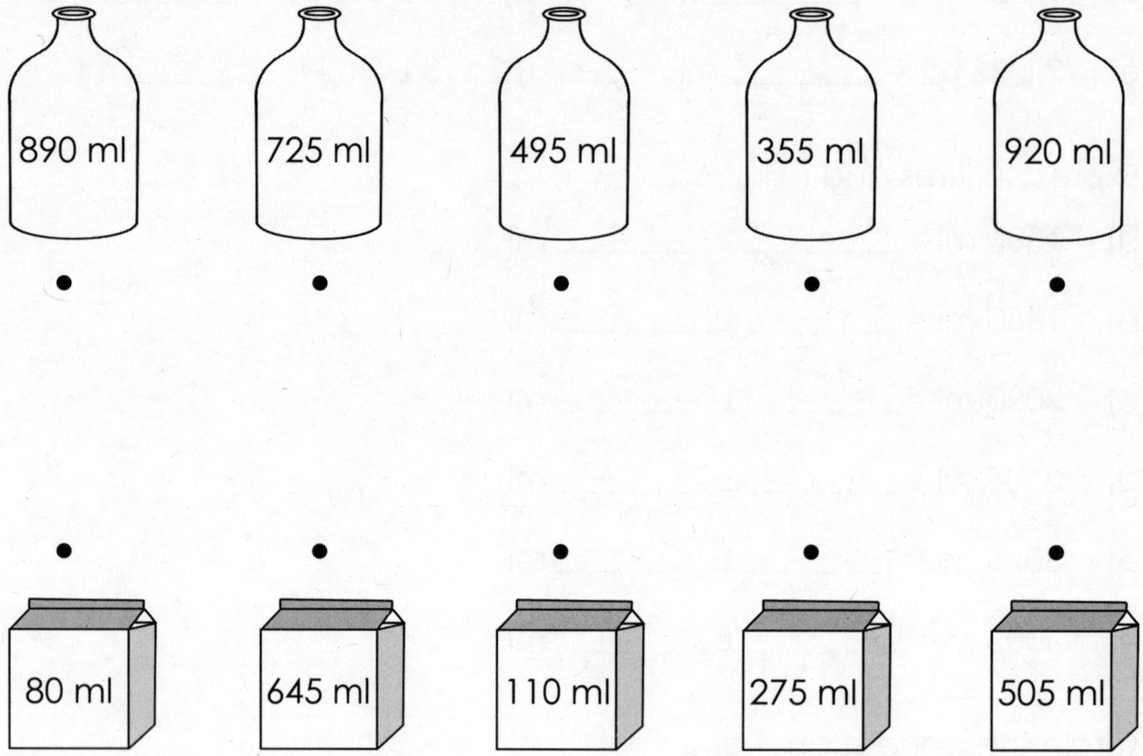

2. Write the missing numbers.

a) b) c)

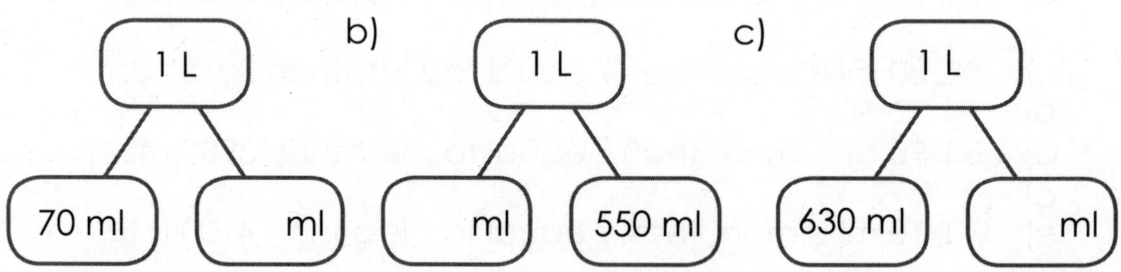

3. Fill in the missing numbers.

a) 1 L – 860 ml = ________ ml b) 1 L – 420 ml = ________ ml

c) 1 L – 750 ml = ________ ml d) 1 L – 340 ml = ________ ml

 ISBN 978-93-5103-030-0

4. Add.

a) 1 L 400 ml + 350 ml = ________ L ________ ml

400 ml + 350 ml = 750 ml

b) 2 L 450 ml + 550 ml = ________ L ________ ml

1000 ml = 1 L

c) 3 L 750 ml + 400 ml = ________ L ________ ml

d) 4 L 850 ml + 640 ml = ________ L ________ ml

5. Add.

a) 1 L 340 ml + 2 L 420 ml = ________ L ________ ml

1 L 340 ml $\xrightarrow{+\,2\text{ L}}$ 3 L 340 ml $\xrightarrow{+\,420\text{ ml}}$?

b) 2 L 250 ml + 1 L 640 ml = ________ L ________ ml

c) 3 L 670 ml + 1 L 400 ml = ________ L ________ ml

3 L 670 ml $\xrightarrow{+\,1\text{ L}}$ 4 L 670 ml $\xrightarrow{+\,400\text{ ml}}$?

3 L 670 ml = 3670 ml
1 L 400 ml = 1400 ml
3670 ml + 1400 ml = ?

d) 3 L 85 ml + 2 L 960 ml = ________ L ________ ml

e) 4 L 706 ml + 3 L 308 ml = ________ L ________ ml

 ISBN 978-93-5103-030-0

6. Subtract.

a) 3 L 740 ml – 560 ml = ________ L ________ ml

b) 4 L 820 ml – 780 ml = ________ L ________ ml

c) 5 L 30 ml – 360 ml = ________ L ________ ml

d) 6 L – 50 ml = ________ L ________ ml

7. Subtract.

a) 3 L 830 ml – 1 L 650 ml = ________ L ________ ml

b) 2 L 824 ml – 1 L 760 ml = ________ L ________ ml

c) 4 L 40 ml – 1 L 375 ml = ________ L ________ ml

d) 3 L 150 ml – 2 L 390 ml = ________ L ________ ml

e) 9 L 5 ml – 3 L 84 ml = ________ L ________ ml

 ISBN 978-93-5103-030-0

Exercise 9 Litres and Millilitres

Fill in the blanks.

1. The jug and the water bottle are filled with water.

3 L

1 L 50 ml

a) The jug contains ________ litre ________ millilitres more water than the water bottle.

b) The total volume of water in the two containers is

________ litres ________ millilitres.

2. Mr. Kumar bought three tins of paint.

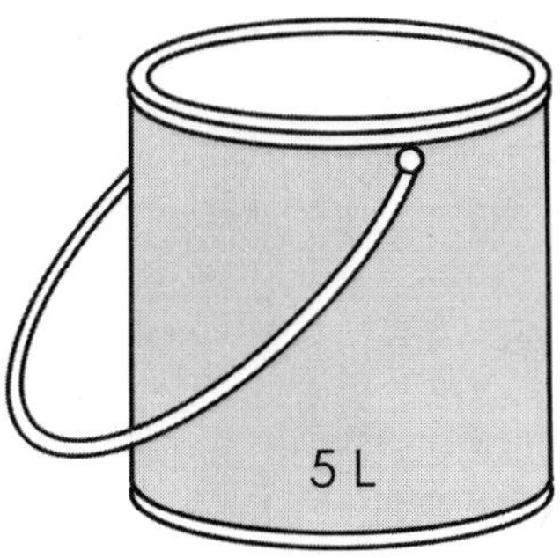

A

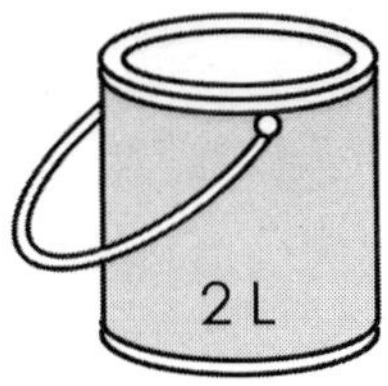

B

C

a) Tin A can hold ________ litres more paint than Tin C.

b) The total capacity of the three tins is ________ litres.

c) Mr. Kumar used 8 litres 400 millilitres of paint to paint his house.

He had ________ litre ________ millilitres of paint left.

 ISBN 978-93-5103-030-0

Exercise 10 Problem Solving

Solve the word problems. You may draw bar models to help you.
Show your work clearly.

1. The capacity of a tank is 250 litres. It contains 105 litres of water. How many litres more are needed to fill up the tank?

☐ 1. Understand
☐ 2. Plan
☐ 3. Answer
☐ 4. Check

2. Mrs. Roy poured 750 millilitres of orange juice equally into 6 cups. How many millilitres of orange juice were there in each cup?

☐ 1. Understand
☐ 2. Plan
☐ 3. Answer
☐ 4. Check

 ISBN 978-93-5103-030-0

3. There are 375 millilitres of milk in a carton. What is the total amount of milk in 6 cartons? Express your answer in litres and millilitres.

- [ ] 1. Understand
- [ ] 2. Plan
- [ ] 3. Answer
- [ ] 4. Check

4. Container X holds 2 litres 800 millilitres of water. Container Y holds 1 litre 600 millilitres more water than Container X.

   a) How much water does Container Y hold?
   b) What is the total amount of water in Container X and Container Y?

- [ ] 1. Understand
- [ ] 2. Plan
- [ ] 3. Answer
- [ ] 4. Check

 ISBN 978-93-5103-030-0

5. Gopal bought 2 tins of paint. Each tin contained 3 litres of paint. After painting his house, he had 2 litres 450 millilitres of paint left. How much paint did he use for painting his house?

- [ ] 1. Understand
- [ ] 2. Plan
- [ ] 3. Answer
- [ ] 4. Check

6. The capacity of a fish tank is 8 litres. There are 7 litres 50 millilitres of water in the fish tank. If 5 similar cups full of water are needed to fill up the tank completely, what is the capacity of each cup?

- [ ] 1. Understand
- [ ] 2. Plan
- [ ] 3. Answer
- [ ] 4. Check

 ISBN 978-93-5103-030-0

7. There are 2 litres 250 millilitres of juice left in a jug after Max and 2 of his friends drank some juice. Each of them drank 280 millilitres of juice. How much juice was there in the jug at first?

- [ ] 1. Understand
- [ ] 2. Plan
- [ ] 3. Answer
- [ ] 4. Check

8. A barrel contains 95 litres of water. Anil pours another 25 litres of water into the barrel. All the water is then poured equally into 8 fish tanks. How much water is there in each fish tank?

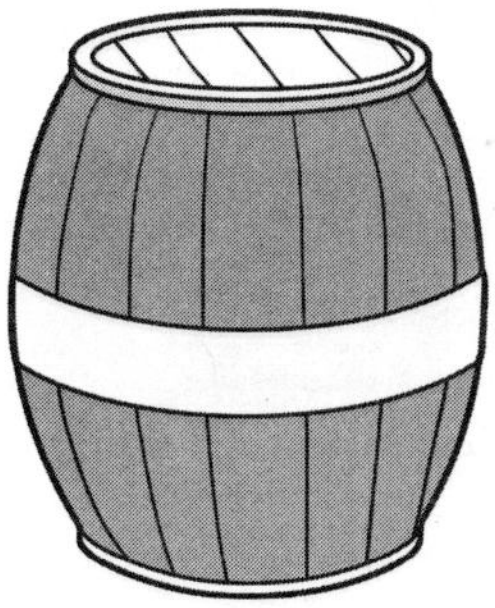

- [ ] 1. Understand
- [ ] 2. Plan
- [ ] 3. Answer
- [ ] 4. Check

 ISBN 978-93-5103-030-0

11 Fractions

Exercise 1 Fraction of a Whole

1. Write the numerator of each fraction.

   a) $\frac{2}{3}$ ________ b) $\frac{7}{10}$ ________ c) $\frac{11}{12}$ ________

2. Write the denominator of each fraction.

   a) $\frac{5}{8}$ ________ b) $\frac{4}{9}$ ________ c) $\frac{3}{10}$ ________

3. Write the numerator of each fraction.

	Fraction	Numerator
a)	$\frac{1}{4}$	
b)	$\frac{3}{5}$	
c)	$\frac{8}{9}$	

4. Write the denominator of each fraction.

	Fraction	Denominator
a)	$\frac{4}{5}$	
b)	$\frac{6}{11}$	
c)	$\frac{2}{7}$	

5. Circle the greater fraction.

Example

$\frac{2}{3}$ (circled), $\frac{1}{3}$

a) $\frac{3}{5}$, $\frac{2}{5}$	b) $\frac{4}{8}$, $\frac{6}{8}$
c) $\frac{1}{6}$, $\frac{5}{6}$	d) $\frac{7}{12}$, $\frac{7}{9}$
e) $\frac{4}{10}$, $\frac{4}{6}$	f) $\frac{6}{11}$, $\frac{6}{7}$

 ISBN 978-93-5103-030-0

6. Circle the smallest fraction.

a) $\frac{8}{10}$, $\frac{1}{10}$, $\frac{7}{10}$	b) $\frac{1}{4}$, $\frac{3}{4}$, $\frac{2}{4}$
c) $\frac{5}{7}$, $\frac{7}{7}$, $\frac{4}{7}$	d) $\frac{5}{11}$, $\frac{5}{8}$, $\frac{5}{9}$
e) $\frac{3}{9}$, $\frac{3}{5}$, $\frac{3}{7}$	f) $\frac{2}{5}$, $\frac{2}{10}$, $\frac{2}{3}$

7. Circle the smaller fraction.

a) $\frac{3}{7}$, $\frac{1}{2}$

b) $\frac{1}{2}$, $\frac{7}{12}$

c) $\frac{1}{2}$, $\frac{4}{9}$

8. Circle the greatest fraction.

a) $\frac{1}{2}$, $\frac{2}{3}$, $\frac{5}{6}$

b) $\frac{4}{5}$, $\frac{1}{3}$, $\frac{1}{2}$

c) $\frac{7}{10}$, $\frac{1}{2}$, $\frac{3}{8}$

9. Arrange the fractions in order. Begin with the smallest.

$\frac{1}{2}$, $\frac{7}{9}$, $\frac{4}{9}$

__________, __________, __________
(smallest)

Exercise 2 Equivalent Fractions

1. Write the missing numerators.

$\frac{1}{2}$ of the bar is shaded.

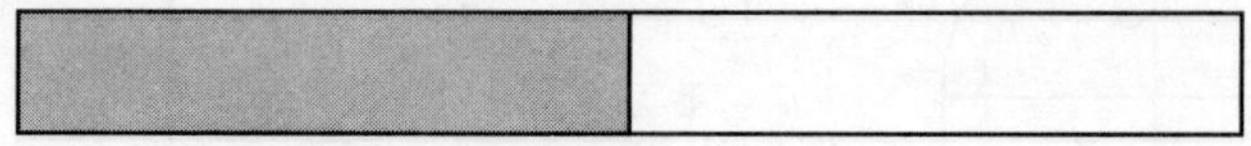

a) $\frac{1}{2} = \frac{\square}{4}$

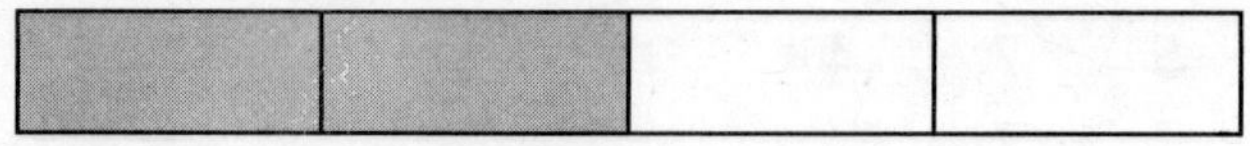

b) $\frac{1}{2} = \frac{\square}{6}$

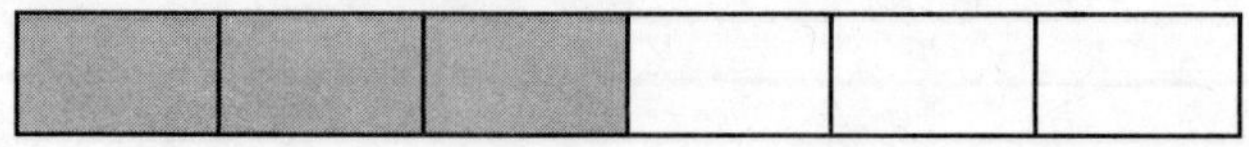

c) $\frac{1}{2} = \frac{\square}{8}$

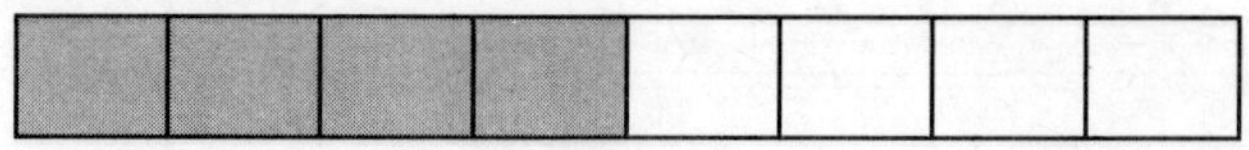

d) $\frac{1}{2} = \frac{\square}{10}$

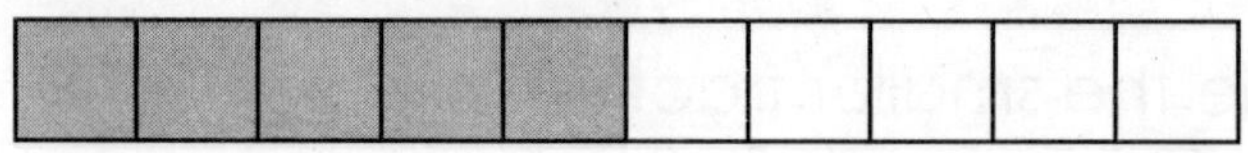

2. Write the missing denominators.

$\frac{3}{4}$ of the bar is shaded.

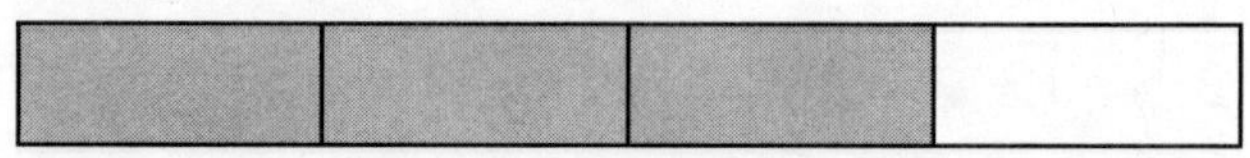

a) $\frac{3}{4} = \frac{6}{\square}$

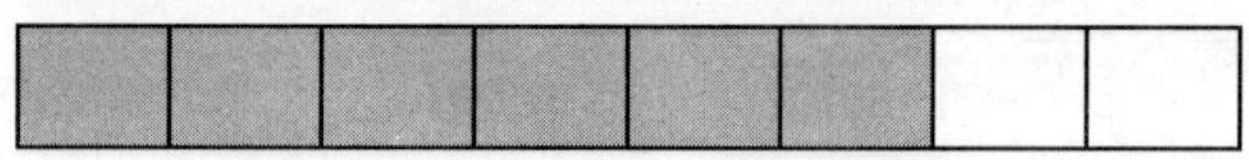

b) $\frac{3}{4} = \frac{9}{\square}$

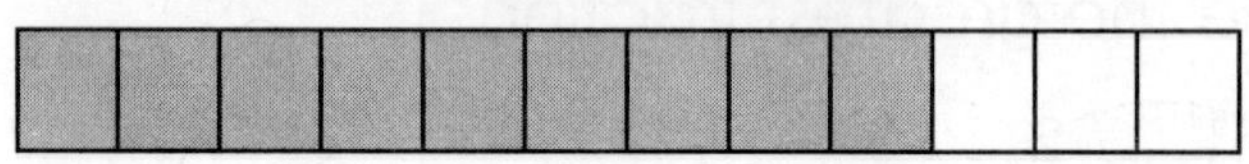

3. Write the missing numerator and denominator.

a)

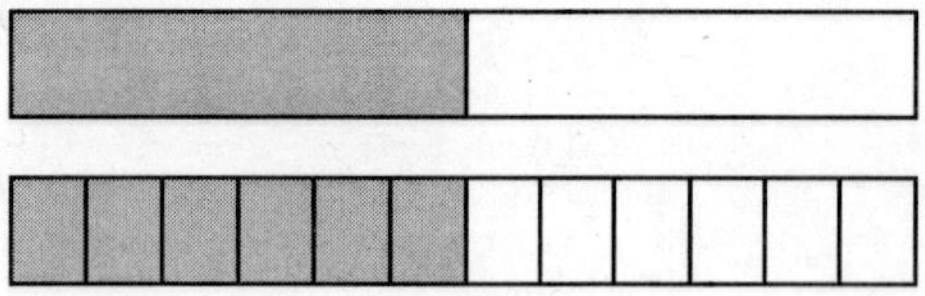

$\frac{1}{2} = \frac{6}{\square}$

b)

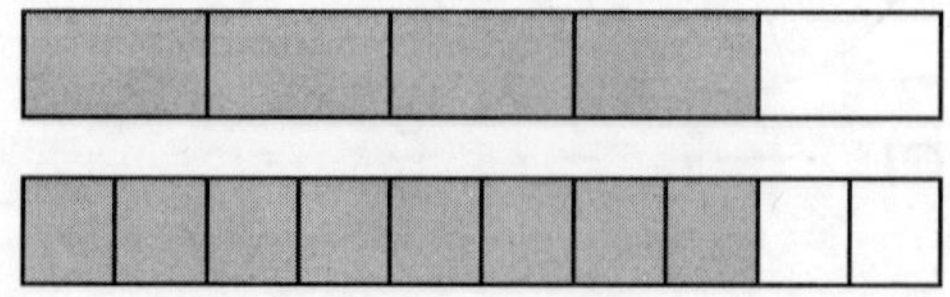

$\frac{4}{5} = \frac{\square}{10}$

 ISBN 978-93-5103-030-0

4. Join each pair of equivalent fractions.

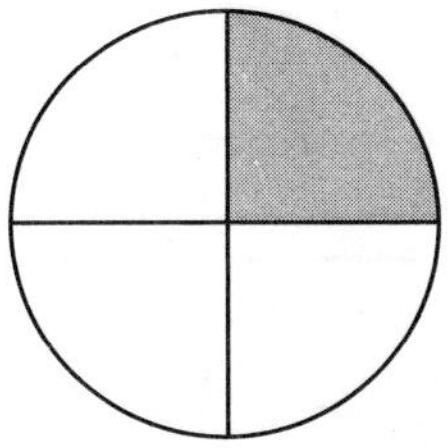 $\frac{1}{4}$ • • $\frac{1}{2}$ 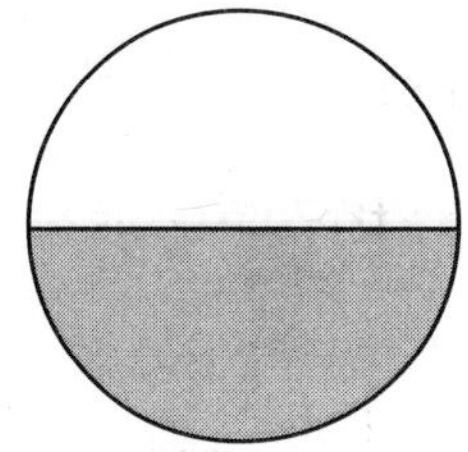

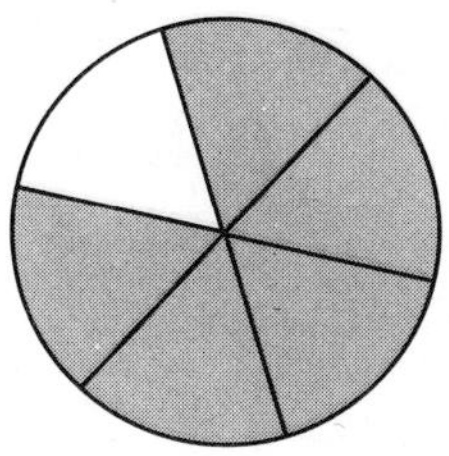 $\frac{5}{6}$ • • $\frac{6}{9}$ 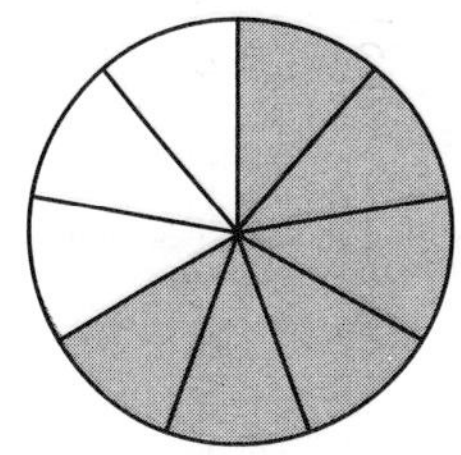

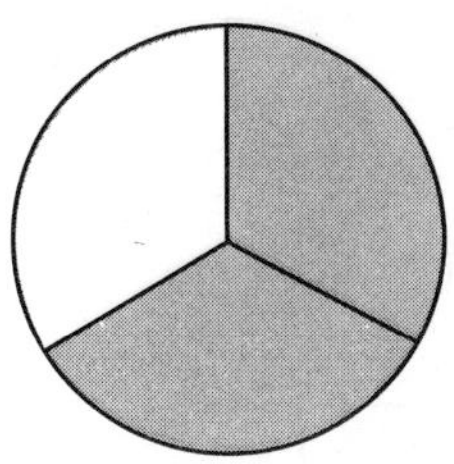 $\frac{2}{3}$ • • $\frac{2}{8}$ 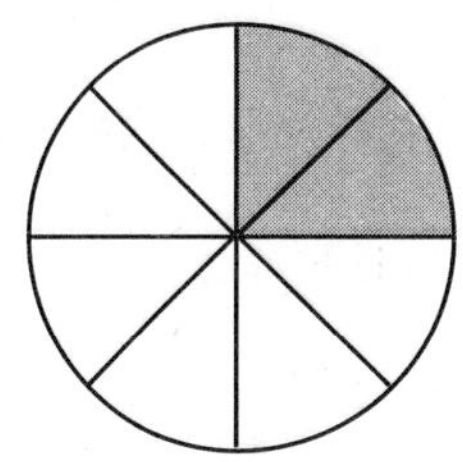

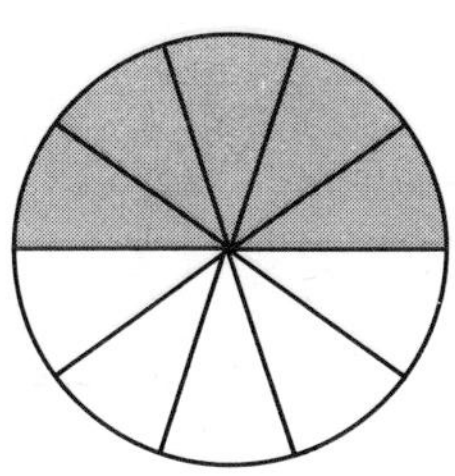 $\frac{5}{10}$ • • $\frac{3}{5}$ 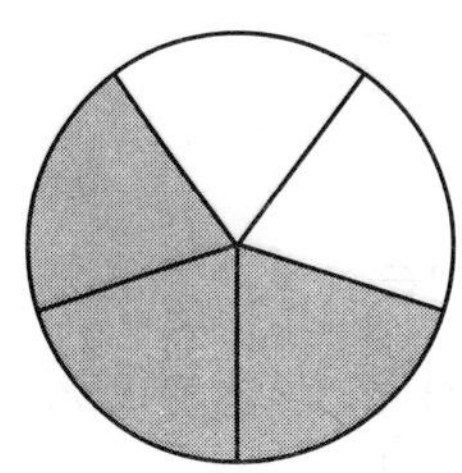

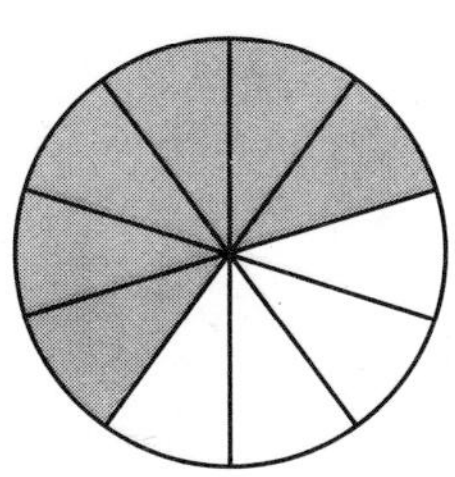 $\frac{6}{10}$ • • $\frac{10}{12}$ 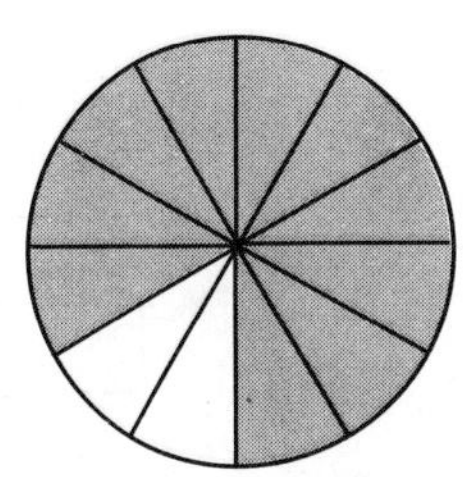

 ISBN 978-93-5103-030-0

Exercise 3 Equivalent Fractions

1. Write the missing numerators and denominators.

Example

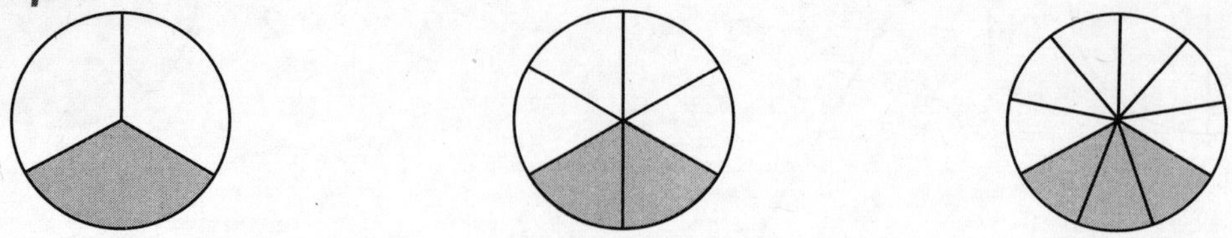

$$\frac{1}{3} = \frac{2}{\boxed{6}} = \frac{\boxed{3}}{9}$$

a)

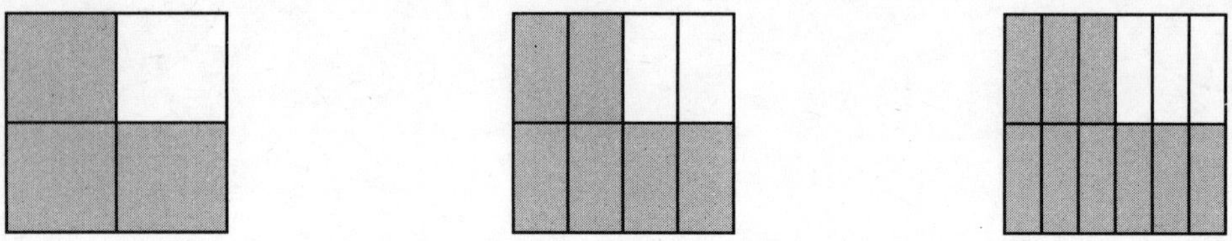

$$\frac{3}{4} = \frac{\square}{8} = \frac{9}{\square}$$

b)

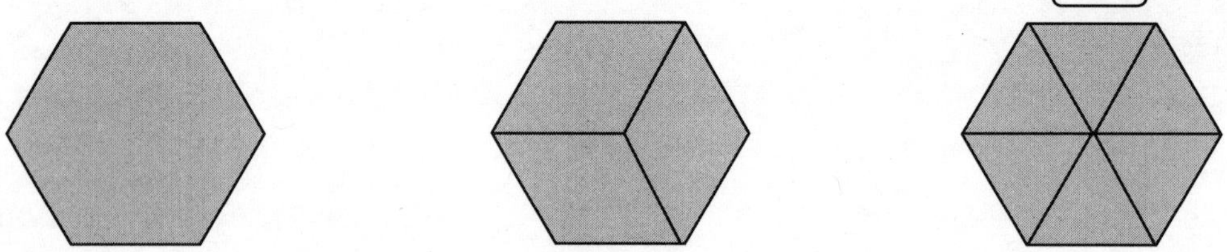

$$1 = \frac{\square}{3} = \frac{6}{\square}$$

2. Write the missing numerators and denominators.

a) $\frac{4}{5} = \frac{\square}{\square}$ (×2 above, ×2 below)

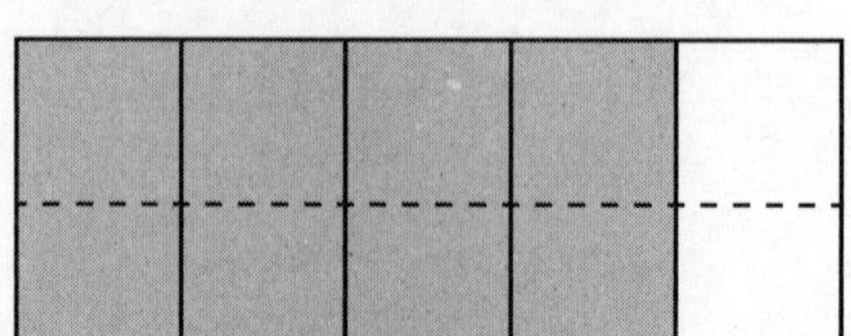

b) $\frac{2}{3} = \frac{\square}{\square}$ (×4 above, ×4 below)

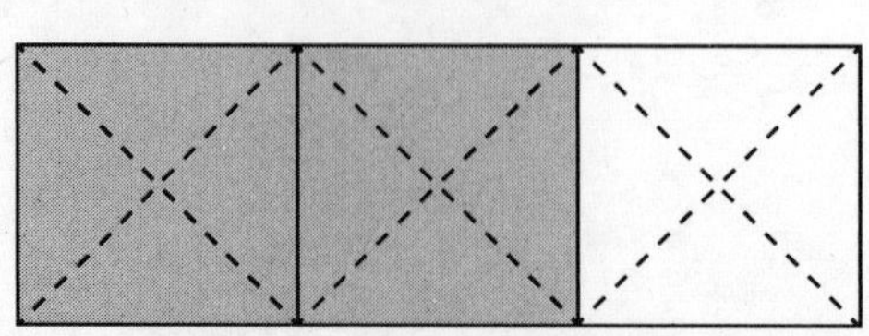

 ISBN 978-93-5103-030-0

3. Circle 8 pairs of equivalent fractions.
One pair has been circled for you.

$\frac{1}{2}$	$\frac{1}{5}$	$\frac{9}{10}$	$\frac{4}{5}$	$\frac{8}{10}$
$\frac{2}{4}$	$\frac{1}{12}$	$\frac{2}{10}$	$\frac{4}{10}$	$\frac{1}{4}$
$\frac{2}{6}$	$\frac{1}{3}$	$\frac{2}{3}$	$\frac{3}{8}$	$\frac{2}{8}$
$\frac{2}{9}$	$\frac{1}{7}$	$\frac{2}{12}$	$\frac{4}{6}$	$\frac{5}{9}$
$\frac{5}{10}$	$\frac{5}{6}$	$\frac{1}{6}$	$\frac{1}{9}$	$\frac{4}{9}$
$\frac{10}{12}$	$\frac{3}{5}$	$\frac{6}{10}$	$\frac{6}{7}$	$\frac{5}{7}$

 ISBN 978-93-5103-030-0

Exercise 4 Equivalent Fractions

1. Write the equivalent fraction for each of the following.

Example

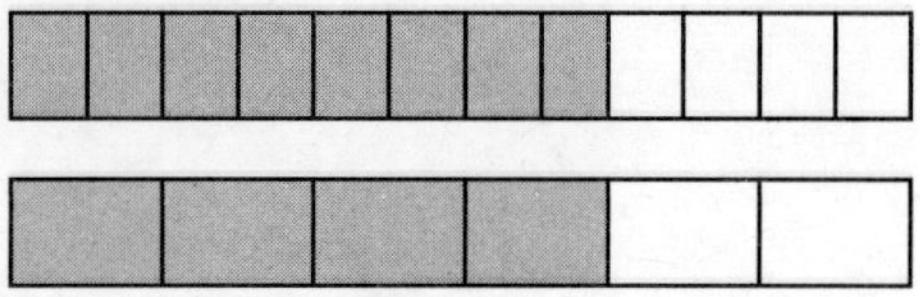

$\frac{8}{12} = \frac{4}{6}$

a)

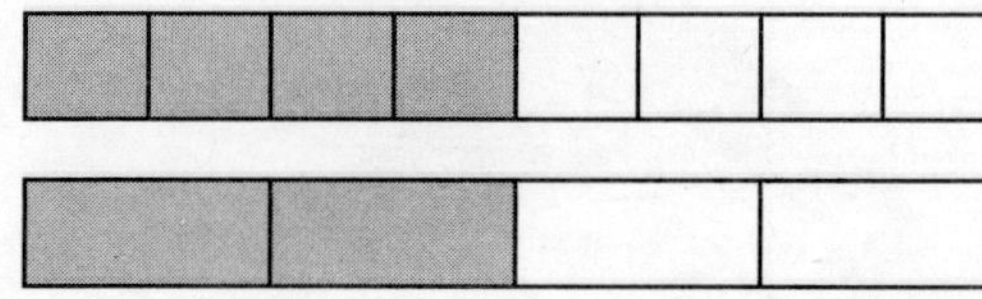

$\frac{4}{8} =$ ________

b)

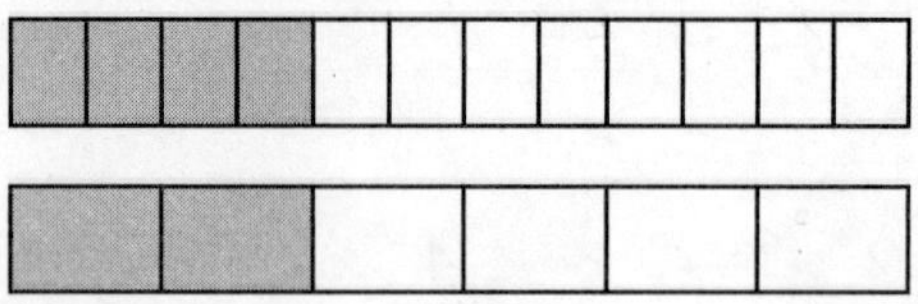

$\frac{4}{12} =$ ________

c)

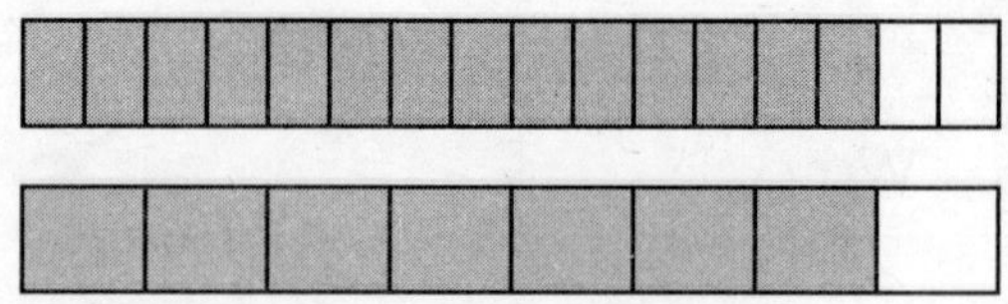

$\frac{14}{16} =$ ________

d)

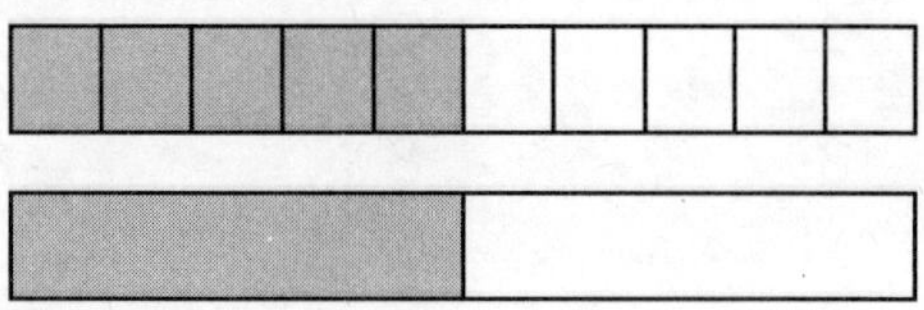

$\frac{5}{10} =$ ________

e)

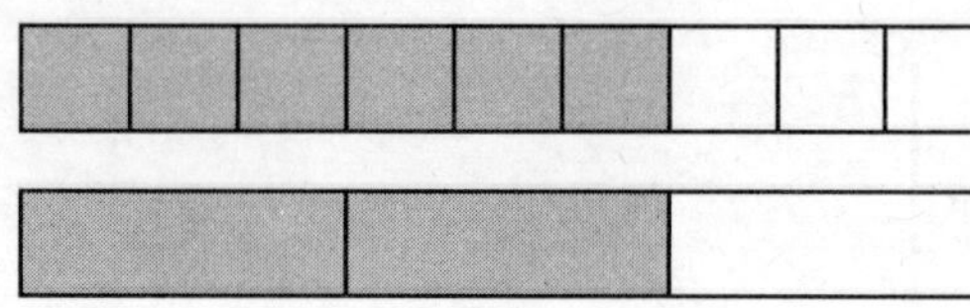

$\frac{6}{9} =$ ________

f)

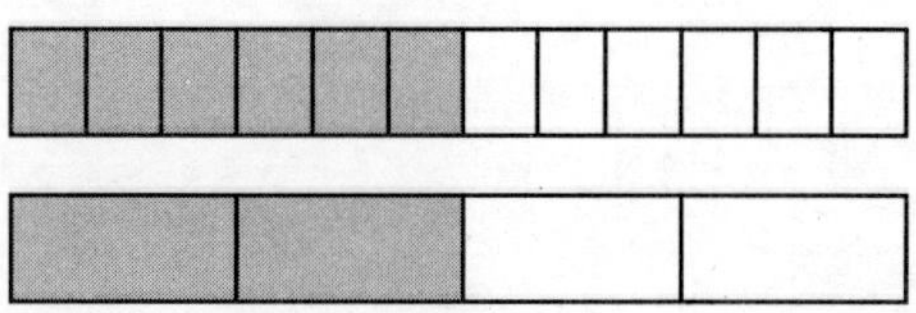

$\frac{6}{12} =$ ________

g)

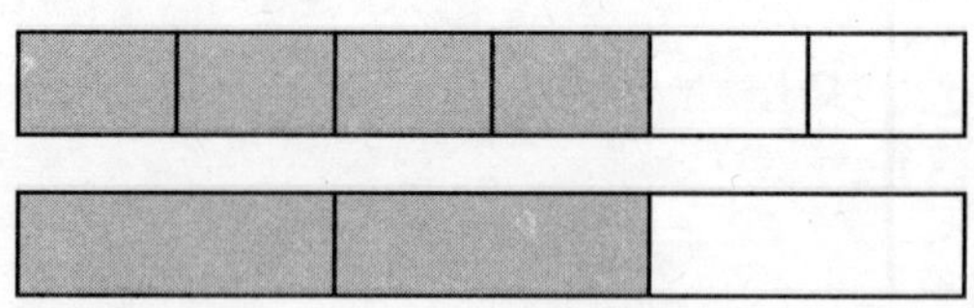

$\frac{4}{6} =$ ________

2. Write the missing numerators and denominators.

a) $\frac{8}{12} = \frac{\square}{3}$ (÷ 4 above, ÷ 4 below)

b) $\frac{6}{10} = \frac{\square}{5}$ (÷ 2 above, ÷ 2 below)

c) $\frac{2}{8} = \frac{1}{\square}$

d) $\frac{8}{10} = \frac{4}{\square}$

 ISBN 978-93-5103-030-0

Exercise 5 Equivalent Fractions

1. Write each fraction in its simplest form.

a) 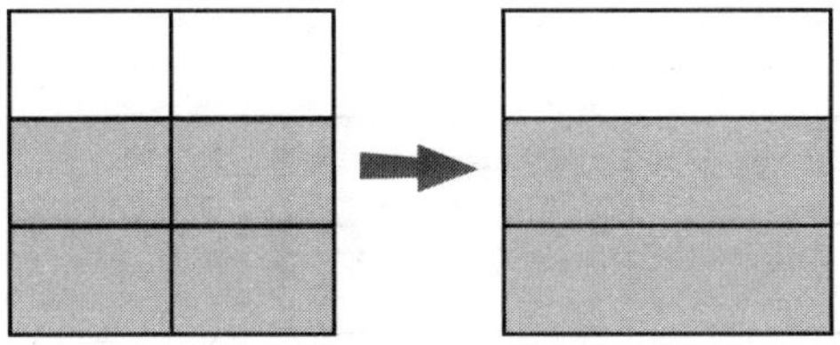

$$\frac{4}{6} \overset{\div 2}{=} \frac{\square}{\square}$$

b) 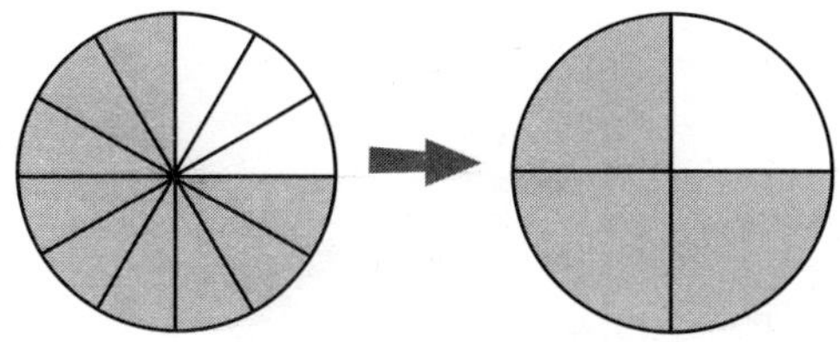

$$\frac{9}{12} \overset{\div 3}{=} \frac{\square}{\square}$$

2. Write each fraction in its simplest form.

a) $\frac{5}{10}$ = ________ b) $\frac{6}{9}$ = ________ c) $\frac{4}{12}$ = ________

3. Circle the equivalent fractions for each of the given fractions.

Example $\frac{2}{3}$	$\frac{3}{4}$,	($\frac{4}{6}$),	$\frac{5}{10}$,	($\frac{6}{9}$)
a) $\frac{4}{5}$	$\frac{2}{8}$,	$\frac{3}{4}$,	$\frac{8}{10}$,	$\frac{4}{10}$
b) $\frac{4}{10}$	$\frac{2}{5}$,	$\frac{5}{8}$,	$\frac{6}{12}$,	$\frac{4}{5}$
c) $\frac{3}{3}$	$\frac{4}{8}$,	$\frac{6}{6}$,	$\frac{8}{12}$,	$\frac{4}{4}$
d) $\frac{9}{12}$	$\frac{2}{3}$,	$\frac{3}{4}$,	$\frac{6}{10}$,	$\frac{8}{11}$
e) $\frac{1}{6}$	$\frac{1}{3}$,	$\frac{2}{12}$,	$\frac{3}{8}$,	$\frac{2}{7}$
f) $\frac{6}{8}$	$\frac{2}{5}$,	$\frac{3}{4}$,	$\frac{8}{12}$,	$\frac{8}{10}$
g) $\frac{1}{2}$	$\frac{2}{3}$,	$\frac{6}{9}$,	$\frac{5}{10}$,	$\frac{6}{12}$

 ISBN 978-93-5103-030-0

4. Join each pair of equivalent fractions with a straight line. Each line will pass through a letter.

a) $\frac{4}{6}$

b) $\frac{4}{12}$

c) $\frac{2}{10}$

d) $\frac{3}{12}$

e) $\frac{4}{8}$

f) $\frac{8}{10}$

g) $\frac{6}{8}$

h) $\frac{10}{12}$

i) $\frac{2}{12}$

j) $\frac{4}{10}$

Letters: D, V, I, M, I, G, A, N, S, K

- $\frac{1}{5}$
- $\frac{3}{4}$
- $\frac{5}{6}$
- $\frac{2}{3}$
- $\frac{1}{4}$
- $\frac{1}{3}$
- $\frac{4}{5}$
- $\frac{1}{6}$
- $\frac{1}{2}$
- $\frac{2}{5}$

What do scuba divers wear to see underwater?
Write the letters in order from a) to j) to find out.

D					
a)	b)	c)	d)	e)	f)

g)	h)	i)	j)

 ISBN 978-93-5103-030-0

Exercise 6 Equivalent Fractions

1. Circle the greater fraction.

Example

$\frac{1}{2}$ (circled), $\frac{1}{4}$ $\quad \frac{1}{2} = \frac{2}{4}$

a) $\frac{7}{8}$, $\frac{3}{4}$	b) $\frac{4}{5}$, $\frac{7}{10}$
c) $\frac{5}{9}$, $\frac{2}{3}$	d) $\frac{2}{3}$, $\frac{1}{6}$
e) $\frac{1}{2}$, $\frac{3}{4}$	f) $\frac{5}{6}$, $\frac{11}{12}$

2. Circle the smaller fraction.

a) $\frac{7}{10}$, $\frac{3}{5}$	b) $\frac{3}{4}$, $\frac{11}{12}$
c) $\frac{2}{3}$, $\frac{5}{12}$	d) $\frac{5}{12}$, $\frac{1}{2}$
e) $\frac{1}{4}$, $\frac{3}{8}$	f) $\frac{7}{8}$, $\frac{3}{4}$

 ISBN 978-93-5103-030-0

Exercise 7 Adding Fractions

1. Colour each figure to show the given fractions.
   Then, add the fractions.

a) $\frac{2}{5}$ red, $\frac{1}{5}$ yellow

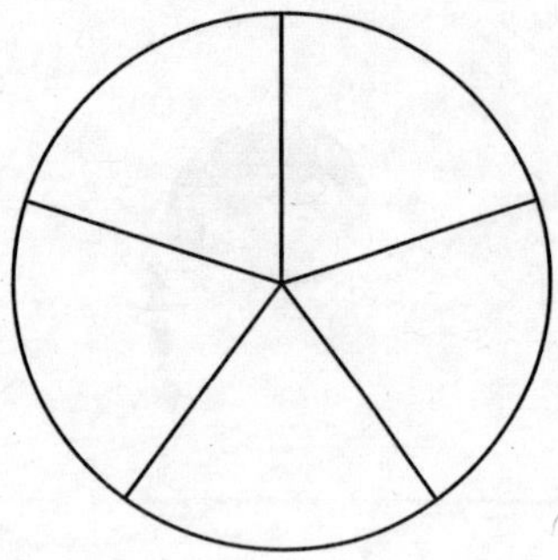

$\frac{2}{5} + \frac{1}{5} =$ ________

b) $\frac{2}{8}$ blue, $\frac{5}{8}$ green

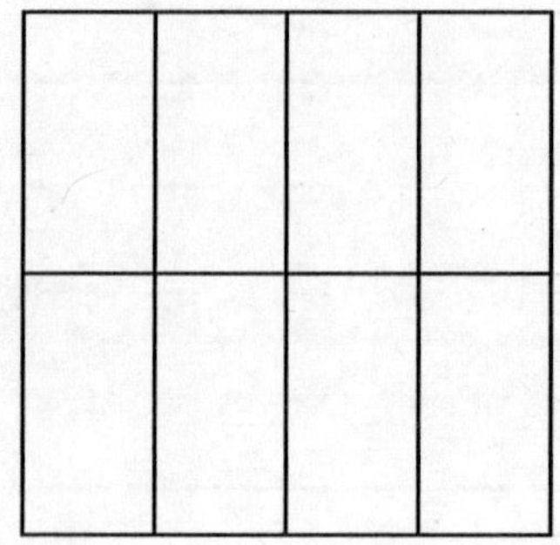

$\frac{2}{8} + \frac{5}{8} =$ ________

c) $\frac{3}{6}$ red, $\frac{2}{6}$ blue

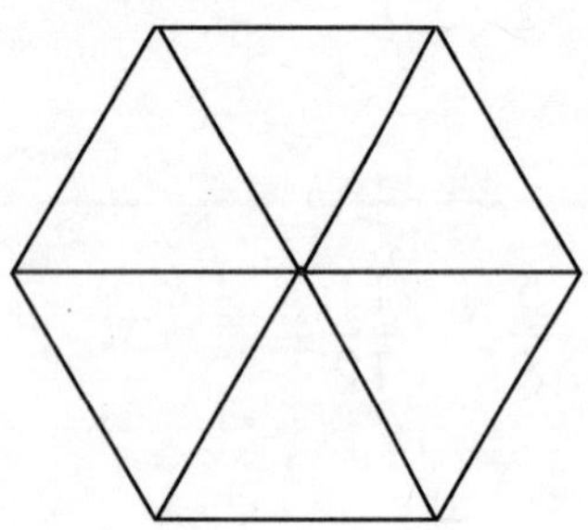

$\frac{3}{6} + \frac{2}{6} =$ ________

d) $\frac{4}{10}$ yellow, $\frac{3}{10}$ red

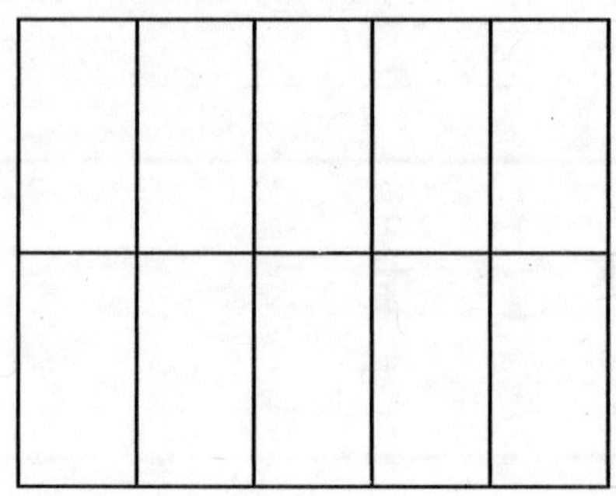

$\frac{4}{10} + \frac{3}{10} =$ ________

e) $\frac{1}{4}$ blue, $\frac{2}{4}$ yellow

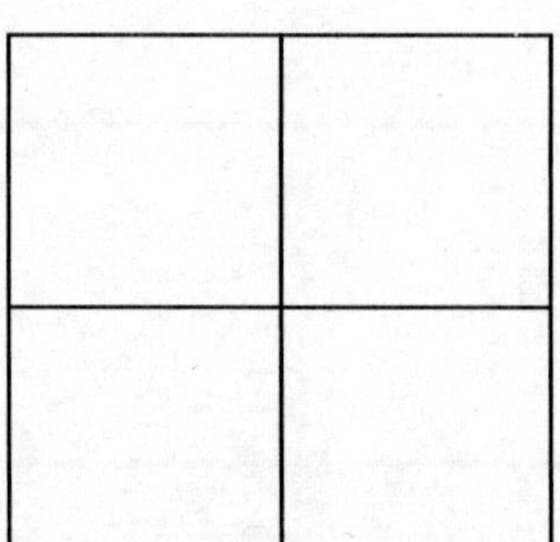

$\frac{1}{4} + \frac{2}{4} =$ ________

f) $\frac{3}{7}$ green, $\frac{2}{7}$ red

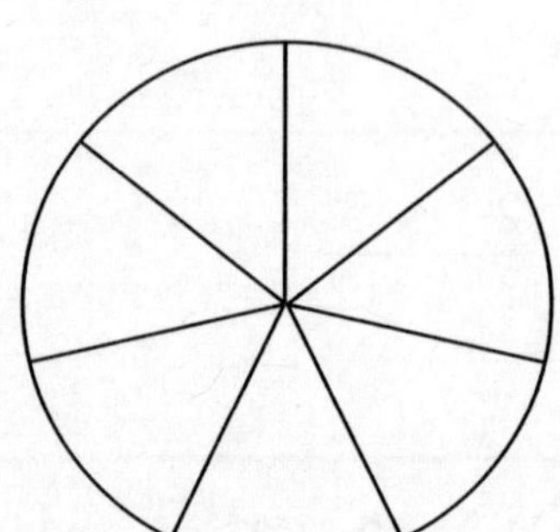

$\frac{3}{7} + \frac{2}{7} =$ ________

 ISBN 978-93-5103-030-0

2. Add. Write the answer in its simplest form.

$\frac{1}{2} + \frac{1}{2} =$	$\frac{1}{4} + \frac{1}{4} =$	$\frac{1}{3} + \frac{1}{3} =$
$\frac{1}{5} + \frac{2}{5} =$	$\frac{3}{6} + \frac{2}{6} =$	$\frac{1}{7} + \frac{4}{7} =$
$\frac{5}{8} + \frac{1}{8} =$	$\frac{2}{9} + \frac{5}{9} =$	$\frac{2}{10} + \frac{7}{10} =$

Colour the spaces which contain the answers.
How many sides does an octagon have? ________

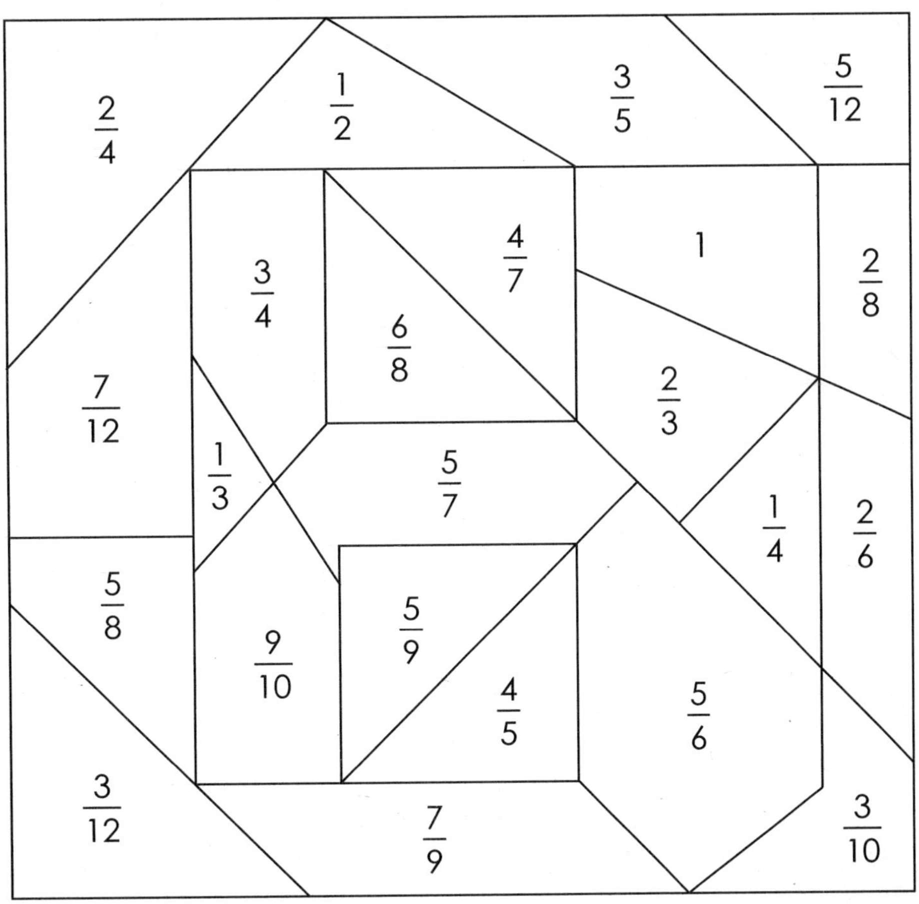

 ISBN 978-93-5103-030-0

Exercise 8 Adding Fractions

1. Add. Write the answer in its simplest form.

Example $\frac{1}{2}+\frac{1}{4}=\frac{\mathbf{2}}{\mathbf{4}}+\frac{\mathbf{1}}{\mathbf{4}}$ $=\frac{\mathbf{3}}{\mathbf{4}}$	a) $\frac{1}{6}+\frac{2}{3}=$
b) $\frac{2}{9}+\frac{2}{3}=$	c) $\frac{1}{9}+\frac{1}{3}=$
d) $\frac{1}{5}+\frac{1}{10}=$	e) $\frac{3}{10}+\frac{1}{5}=$
f) $\frac{1}{8}+\frac{3}{4}=$	g) $\frac{3}{8}+\frac{1}{4}=$
h) $\frac{1}{12}+\frac{2}{3}=$	i) $\frac{1}{4}+\frac{1}{12}=$

 ISBN 978-93-5103-030-0

Exercise 9 Subtracting Fractions

1. Subtract. Write the answer in its simplest form.

a)

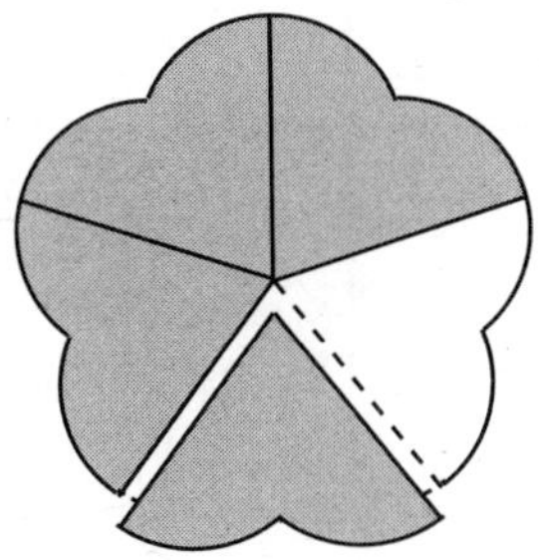

$\frac{4}{5} - \frac{1}{5} =$ ________

b)

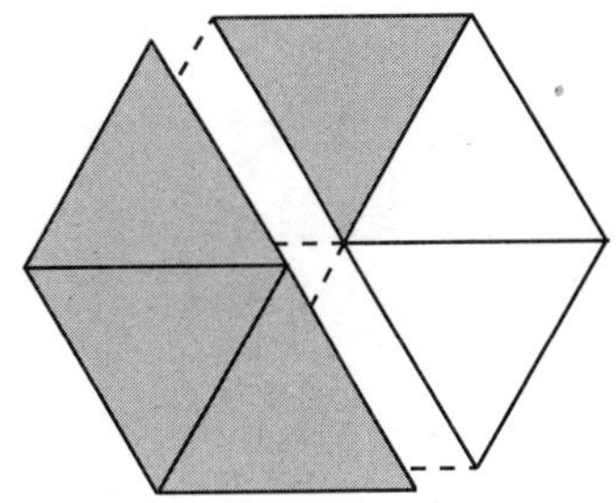

$\frac{4}{6} - \frac{3}{6} =$ ________

c)

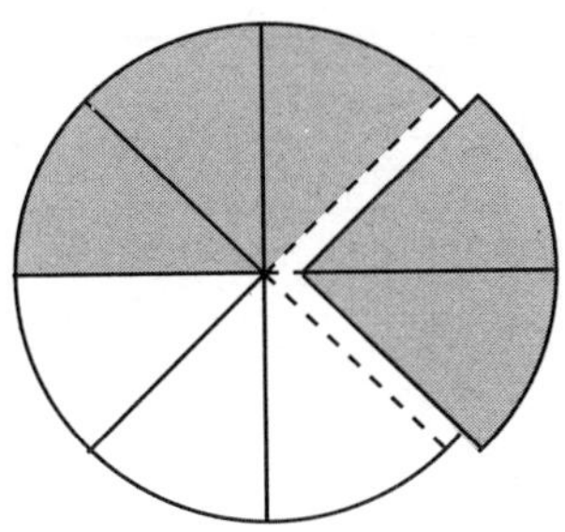

$\frac{5}{8} - \frac{2}{8} =$ ________

d)

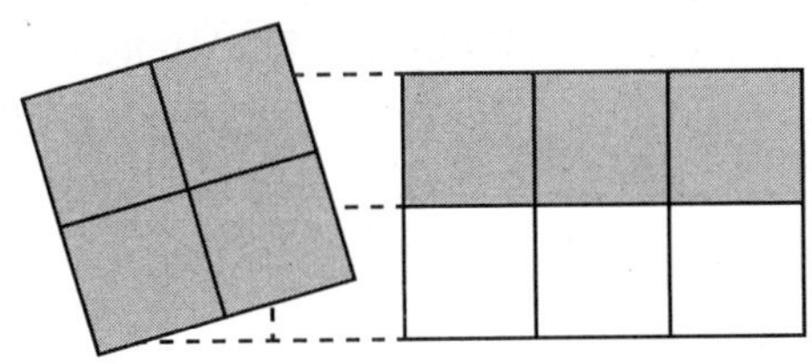

$\frac{7}{10} - \frac{4}{10} =$ ________

e)

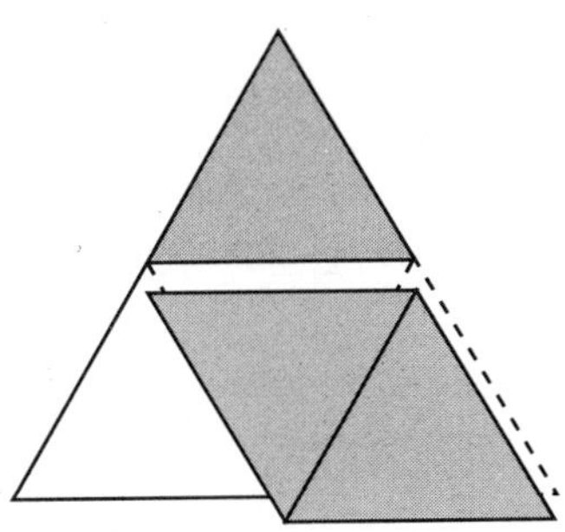

$\frac{3}{4} - \frac{2}{4} =$ ________

f)

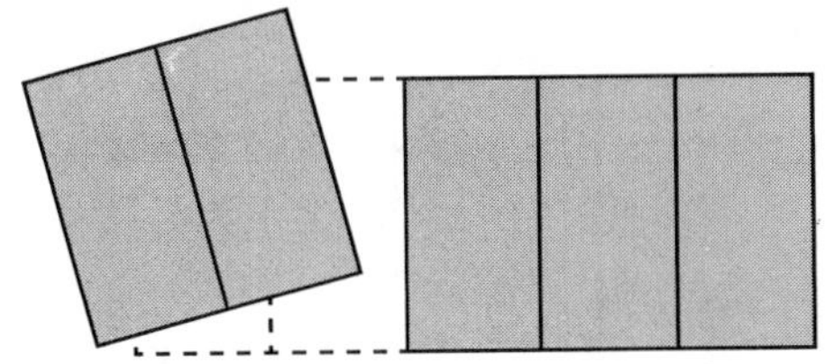

$1 - \frac{2}{5} =$ ________

2. Subtract. Write the answer in its simplest form.

$\frac{2}{3} - \frac{1}{3} =$	$\frac{4}{5} - \frac{2}{5} =$	$\frac{5}{6} - \frac{1}{6} =$
$1 - \frac{3}{8} =$	$\frac{5}{8} - \frac{3}{8} =$	$\frac{7}{8} - \frac{1}{8} =$
$\frac{9}{10} - \frac{3}{10} =$	$1 - \frac{7}{10} =$	$\frac{11}{12} - \frac{5}{12} =$

Colour the spaces which contain the answers.
What is the product of 7 and 2? ________

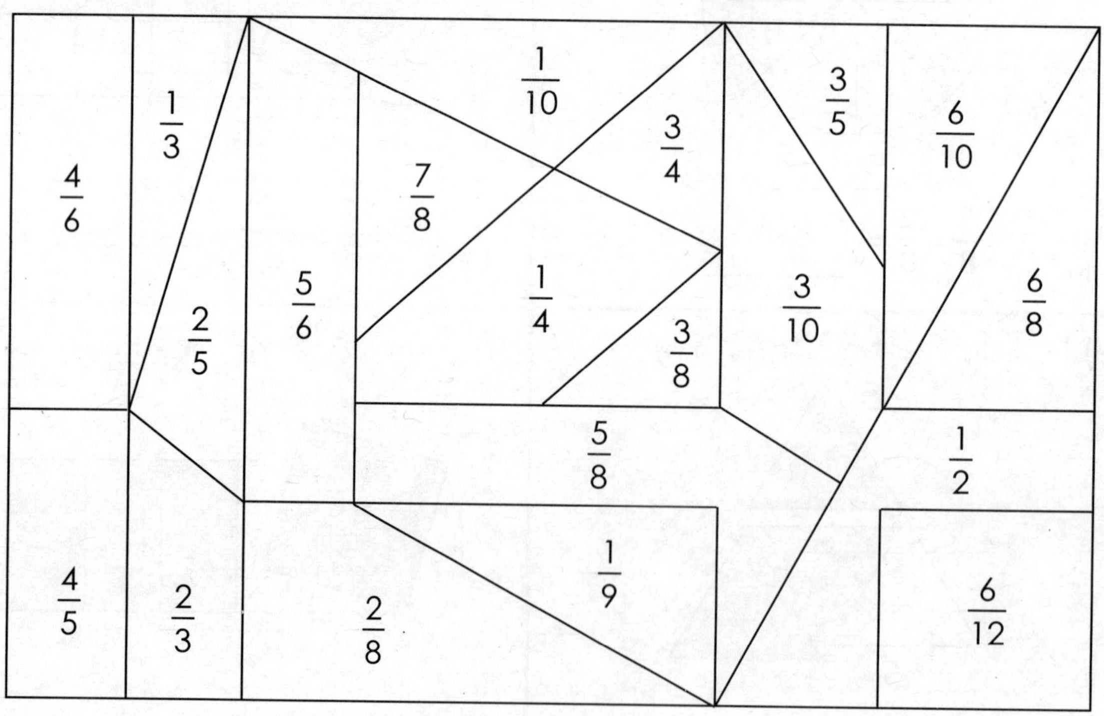

 ISBN 978-93-5103-030-0

Exercise 10 Subtracting Fractions

1. Subtract. Write the answer in its simplest form.

$\frac{1}{2} - \frac{1}{6} = \frac{\square}{6} - \frac{1}{6}$ $= \frac{\square}{6}$ $=$ ______ A	$\frac{3}{4} - \frac{5}{8} =$ D	$\frac{2}{3} - \frac{2}{9} =$ E
$\frac{3}{4} - \frac{1}{12} =$ I	$\frac{2}{5} - \frac{1}{10} =$ L	$\frac{5}{6} - \frac{5}{12} =$ Q
$\frac{4}{5} - \frac{3}{10} =$ R	$\frac{1}{2} - \frac{5}{12} =$ T	$\frac{7}{12} - \frac{1}{3} =$ U

A 3-sided figure is called a triangle.
What is a 4-sided figure called?
Write the letters which match the answers to find out.

		A					A				A	
$\frac{5}{12}$	$\frac{1}{4}$	$\frac{1}{3}$	$\frac{1}{8}$	$\frac{1}{2}$	$\frac{2}{3}$	$\frac{3}{10}$	$\frac{1}{3}$	$\frac{1}{12}$	$\frac{4}{9}$	$\frac{1}{2}$	$\frac{1}{3}$	$\frac{3}{10}$

 ISBN 978-93-5103-030-0

Exercise 11 Problem Solving

Solve the word problems. You may draw bar models to help you.
Show your work clearly.

1. Sonia used $\frac{3}{8}$ of a piece of cloth to sew a blouse.
   She used the rest of the cloth to sew a shirt.
   What fraction of the piece of cloth did she use to sew the shirt?

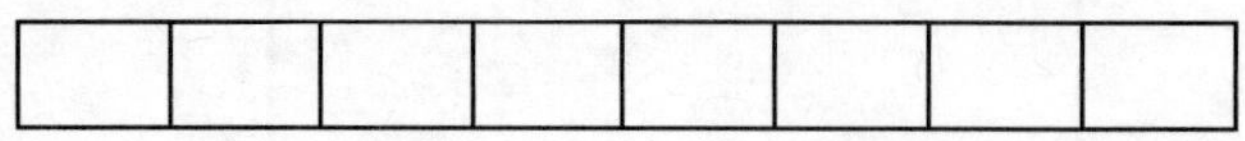

- ☐ **1. Understand**
- ☐ **2. Plan**
- ☐ **3. Answer**
- ☐ **4. Check**

2. Peter spent $\frac{1}{5}$ of his money on a toy car.
   He spent $\frac{2}{5}$ of his money on a kite.
   What fraction of his money did he spend altogether?

- ☐ **1. Understand**
- ☐ **2. Plan**
- ☐ **3. Answer**
- ☐ **4. Check**

 ISBN 978-93-5103-030-0

3. Surya drank $\frac{3}{10}$ litre of grape juice. Atul drank $\frac{1}{5}$ litre of grape juice. How much grape juice did they drink altogether?

- [ ] 1. Understand
- [ ] 2. Plan
- [ ] 3. Answer
- [ ] 4. Check

4. Mala bought $\frac{5}{6}$ metre of string. She used $\frac{1}{2}$ metre to tie a parcel. How much string did she have left?

- [ ] 1. Understand
- [ ] 2. Plan
- [ ] 3. Answer
- [ ] 4. Check

 ISBN 978-93-5103-030-0

5. Akbar used $\frac{2}{3}$ of a roll of ribbon to make some bows.
Rita used $\frac{4}{12}$ of the same roll of ribbon to make some flowers. Who used more ribbon?

- [ ] 1. Understand
- [ ] 2. Plan
- [ ] 3. Answer
- [ ] 4. Check

6. Arun broke a stick $\frac{3}{4}$ metre long into two smaller pieces. One piece was $\frac{5}{12}$ metre long. What was the length of the other piece?

- [ ] 1. Understand
- [ ] 2. Plan
- [ ] 3. Answer
- [ ] 4. Check

 ISBN 978-93-5103-030-0

12 Time

Exercise 1 Hours and Minutes

1. What time is shown on each clock?
   Match the clocks to the correct time.

4:36

7:17

8:03

8:14

2:41

12:21

4:02

11:52

 ISBN 978-93-5103-030-0

2. What time is it?

7 : 30

or half past 7

5 : 24

or 24 minutes past 5

______

or ______

______

or ______

______

or ______

______

or ______

3. Draw the minute hand to show the time.

4 : 55

11 : 05

1 : 27

7 : 25

10 : 36

8 : 53

 ISBN 978-93-5103-030-0

Exercise 2 Hours and Minutes

1. Complete the following.

Example

25 minutes later

3 : 15 p.m.	**3 : 40 p.m.**

a)

_____ minutes later

a.m.	a.m.

b)

_____ hours later

p.m.	p.m.

c)

_____ hours later

a.m.	a.m.

 ISBN 978-93-5103-030-0

2. Complete the following.

a)

____ h ____ min later

p.m.		p.m.

b)

____ h ____ min later

a.m.		p.m.

c)

____ h ____ min later

p.m.		p.m.

d)

____ h ____ min later

a.m.		p.m.

 ISBN 978-93-5103-030-0

Exercise 3 Hours and Minutes

1. Match.

120 min •	• 1 h 30 min •	• 90 min
	• 2 h •	
135 min •	• 2 h 15 min •	• 210 min
	• 3 h 30 min •	

2. Write the missing numbers.

a) 1 h 45 min → 1 h, 45 min → ___ min

b) 2 h 5 min → 2 h, 5 min → ___ min

c) 85 min → 60 min, 25 min → ___ h ___ min

d) 150 min → 120 min, 30 min → ___ h ___ min

 ISBN 978-93-5103-030-0

3. Write in minutes.

a) 1 h 5 min = ________ min

b) 1 h 30 min = ________ min

c) 2 h 25 min = ________ min

d) 3 h 10 min = ________ min

4. Write in hours and minutes.

a) 75 min = ________ h ________ min

b) 100 min = ________ h ________ min

c) 140 min = ________ h ________ min

d) 225 min = ________ h ________ min

5. The table shows the finishing times of four participants in a marathon.

Name	Time taken
Tom	4 h 50 min
Aisha	305 min
Dinesh	245 min
Andy	5 h 25 min

Answer the questions.

a) Who took the shortest time? ________________

b) Who took the longest time? ________________

 ISBN 978-93-5103-030-0

Exercise 4 Hours and Minutes

1. Fill in the blanks.

   a) 1 h 25 min + 30 min = ________ h ________ min

   b) 1 h 45 min + 40 min = ________ h ________ min

   c) 2 h 30 min + 50 min = ________ h ________ min

   d) 2 h 35 min + 35 min = ________ h ________ min

2. Add.

   a) 1 h 30 min + 2 h 20 min = ________ h ________ min

   b) 1 h 45 min + 1 h 5 min = ________ h ________ min

   c) 2 h 20 min + 1 h 50 min = ________ h ________ min

   d) 2 h 40 min + 1 h 35 min = ________ h ________ min

   e) 3 h 50 min + 1 h 20 min = ________ h ________ min

   f) 3 h 25 min + 2 h 45 min = ________ h ________ min

 ISBN 978-93-5103-030-0

3. Subtract.

a) 1 h 45 min – 10 min = ________ h ________ min

45 min – 10 min = 35 min

b) 2 h 40 min – 15 min = ________ h ________ min

c) 2 h 5 min – 50 min = ________ h ________ min

2 h 5 min = 1 h 65 min

d) 3 h 35 min – 40 min = ________ h ________ min

4. Subtract.

a) 2 h 30 min – 1 h 10 min = ________ h ________ min

2 h 30 min $\xrightarrow{-1\text{ h}}$ 1 h 30 min $\xrightarrow{-10\text{ min}}$?

b) 3 h 45 min – 2 h 40 min = ________ h ________ min

c) 2 h 50 min – 1 h 35 min = ________ h ________ min

d) 3 h 15 min – 1 h 45 min = ________ h ________ min

3 h 15 min $\xrightarrow{-1\text{ h}}$ 2 h 15 min $\xrightarrow{-45\text{ min}}$?

3 h 15 min = 180 min + 15 min
= 195 min
1 h 45 min = 60 min + 45 min
= 105 min
195 min – 105 min = ?

e) 4 h 5 min – 2 h 20 min = ________ h ________ min

f) 4 h 20 min – 1 h 25 min = ________ h ________ min

 ISBN 978-93-5103-030-0

Exercise 5 Hours and Minutes

Solve the word problems. You may draw timelines to help you. Show your work clearly.

1. A film started at 7:30 p.m. It lasted 1 hour and 45 minutes. What time did the film end?

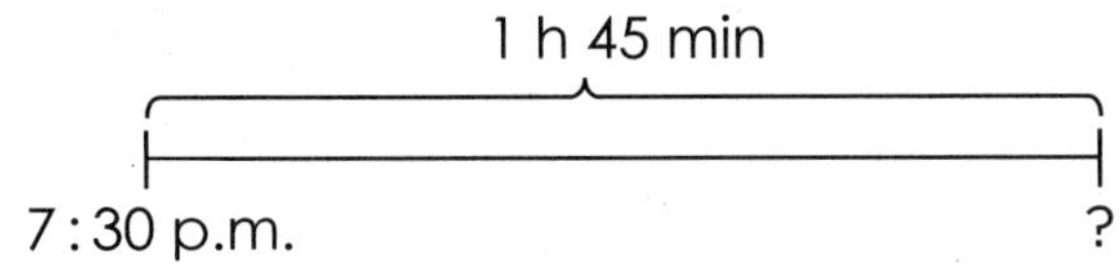

- ☐ 1. Understand
- ☐ 2. Plan
- ☐ 3. Answer
- ☐ 4. Check

2. Mr. Kumar started fishing at 4:40 p.m. He caught his first fish at 6:50 p.m. How long did he take to catch the first fish?

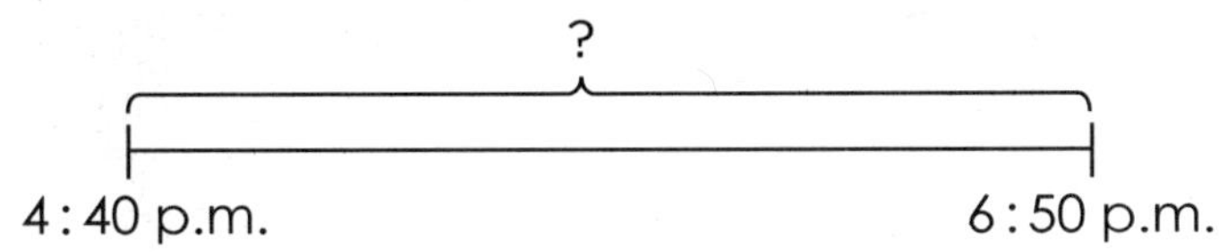

- ☐ 1. Understand
- ☐ 2. Plan
- ☐ 3. Answer
- ☐ 4. Check

3. A concert started at 7:35 p.m. Jack reached the theatre 25 minutes before it started. What time did he reach the theatre?

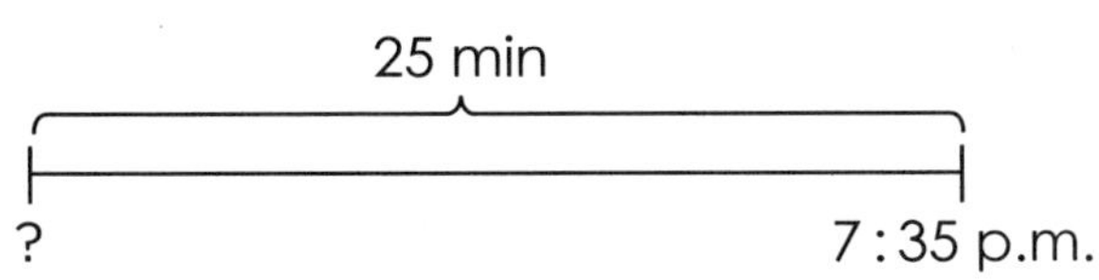

- ☐ 1. Understand
- ☐ 2. Plan
- ☐ 3. Answer
- ☐ 4. Check

 ISBN 978-93-5103-030-0

4. Mrs. Roy arrived at the airport at 7 : 40 p.m. The plane she was taking did not leave until 9 : 00 p.m. How long did she wait at the airport?

- [ ] 1. Understand
- [ ] 2. Plan
- [ ] 3. Answer
- [ ] 4. Check

5. Sam drove from his home to the museum. He left home at 7 : 35 a.m. and arrived at the museum 55 minutes later. What time did he arrive at the museum?

- [ ] 1. Understand
- [ ] 2. Plan
- [ ] 3. Answer
- [ ] 4. Check

6. Kabir took 1 hour and 40 minutes to run from his home to the park. Ahmad took 2 hours and 5 minutes. How much longer did Ahmad take than Kabir?

- [ ] 1. Understand
- [ ] 2. Plan
- [ ] 3. Answer
- [ ] 4. Check

 ISBN 978-93-5103-030-0

Exercise 6 Other Units of Time

1. Match.

1 year 1 month •	• 18 months
1 year 6 months •	• 13 months
2 years •	• 30 months
1 year 8 months •	• 24 months
2 years 6 months •	• 20 months
3 years •	• 26 months
2 years 2 months •	• 36 months

2. Express in months.

   a) 1 year 3 months = ________ months

   b) 2 years 5 months = ________ months

   c) 2 years 11 months = ________ months

   d) 3 years 10 months = ________ months

3. Express in years and months.

   a) 15 months = ________ year ________ months

   b) 25 months = ________ years ________ month

   c) 32 months = ________ years ________ months

   d) 40 months = ________ years ________ months

 ISBN 978-93-5103-030-0

Exercise 7 Other Units of Time

1. Match.

1 week •	• 10 days
1 week 3 days •	• 13 days
2 weeks •	• 7 days
1 week 6 days •	• 20 days
2 weeks 2 days •	• 14 days
2 weeks 6 days •	• 16 days
3 weeks 1 day •	• 22 days

2. Express in days.

   a) 1 week 5 days = ________ days

   b) 2 weeks 4 days = ________ days

   c) 3 weeks 3 days = ________ days

   d) 4 weeks 2 days = ________ days

3. Express in weeks and days.

   a) 14 days = ________ weeks ________ days

   b) 25 days = ________ weeks ________ days

   c) 32 days = ________ weeks ________ days

   d) 51 days = ________ weeks ________ days

 ISBN 978-93-5103-030-0

Exercise 8 Problem Solving

Solve the word problems. You may draw timelines or bar models to help you. Show your work clearly.

1. Seema has Mathematics class from 10 : 35 a.m. to 12 : 20 p.m. for 2 days in a week. What is the total amount of time she spends in Mathematics class in a week?

- [ ] 1. Understand
- [ ] 2. Plan
- [ ] 3. Answer
- [ ] 4. Check

2. Rob and Rita each took 4 hours 45 minutes to complete their homework. Rob completed his homework at 2 : 30 p.m. Rita started doing her homework 1 hour 20 minutes after Rob finished his homework. What time did Rita complete her homework?

- [ ] 1. Understand
- [ ] 2. Plan
- [ ] 3. Answer
- [ ] 4. Check

 ISBN 978-93-5103-030-0

3. Roy took 3 hours 15 minutes to drive from Delhi to Karnal. He then took 2 hours 5 minutes to drive from Karnal to Chandigarh. He arrived in Chandigarh at 4 : 05 p.m. What time did Roy start driving?

- [ ] **1. Understand**
- [ ] **2. Plan**
- [ ] **3. Answer**
- [ ] **4. Check**

4. Mohan took a plane from Tokyo to Singapore at 8 : 20 a.m. The journey took 6 hours 50 minutes. He had a short stopover in Singapore before taking another plane to Jakarta. If the flight time is 1 hour and he arrives in Jakarta at 5 : 05 p.m., how long was the stopover?

- [ ] **1. Understand**
- [ ] **2. Plan**
- [ ] **3. Answer**
- [ ] **4. Check**

 ISBN 978-93-5103-030-0

5. Nitin is 11 years 6 months old. How old will he be in 5 years 8 months? Express your answer in years and months.

- [ ] 1. Understand
- [ ] 2. Plan
- [ ] 3. Answer
- [ ] 4. Check

6. Ashok took 15 days to finish reading a book. Harry took thrice as long to finish the same book. How long did Harry take to finish the book? Express your answer in weeks and days.

- [ ] 1. Understand
- [ ] 2. Plan
- [ ] 3. Answer
- [ ] 4. Check

 ISBN 978-93-5103-030-0

13 Geometry

Exercise 1 Angles

1. Name the following diagrams.
   Use **point, line, line segment** or **ray** in your answers.

a) 

b) 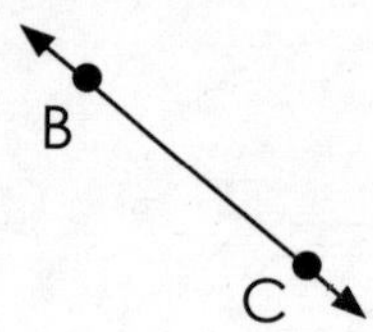

c) 

d) 

__________ __________ __________ __________

2. Tick the diagram that shows an angle.

	Diagram	Angle
a)	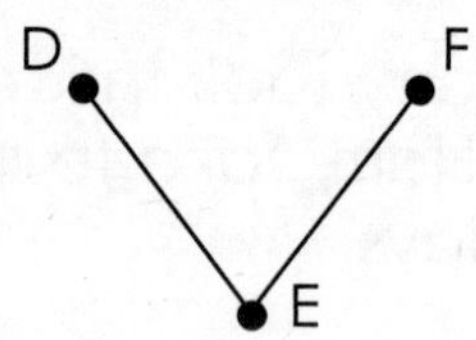	
b)	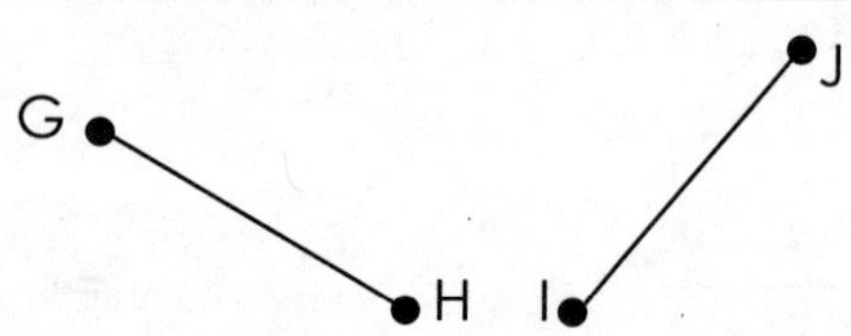	
c)	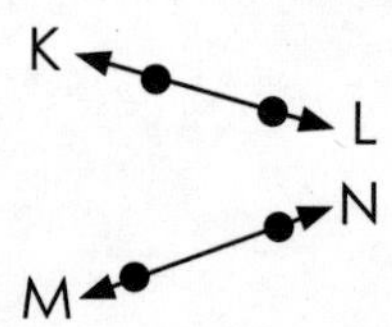	
d)	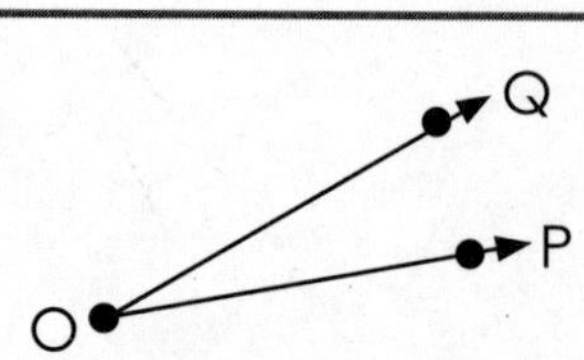	
e)	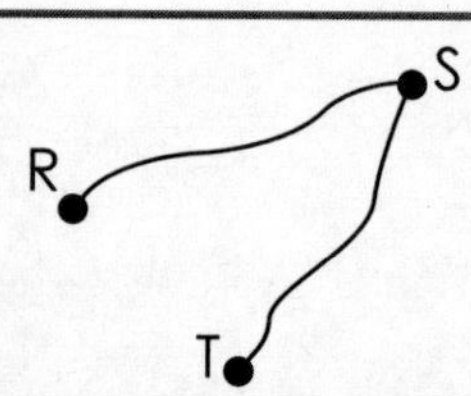	

 ISBN 978-93-5103-030-0

Exercise 2 Angles

1. Compare the angles.

   a) Which angle is greater? ________

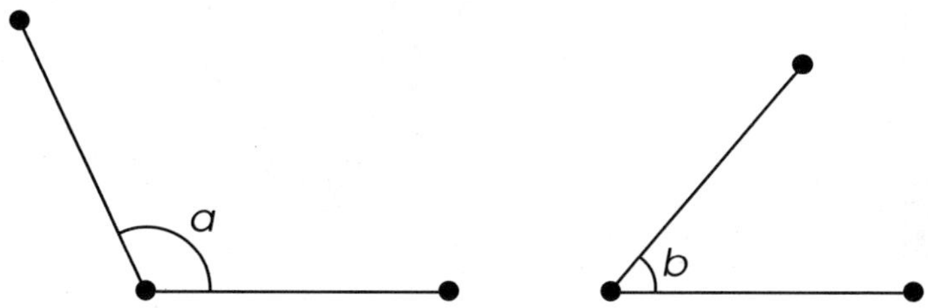

   b) Which angle is smaller? ________

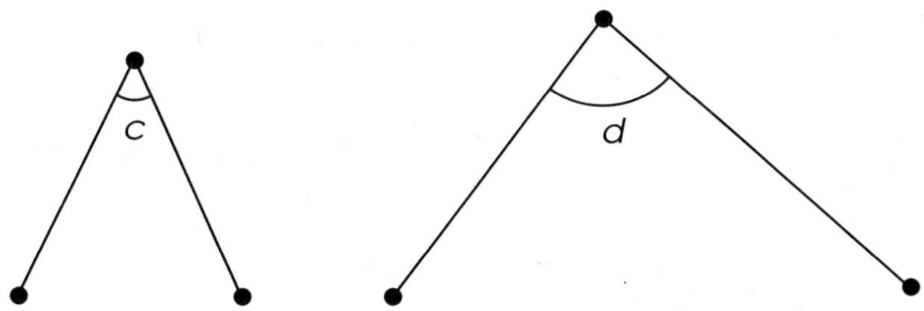

   c) Which angle is the greatest? ________

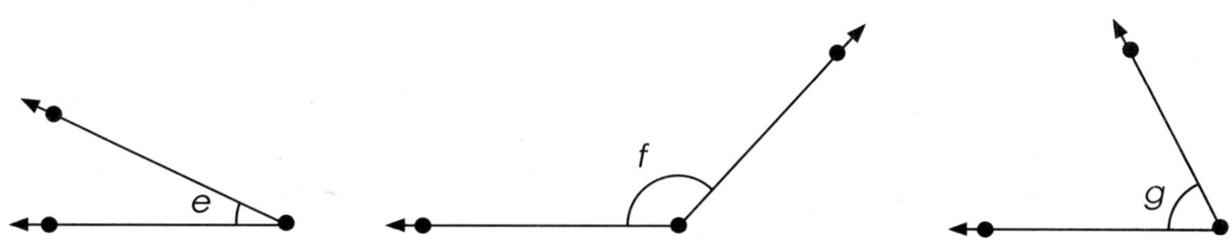

   d) Which angle is the smallest? ________

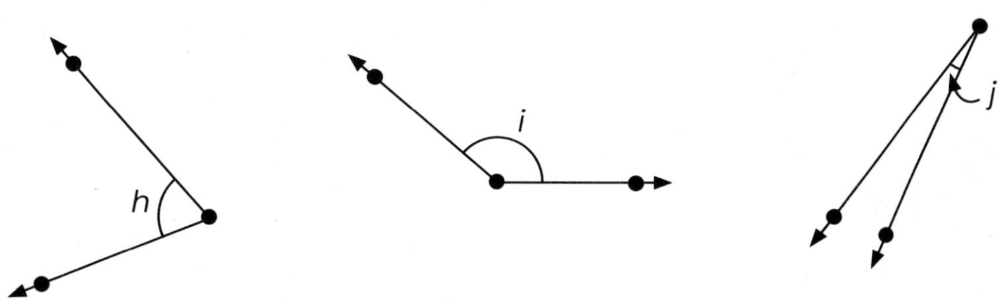

Exercise 3 Angles

1. Mark two angles on each object.

a)

b)

c)

d)

e)

f)

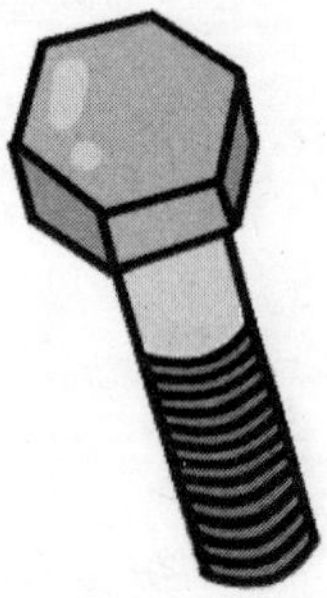

g)

h)

 ISBN 978-93-5103-030-0

Exercise 4 Angles

1. Mark the angles in each shape. Then, complete the table below.

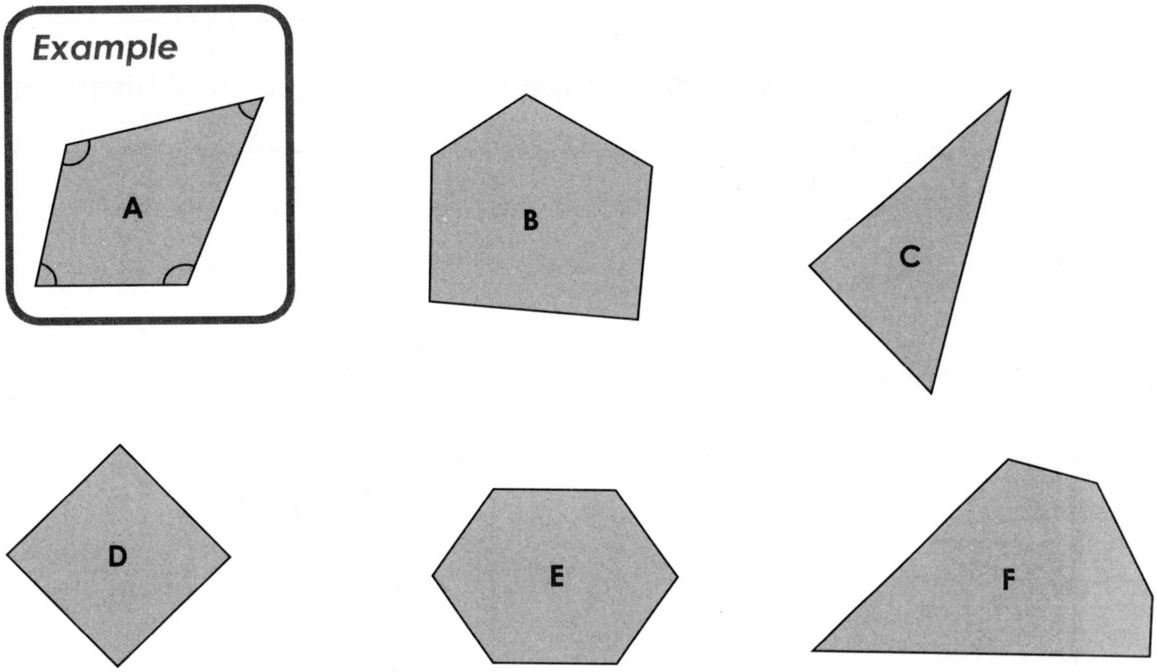

Shape	Number of sides	Number of angles
A	4	4
B		
C		
D		
E		
F		

 ISBN 978-93-5103-030-0

Exercise 5 Right Angles

1. Tick the correct box for each angle.
   Use a folded piece of paper to help you.

	Angle	Acute angle	Right angle	Obtuse angle
a)	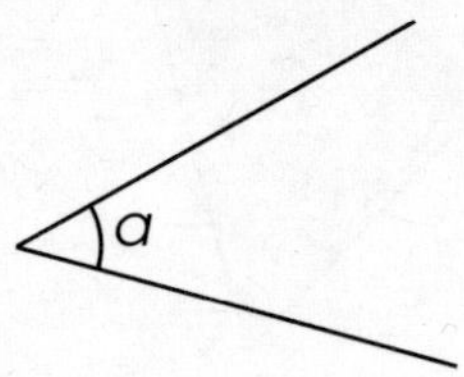			
b)	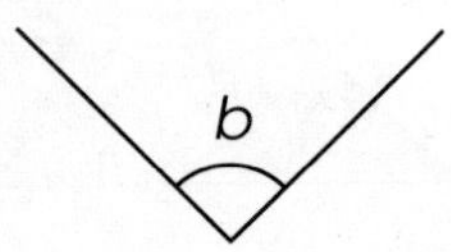			
c)	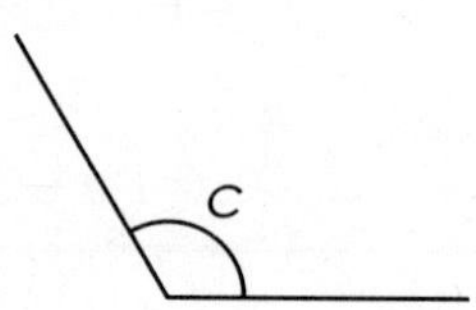			
d)	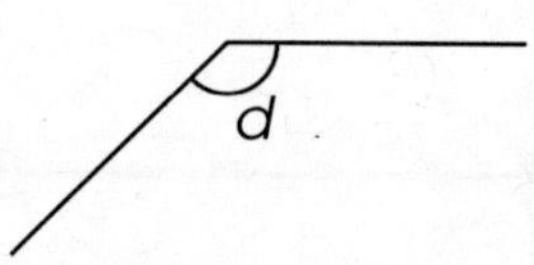			
e)	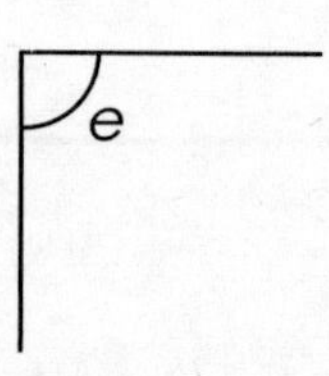			

 ISBN 978-93-5103-030-0

Exercise 6 Right Angles

1. Complete the table.

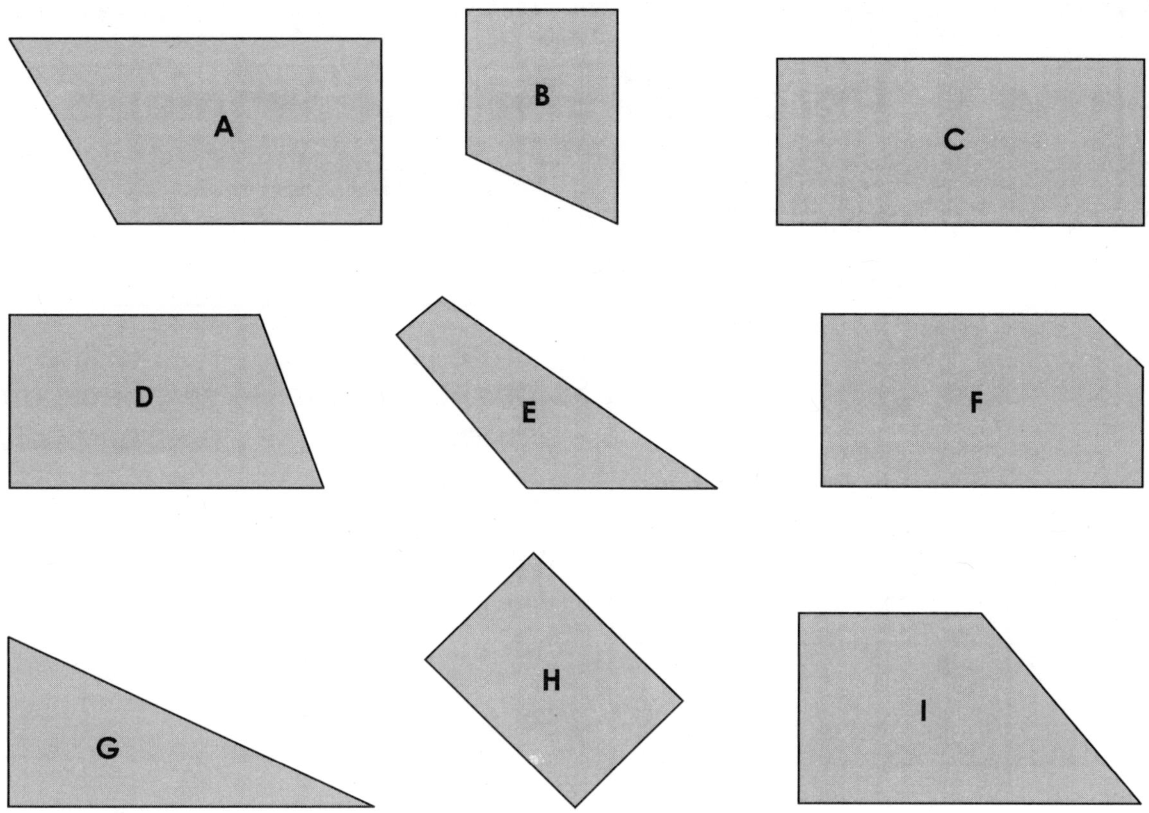

Shape	Number of sides	Number of obtuse angles	Number of right angles	Number of acute angles
A				
B				
C				
D				
E				
F				
G				
H				
I				

 ISBN 978-93-5103-030-0

14 Perpendicular and Parallel Line Segments

Exercise 1 Perpendicular Line Segments

1. Tick the correct answer for each pair of line segments.
   Use a folded piece of paper to help you.

	The line segments are not perpendicular	**The line segments are perpendicular**
a) 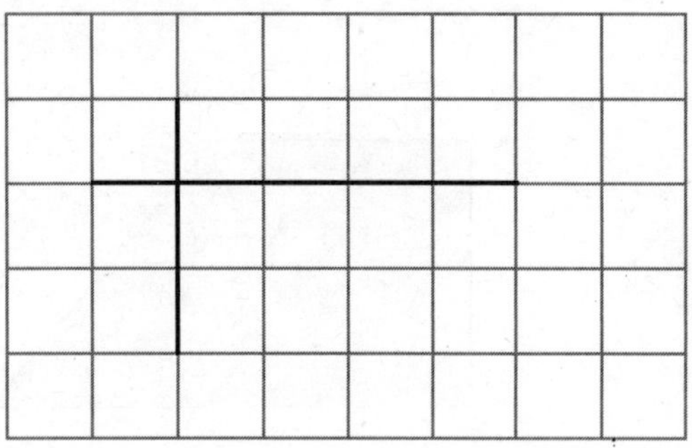		
b) 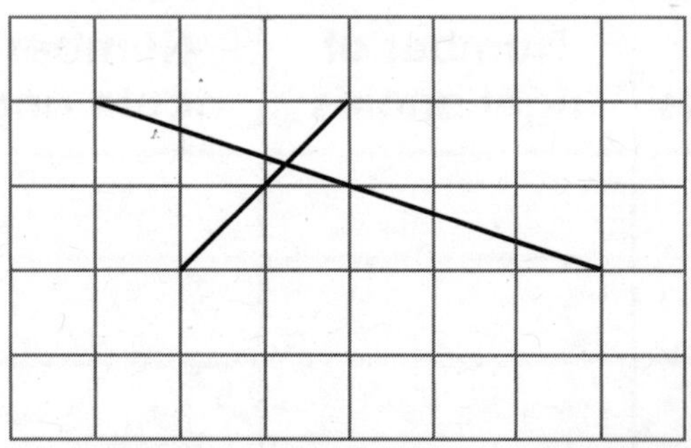		
c) 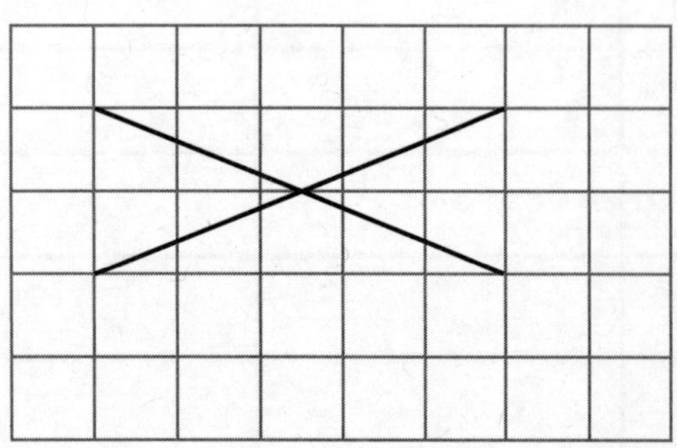		

 ISBN 978-93-5103-030-0

	The line segments are not perpendicular	The line segments are perpendicular
d) 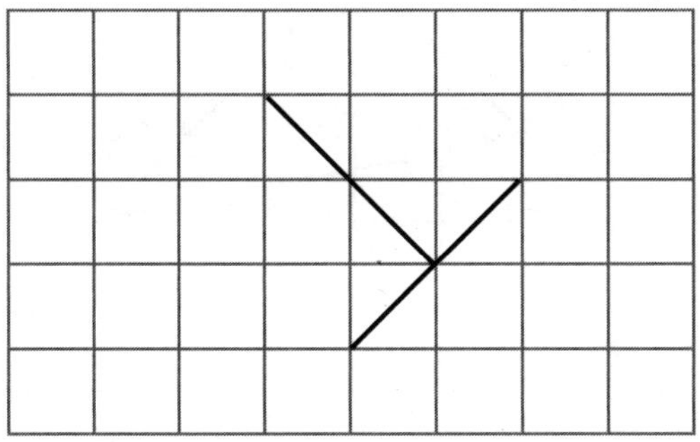		
e) 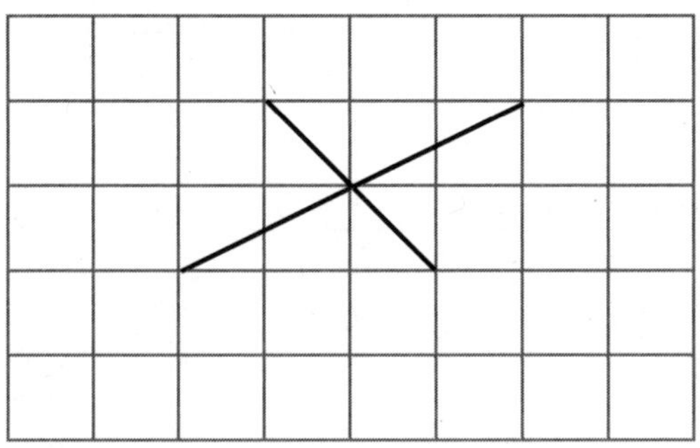		
f) 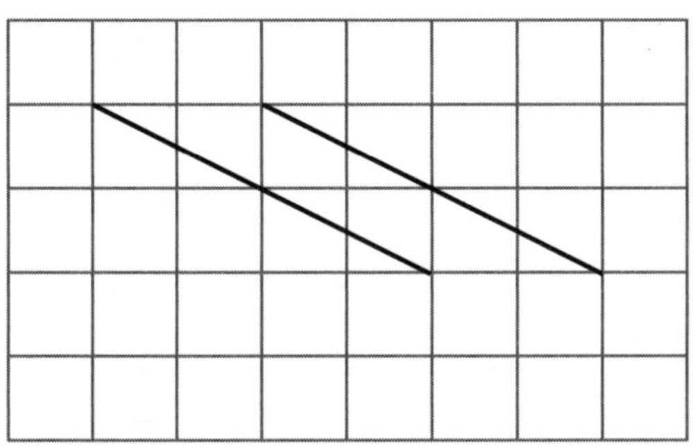		

2. Name each pair of perpendicular line segments.

a)

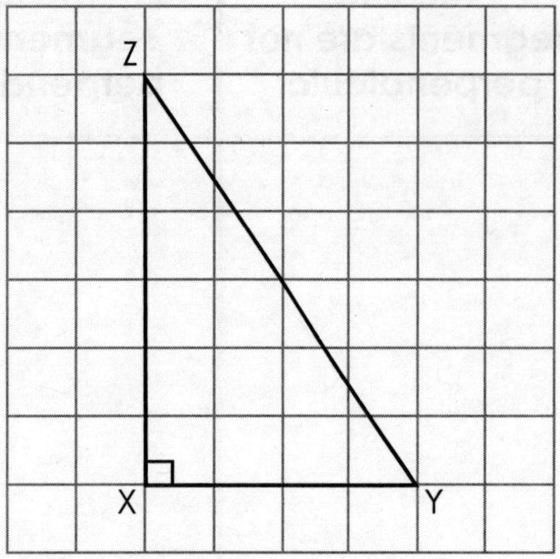

XY ⊥ ________

b)

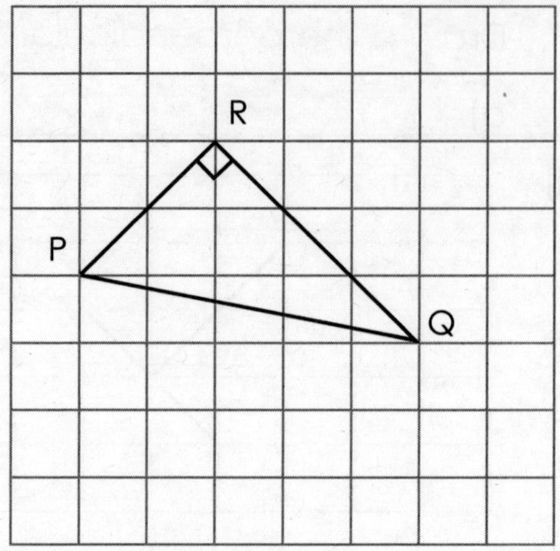

PR ⊥ ________

c)

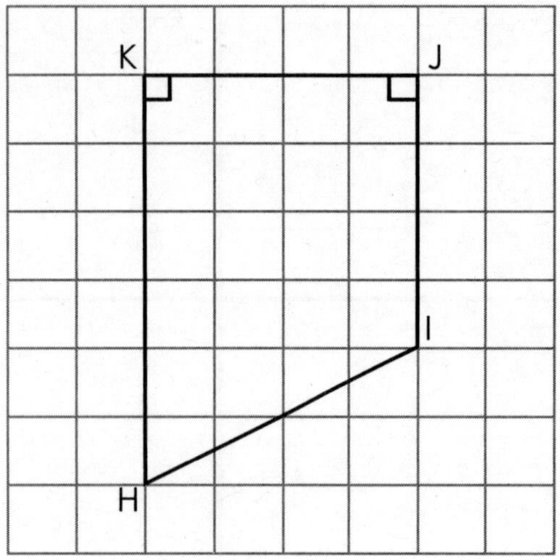

____

____

d)

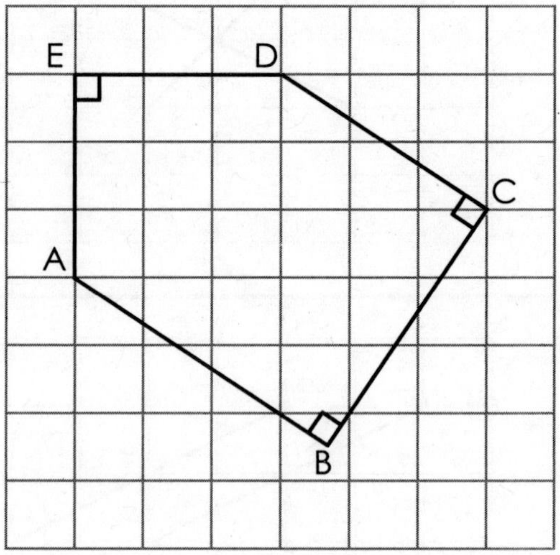

____

____

____

  ISBN 978-93-5103-030-0

Exercise 2 Perpendicular Line Segments

1. Draw a line perpendicular to each of the given line segments.

a)

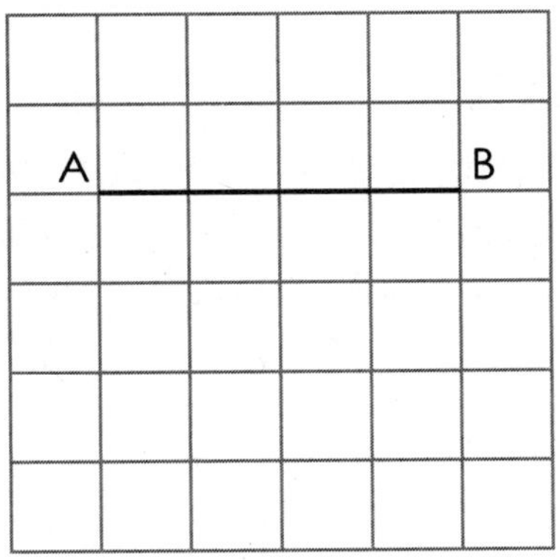

b)

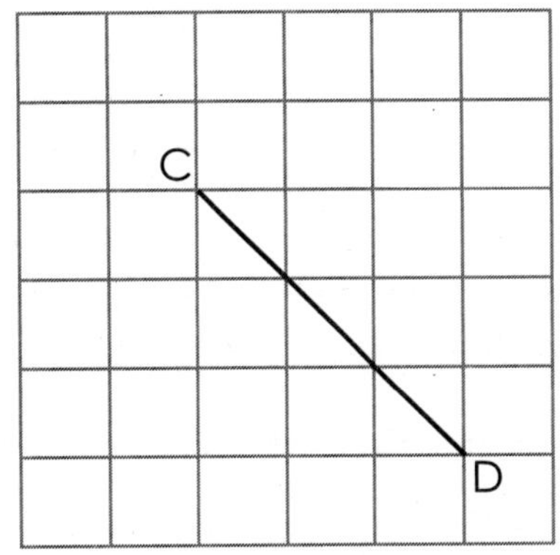

c)

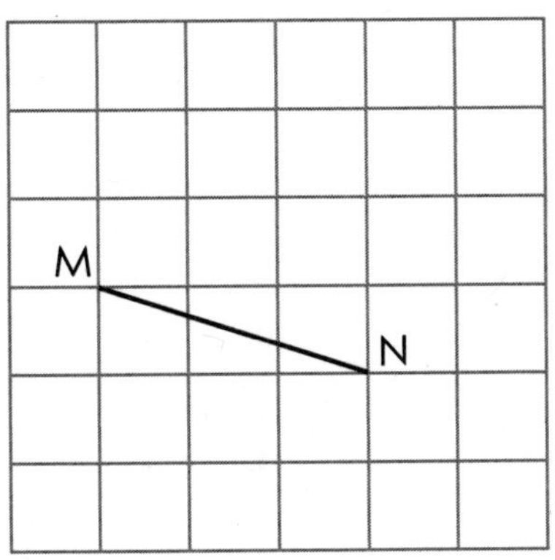

d)

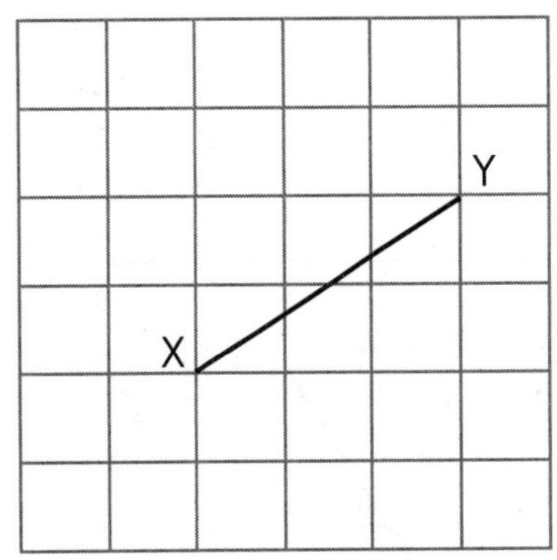

e)

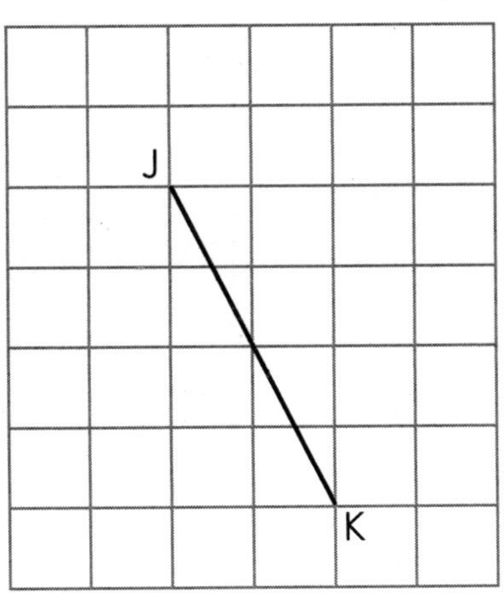

f)

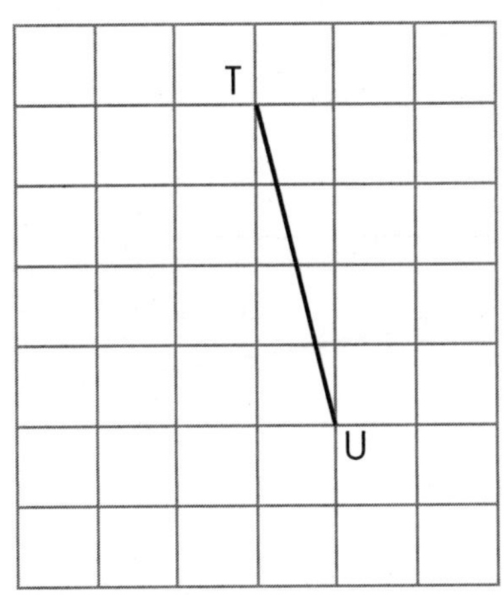

 ISBN 978-93-5103-030-0

Exercise 3 Parallel Line Segments

1. Tick the correct answer for each pair of line segments.

	The line segments are not parallel	The line segments are parallel
a) 		
b) 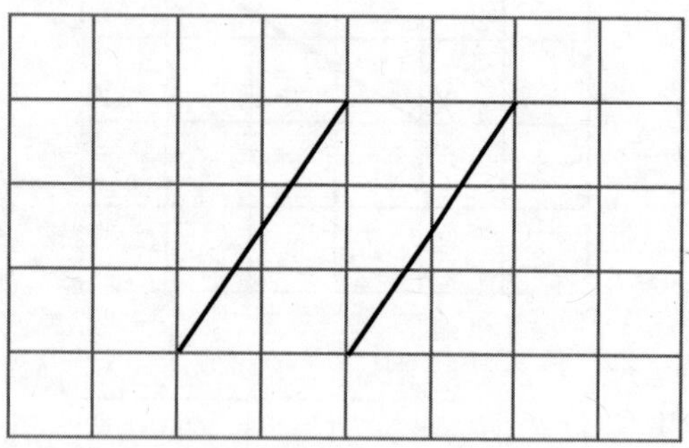		
c) 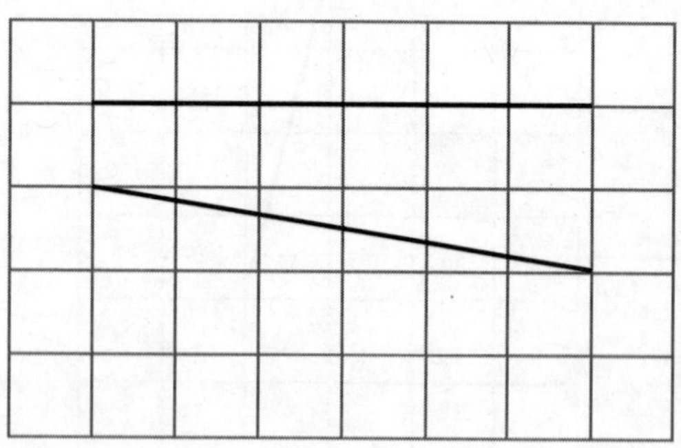		

 ISBN 978-93-5103-030-0

	The line segments are not parallel	The line segments are parallel
d) 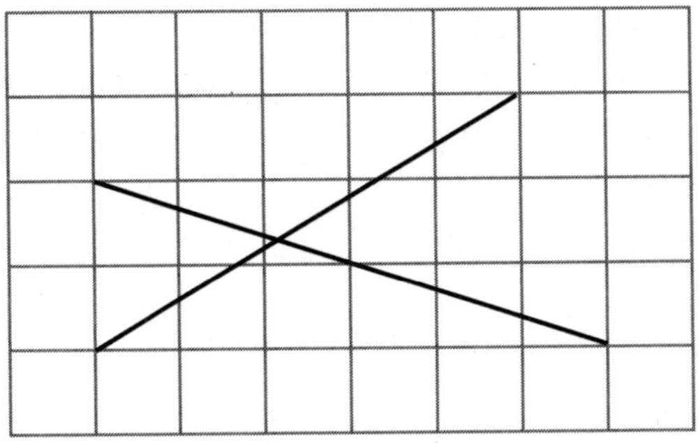		
e) 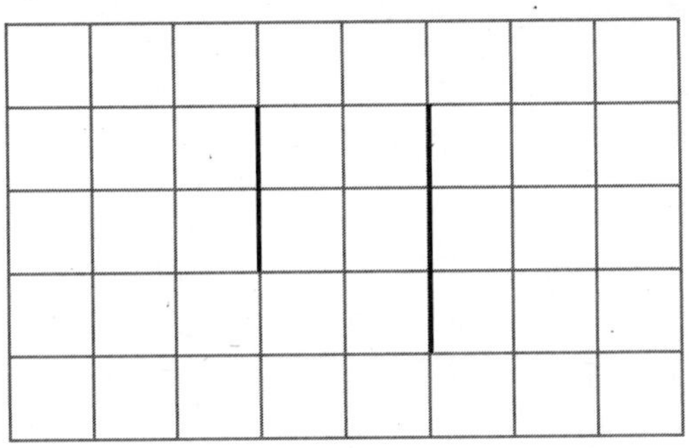		
f) 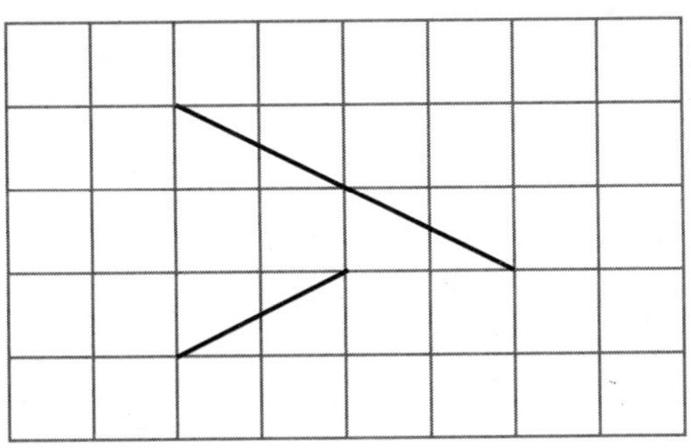		

2. Name each pair of parallel line segments.

a)

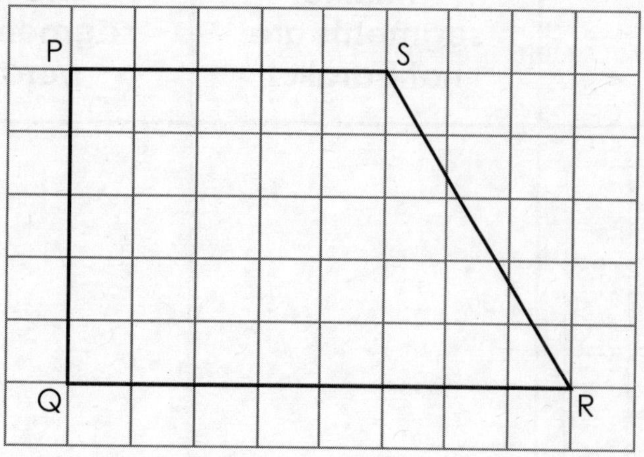

PS || ____________

b)

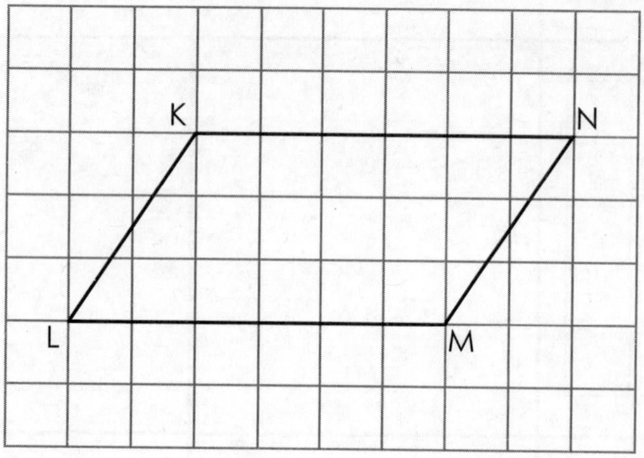

____

____

c)

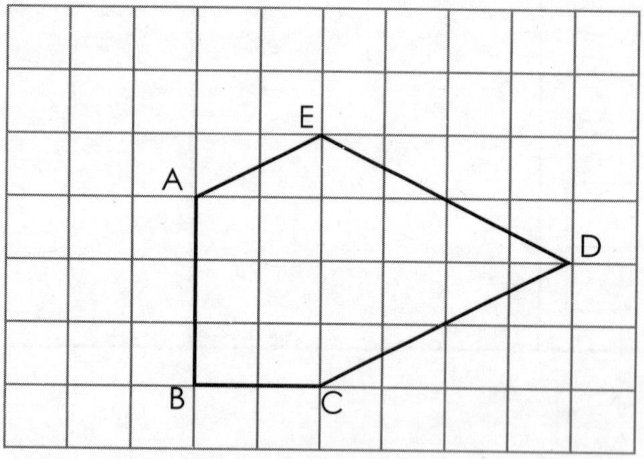

AE || ____________

d)

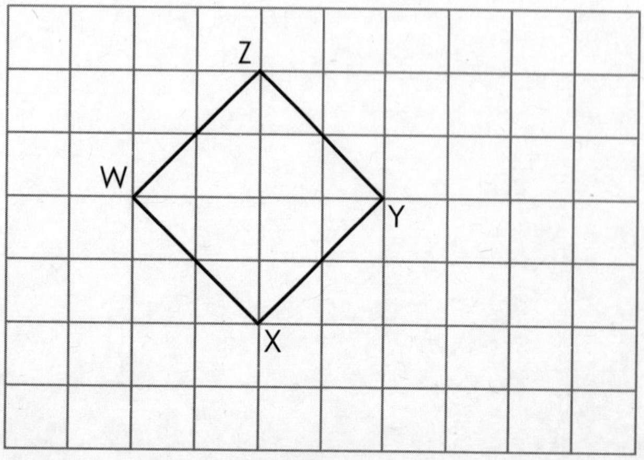

____

____

 ISBN 978-93-5103-030-0

Exercise 4 Parallel Line Segments

1. Draw a line segment parallel to each of the given line segments.

a)

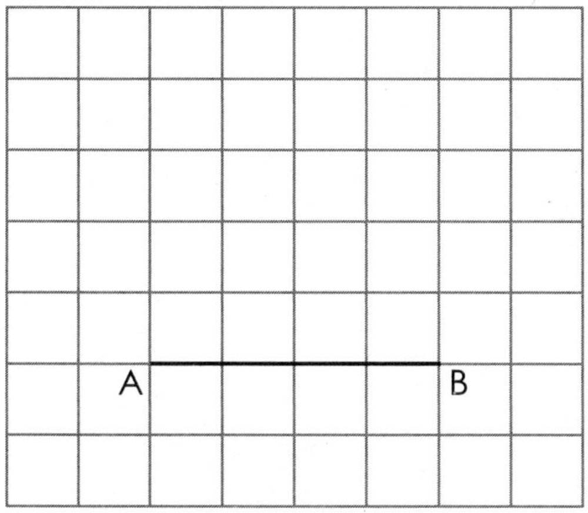

b)

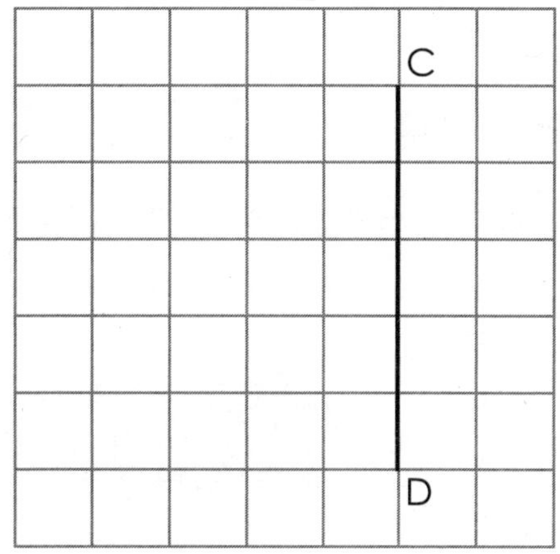

c)

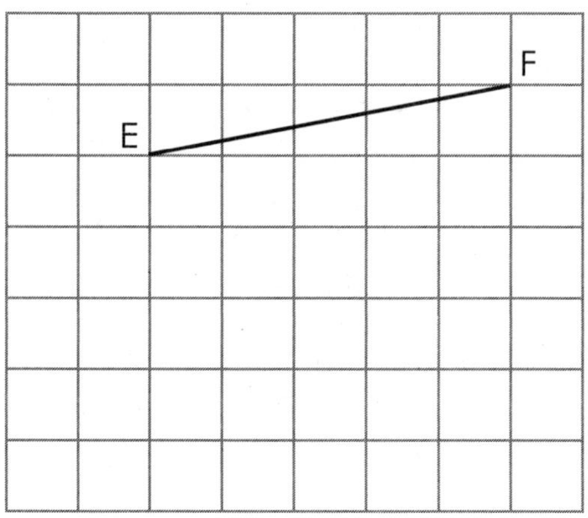

d)

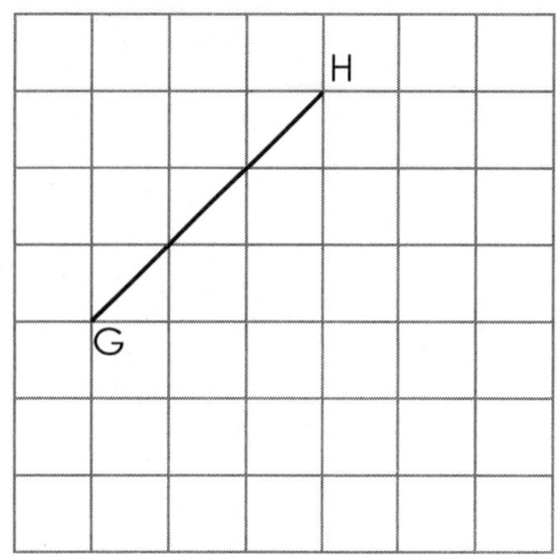

e)

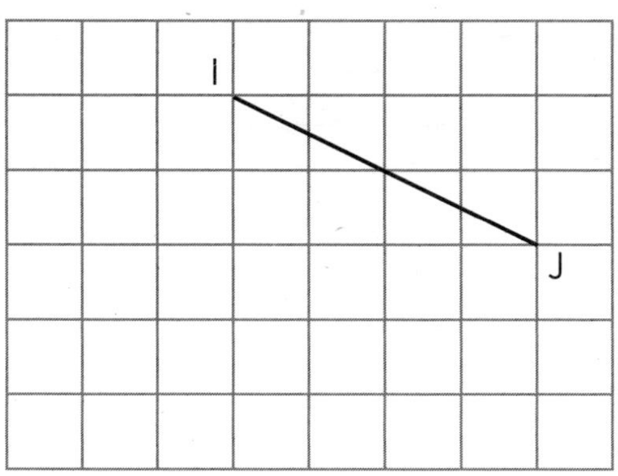

f)

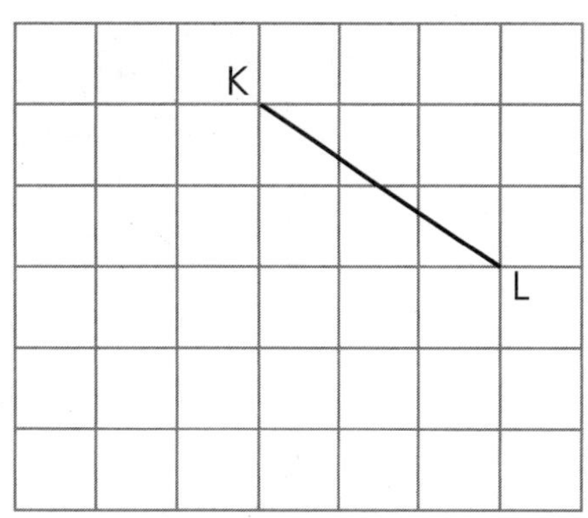

 ISBN 978-93-5103-030-0

15 Area

Exercise 1 Square Units

1. Circle the figure with the greater area.

a)

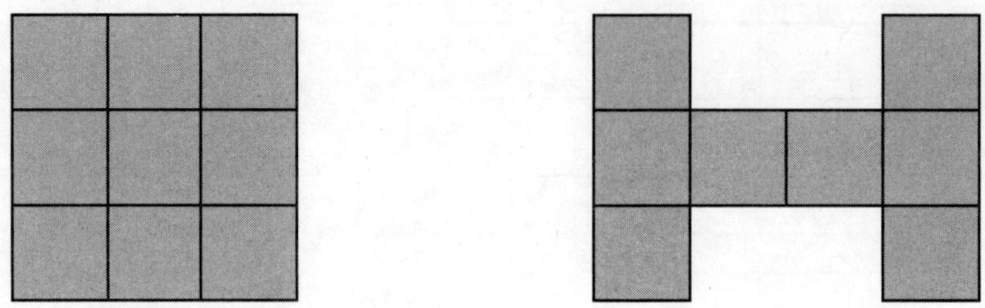

b)

c)

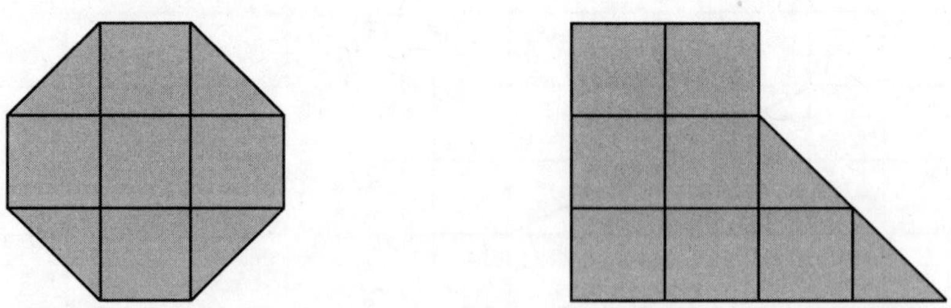

d)

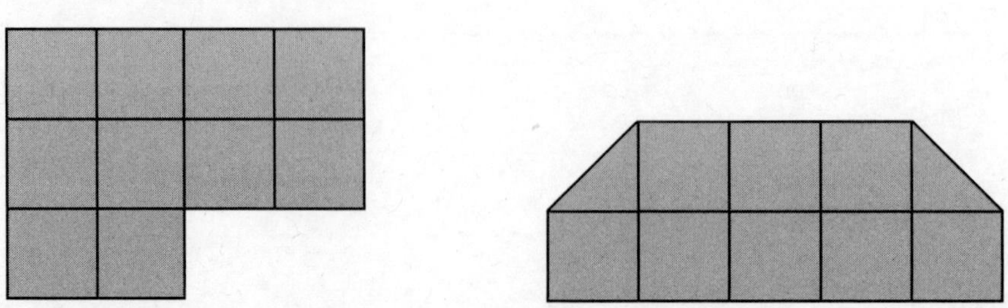

 ISBN 978-93-5103-030-0

2. Draw another figure which has the same area as the given figure and then colour it.

a) 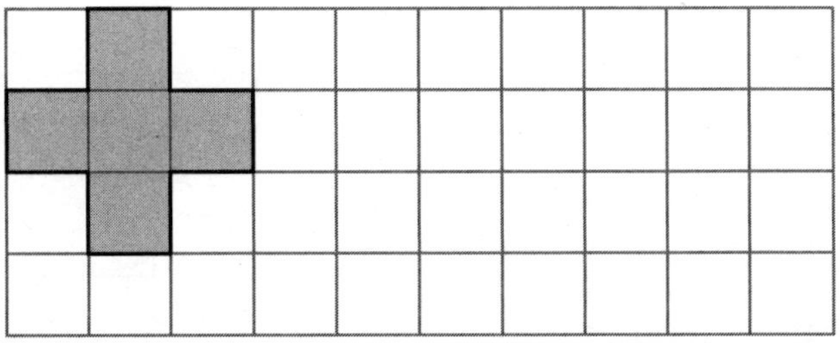

b) 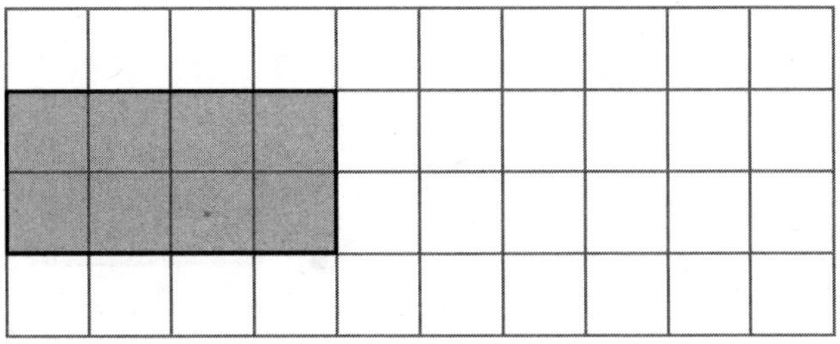

c) 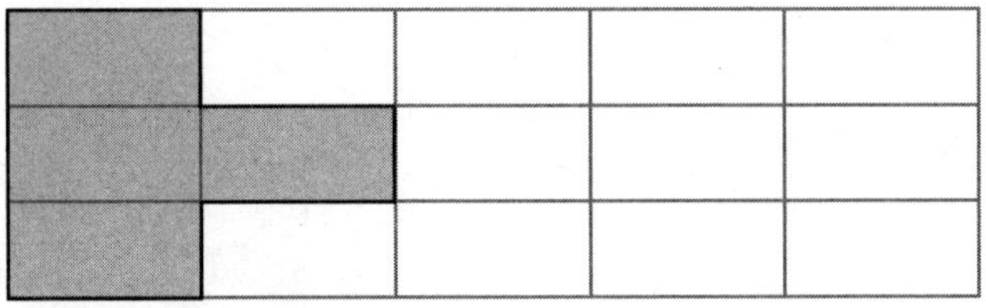

d) 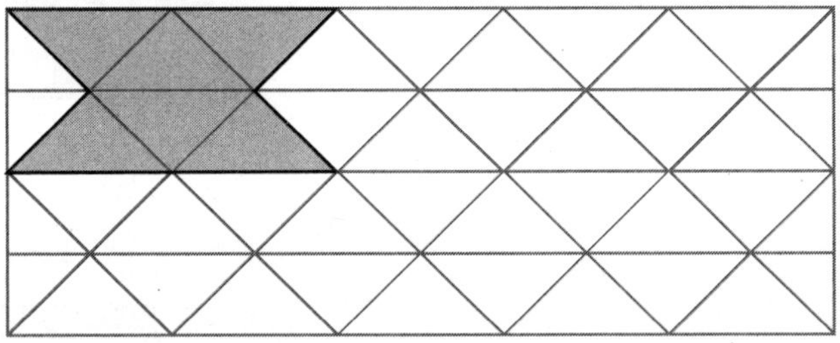

 ISBN 978-93-5103-030-0

Exercise 2 Square Units

1. Join the two figures that have the same area.

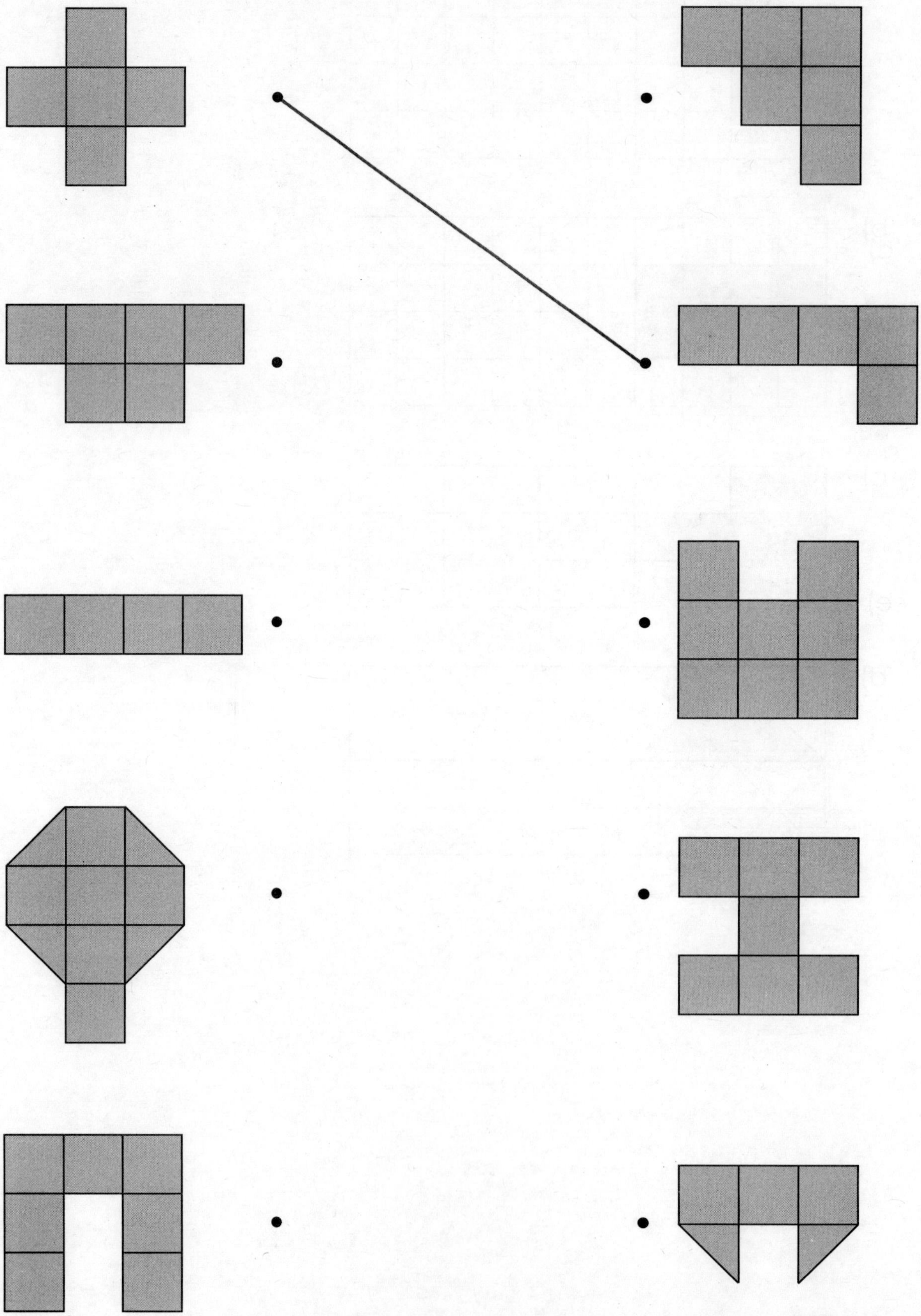

 ISBN 978-93-5103-030-0

2. What is the area of each of the figures?

a)

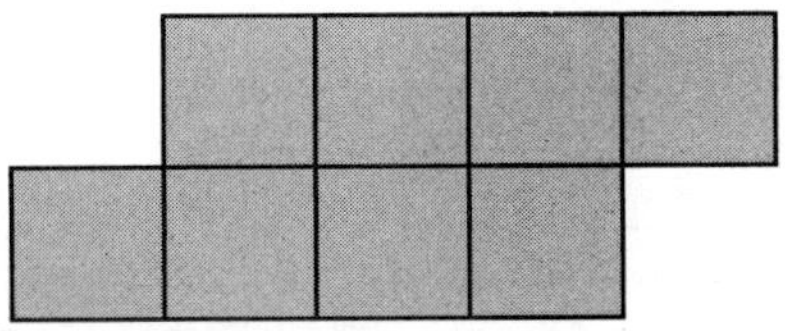

The area is ________ square units.

b)

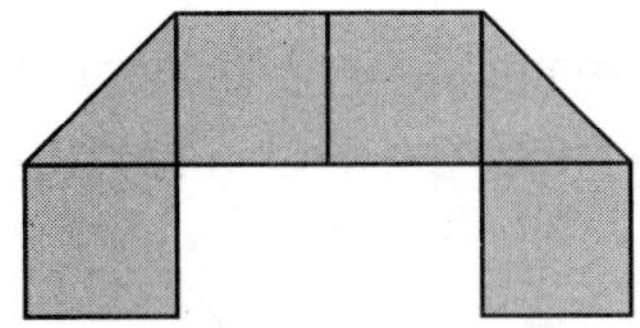

The area is ________ square units.

c)

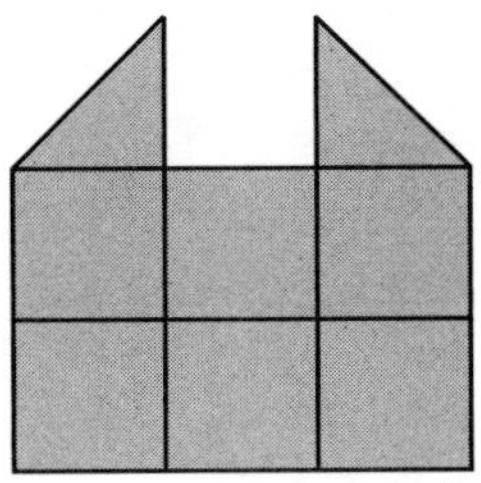

The area is ________ square units.

d)

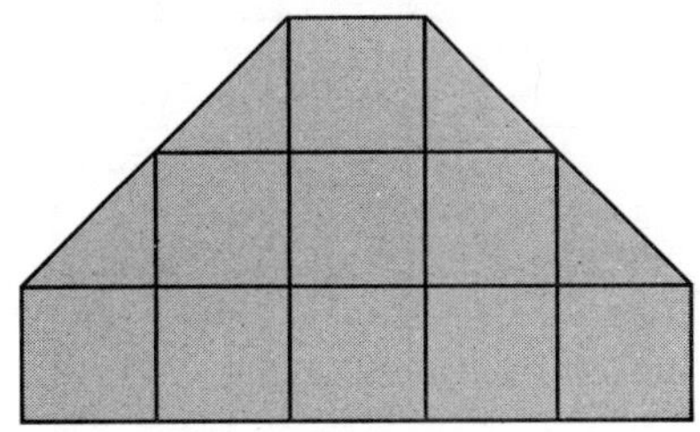

The area is ________ square units.

e)

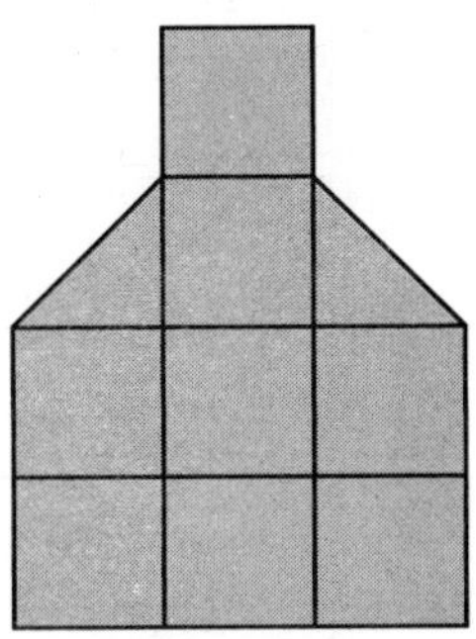

The area is ________ square units.

f)

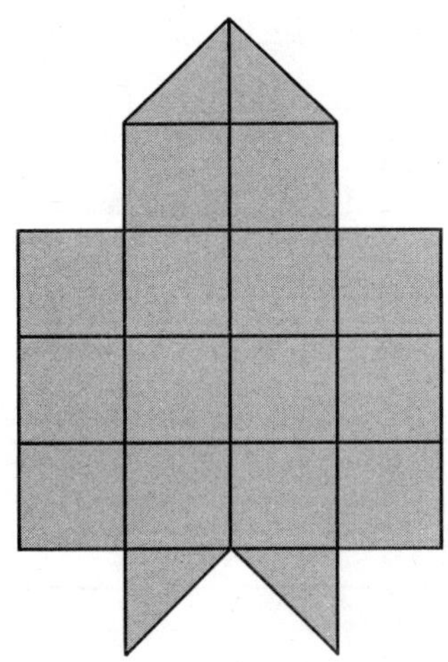

The area is ________ square units.

 ISBN 978-93-5103-030-0

Exercise 3 Square Units

1. Draw another figure which has the same area as the given figure and then colour it.

a)

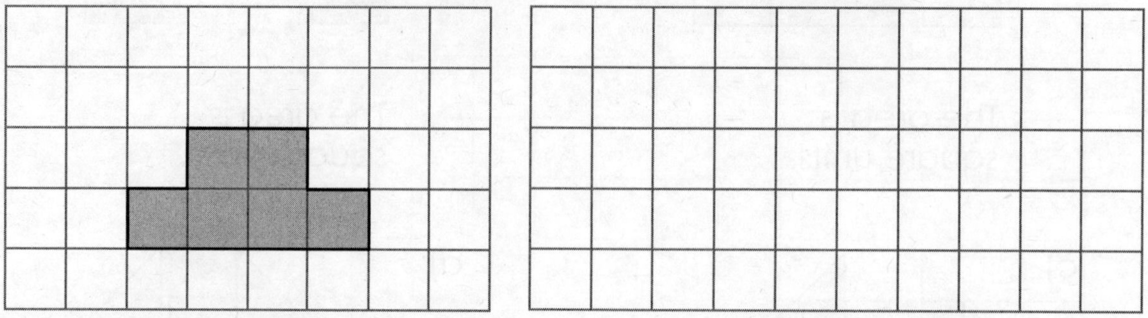

b)

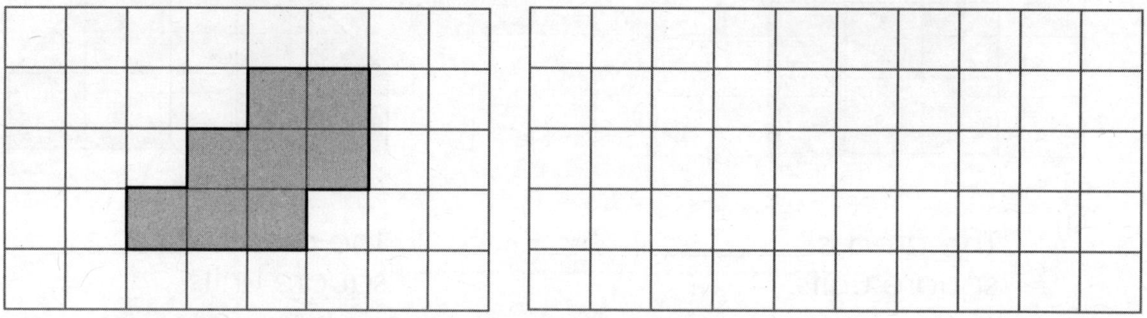

c)

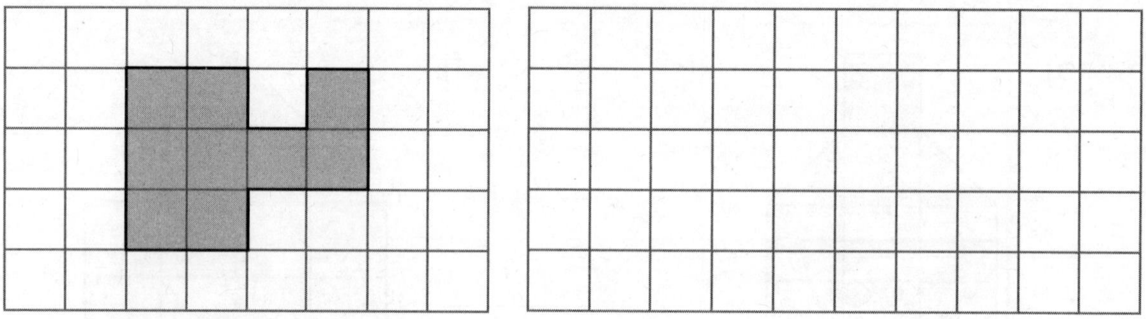

d)

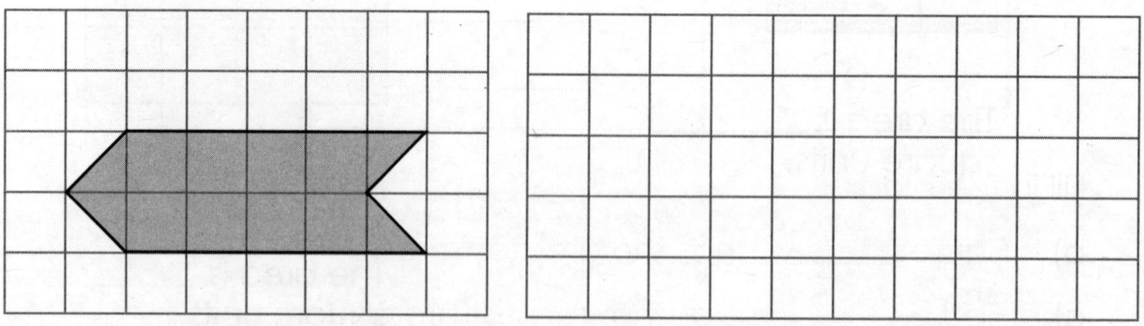

e)

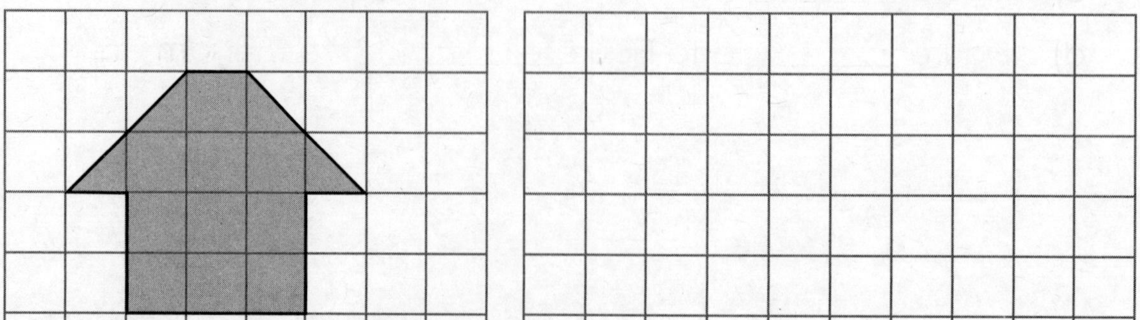

 ISBN 978-93-5103-030-0

2. Look at the figures below.

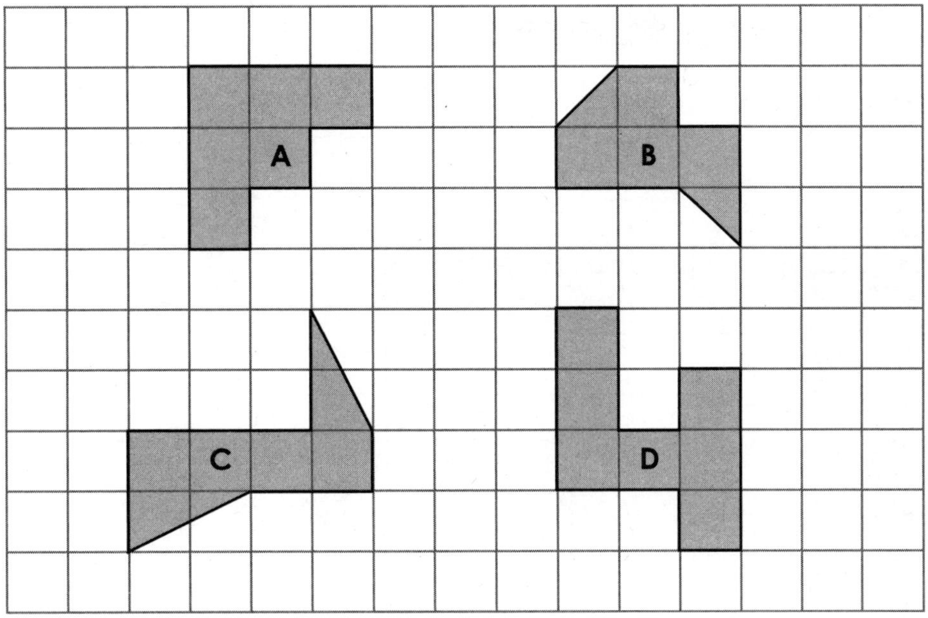

a) Complete the table.

Figure	Area
A	________ square units
B	________ square units
C	________ square units
D	________ square units

Fill in the blanks.

b) Figure ________ has the greatest area.

c) Figure ________ has the smallest area.

d) Figure ________ and Figure ________ have the same area.

 ISBN 978-93-5103-030-0

Exercise 4 Area in Square Centimetres and Square Metres

1. Look at the figures below.

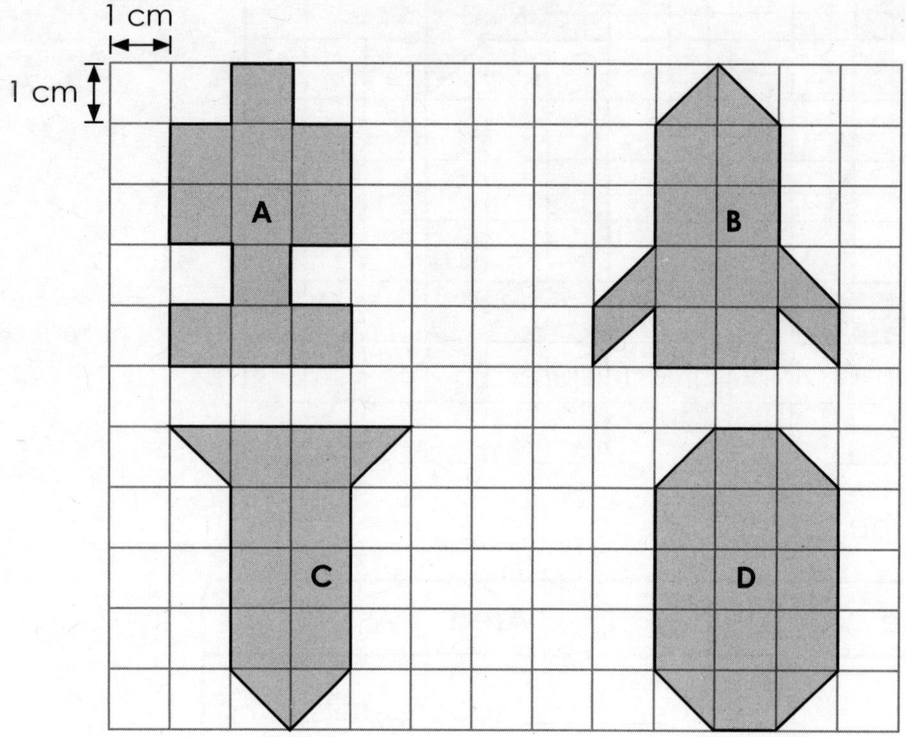

a) Complete the table.

Figure	Area
A	________ cm^2
B	________ cm^2
C	________ cm^2
D	________ cm^2

Fill in the blanks.

b) Figure ________ and Figure ________ have the same area.

c) Figure ________ has the greatest area.

d) Figure ________ has the smallest area.

 ISBN 978-93-5103-030-0

2. a) Find the area of the given figure.
Then, draw another figure with the same area.

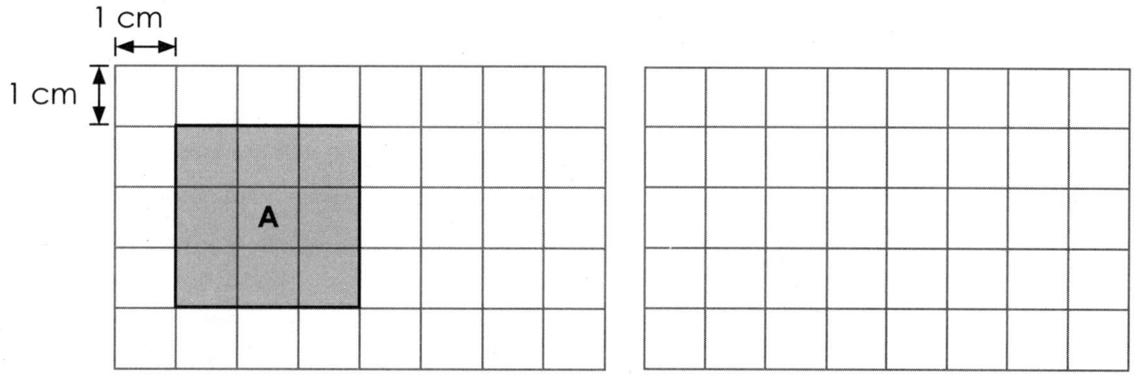

Area = ________

b) Find the area of the given figure.
Then, draw another figure with a smaller area.
Write its area.

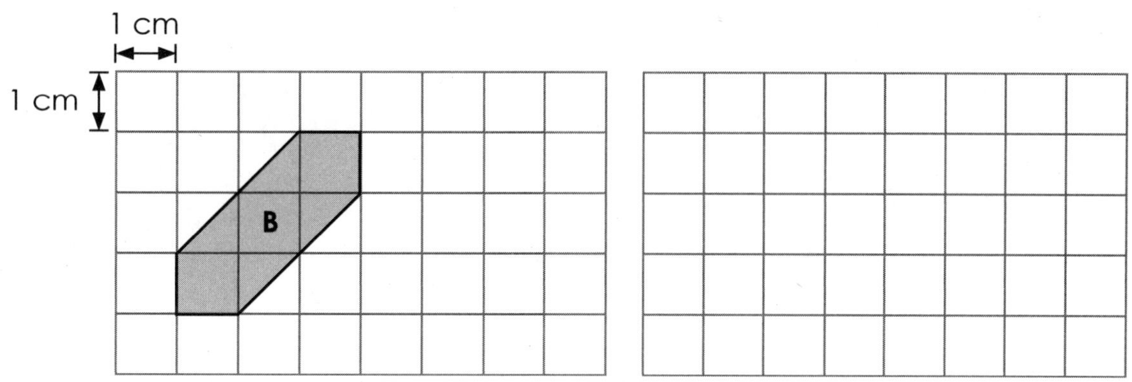

Area = ________ Area = ________

c) Find the area of the given figure.
Then, draw another figure with a greater area.
Write its area.

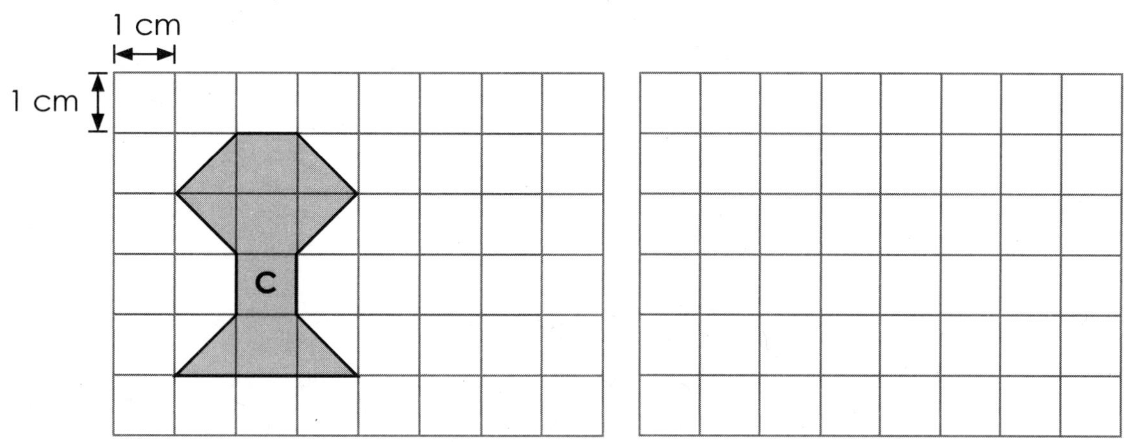

Area = ________ Area = ________

 ISBN 978-93-5103-030-0

Exercise 5 Area in Square Centimetres and Square Metres

1. What is the area of each of the figures?

a)

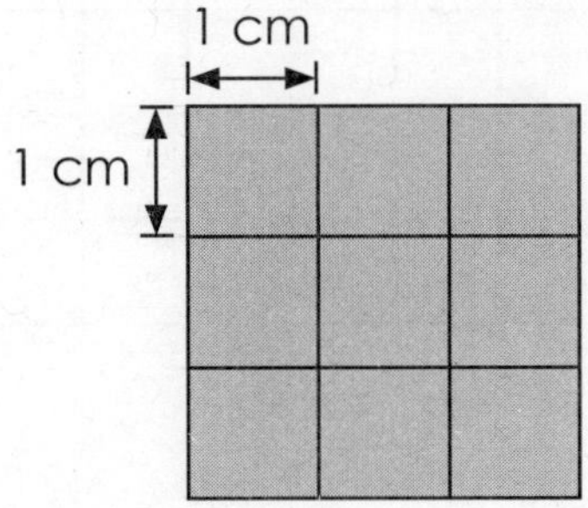

Area = ________

b)

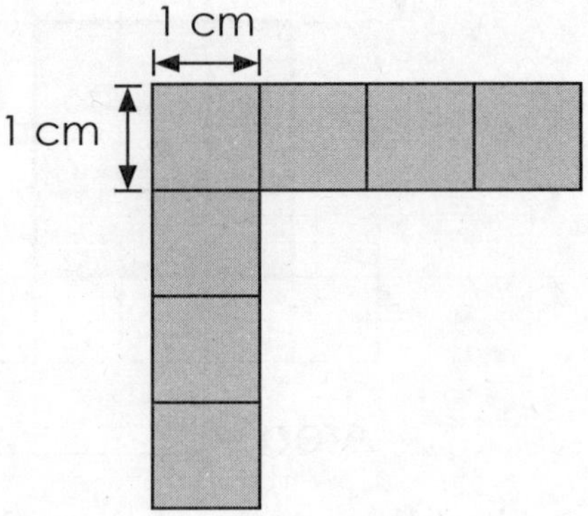

Area = ________

c)

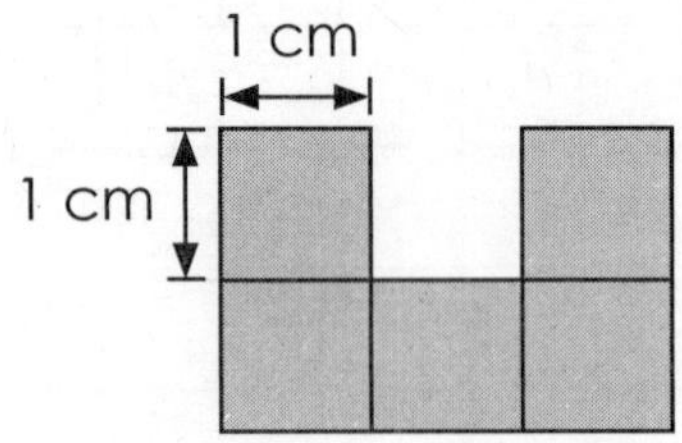

Area = ________

d)

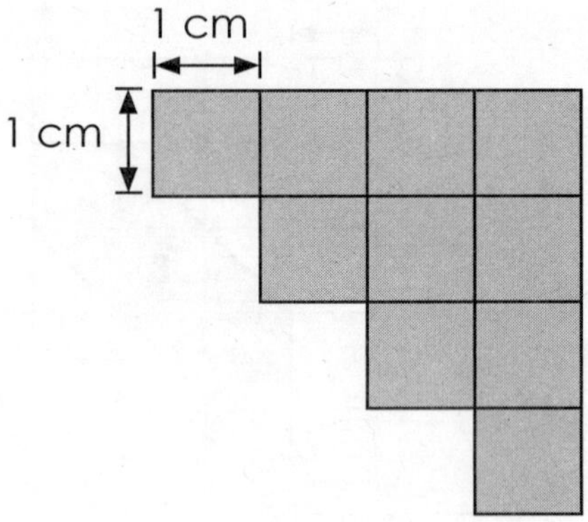

Area = ________

e)

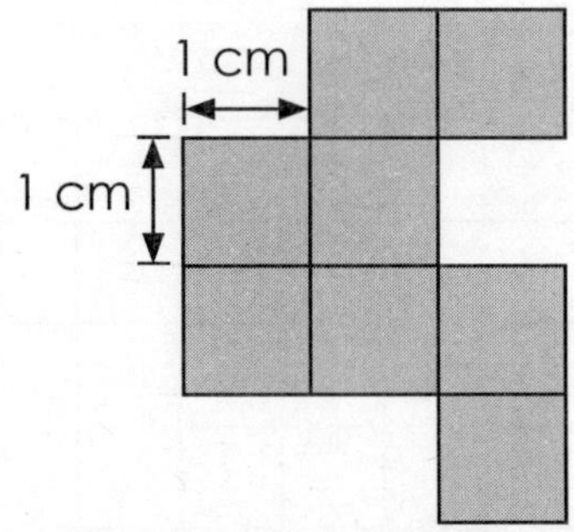

Area = ________

f)

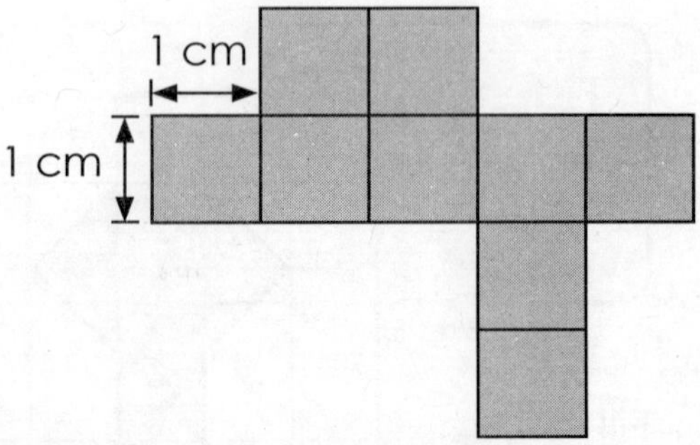

Area = ________

 ISBN 978-93-5103-030-0

Exercise 6 Area in Square Centimetres and Square Metres

1. What is the area of each of the figures?

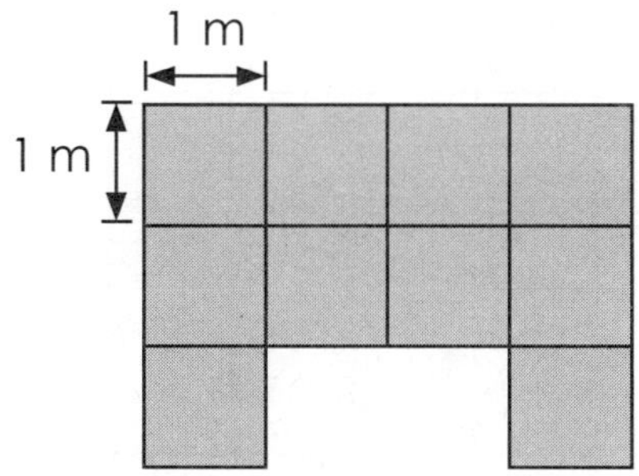

A

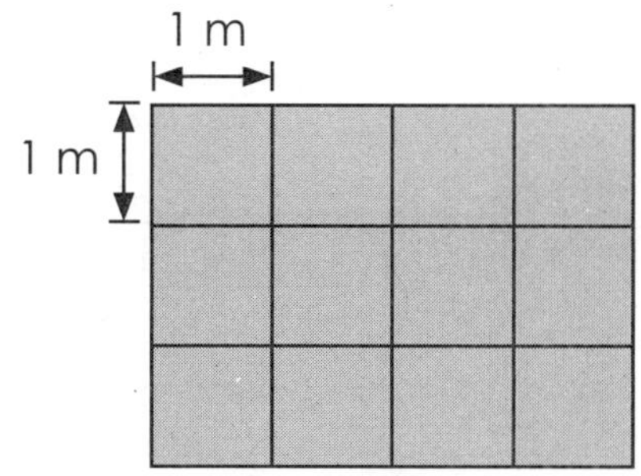

B

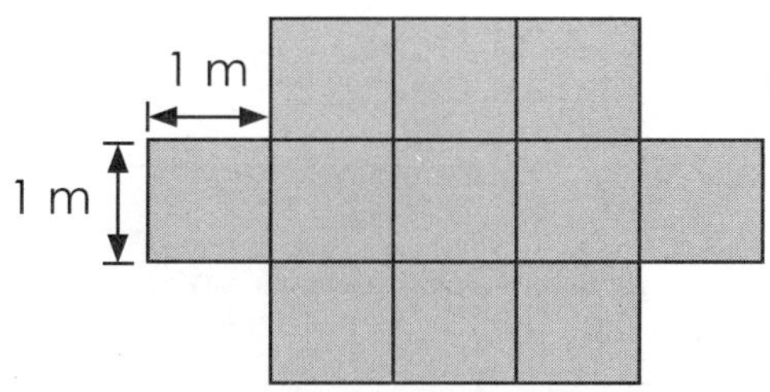

C

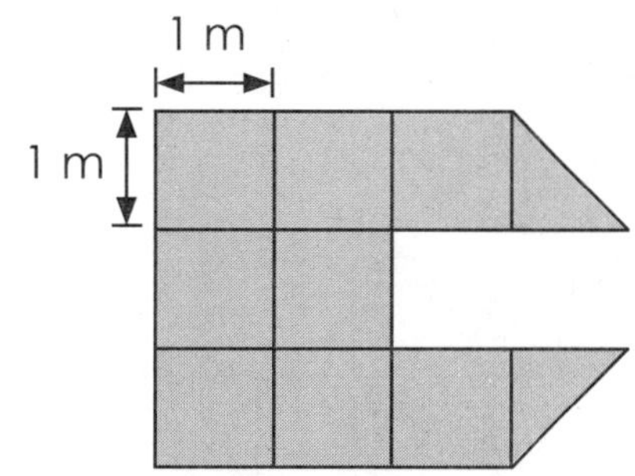

D

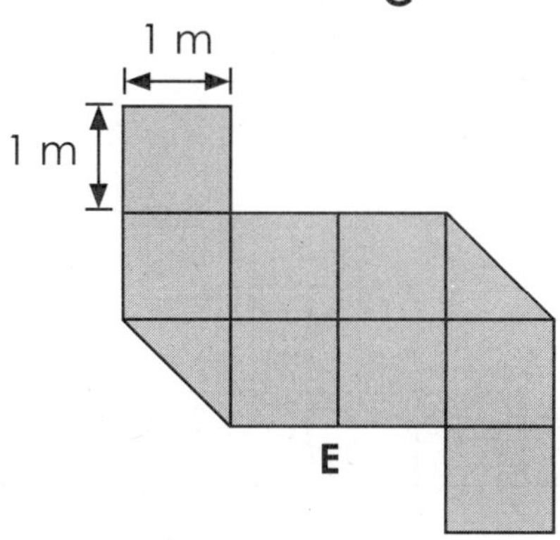

E

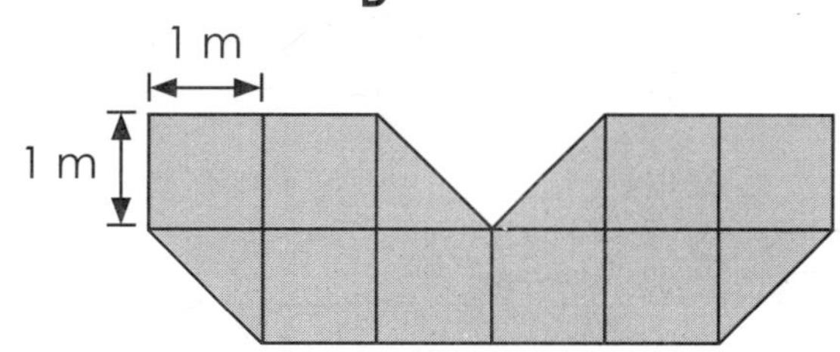

F

Complete the table.

Figure	A	B	C	D	E	F
Area	____ m^2	____ m^2	____ m^2	____ m^2	____ m^2	____ m^2

2. Fill in the blanks with **square centimetres** or **square metres**.

   a) The area of my classroom door is about 2 ________________.

   b) The area of my ruler is about 60 ________________.

   c) The area of my exercise book is about 300 ________________.

 ISBN 978-93-5103-030-0

Exercise 7 Area in Square Centimetres and Square Metres

1. What is the area of each of the figures?

a)

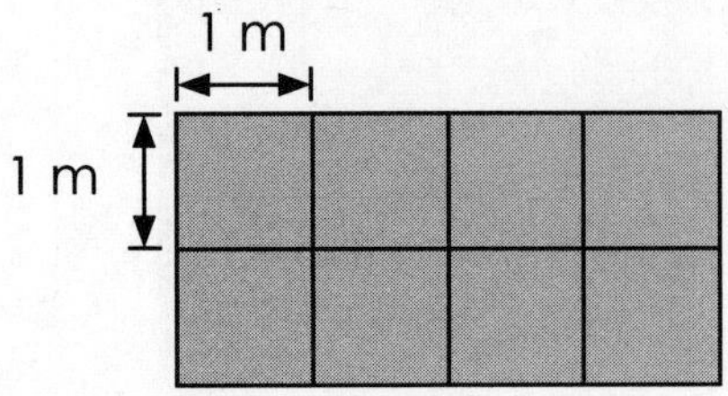

Area = ________

b)

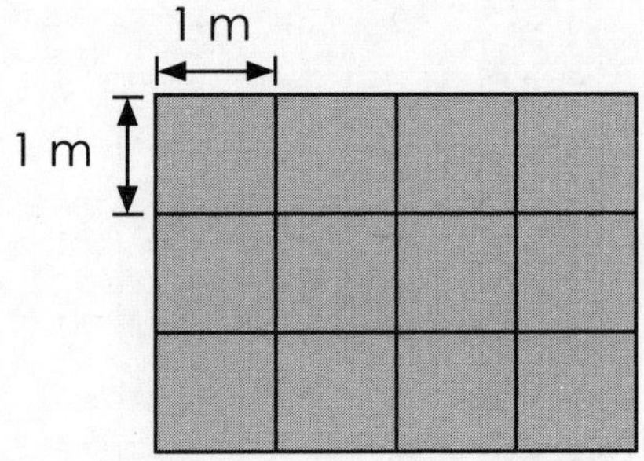

Area = ________

c)

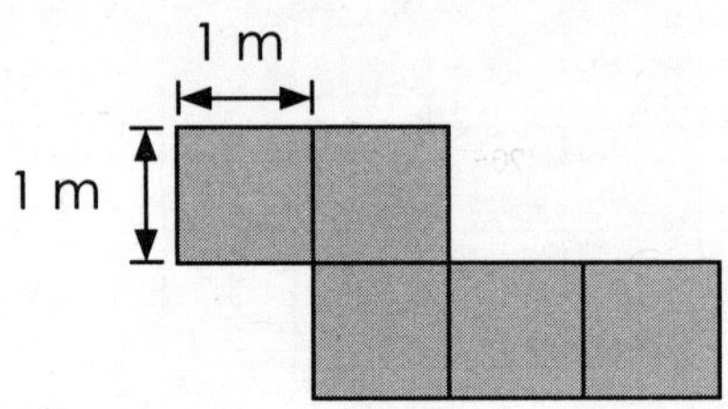

Area = ________

d)

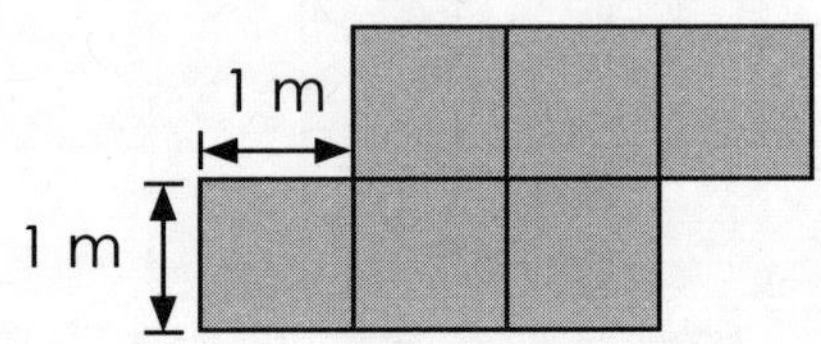

Area = ________

e)

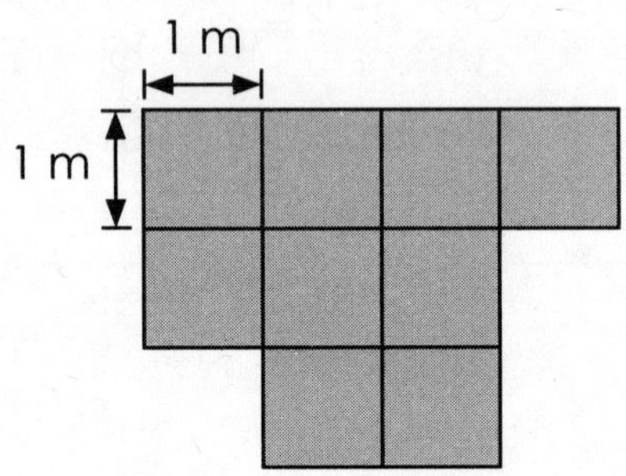

Area = ________

f)

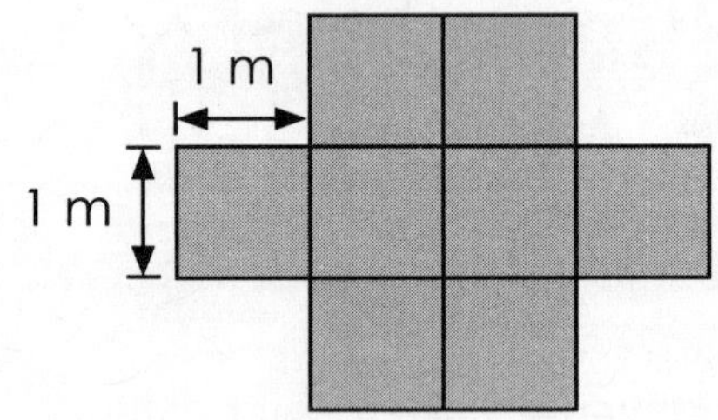

Area = ________

 ISBN 978-93-5103-030-0

Answers

Chapter 1

Exercise 1

1. b) 2048; **c)** 1344; **d)** 4066; **e)** 8009 **2. a)** 5278; **b)** 2050; **c)** 4207; **d)** 6035 **3.** 4548, 3302, 1712, 3400, 6009, 4502 **4.** Five thousand four hundred seventeen; Six thousand nine hundred forty; Eight thousand fifty-three; Seven thousand two hundred nine; Nine thousand four

Exercise 2

1. a) 8, 80, 400; **b)** 7, 40, 400, 6000; **c)** 9, 90, 700, 7000 **2. a)** 90; **b)** 8; **c)** 50; **d)** 700; **e)** 3000; **f)** 600; **g)** 200 **3. a)** 5, 8, 9, 7; **b)** 5000; **c)** 8, 800; **d)** 9, 5 **4. a)** 800; **b)** 6; **c)** 60; **d)** tens; **e)** 5, 8

Exercise 3

1. a) 4073; **b)** 5001 **2. a)** 4082; **b)** 3671 **3. a)** <; **b)** < **4.** 7640, 7604, 7406, 7064 **5. a)** 392, 329, 932, 239, 293, 923; **b)** 932, 239 **6.** 1038

Exercise 4

1. a) 6335; **b)** 2316 **2. a)** 395; **b)** 590; **c)** 4042; **d)** 3507; **e)** 1183; **f)** 2716; **g)** 1225; **h)** 4717 **3. a)** 10; **b)** 1000; **c)** 1; **d)** 100; **e)** 10; **f)** 100; **g)** 1000; **h)** 1 **4. a)** 1; **b)** 100; **c)** 1000; **d)** 10; **e)** 1; **f)** 1000; **g)** 100; **h)** 10 **5. a)** 3809; **b)** 5038; **c)** 2987; **d)** 1299 **6. a)** 1302; **b)** 903; **c)** 4537; **d)** 3698

7.

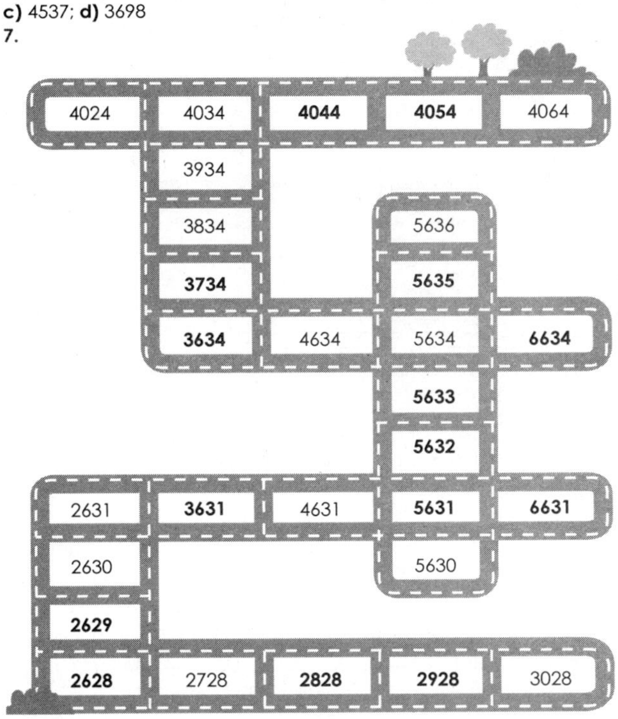

Chapter 2

Exercise 1

1. a) 16, 16; **b)** 2, 2 **2.** +, 14, 14 **3.** –, 7, 7 **4.** 154, 154 **5.** The sum of 145 and 285 is 430. **6.** The difference between 96 and 68 is 28. **7.** The difference between 387 and 512 is 125.

Exercise 2

1. a) 3627, 3674, 3824, 7624; **b)** 5109, 5177, 5707, 8107 **2. a)** 2780; **b)** 5293; **c)** 4965; **d)** 4870; **e)** 5954; **f)** 6818; **g)** 5591; **h)** 7408; **i)** 8934 **3.** 4112, 7346, 1818, 6465, 3074, 8291, 9937, 5713, 7179, VEGETABLES

Exercise 3

1. a) 6661; **b)** 9192; **c)** 4815; **d)** 3127; **e)** 6891; **f)** 9424; **g)** 8692; **h)** 3854; **i)** 7260, UMBRELLA

Exercise 4

1. 4331, 5021, 8160, 6442, 7146, 6554, 8375, 9810, 8301, I SUBTRACT

Exercise 5

1.

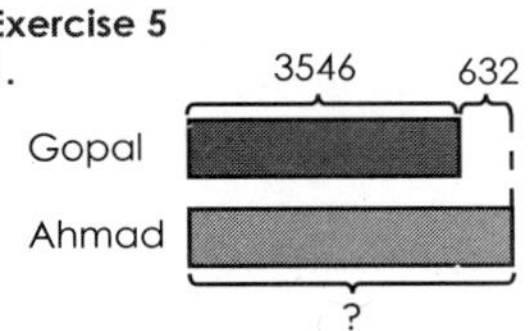

3546 + 632 = 4178 stamps

2.

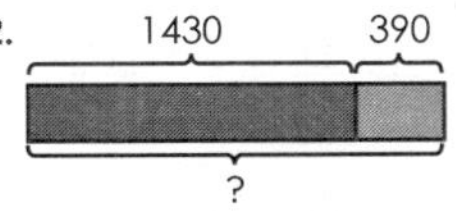

1430 + 390 = 1820 letters

3.

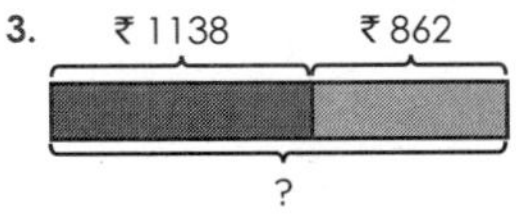

₹ 1138 + ₹ 862 = ₹ 2000 at first

4.

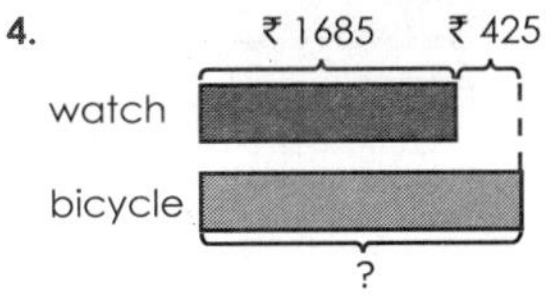

₹ 1685 + ₹ 425 = ₹ 2110

Exercise 6

1. a) 9322; **b)** 6518; **c)** 7400; **d)** 275; **e)** 3313; **f)** 8234; **g)** 5236; **h)** 2593; **i)** 1260, F

Exercise 7

1. 9388, 9589, 2329, 1516, 3497, 1129, 8194, 8258, 3729, COURTEOUS

Exercise 8

1. 8268, 2949, 1868, 5785, 6786, 2837, 4726, 3859, 6283, RASPBERRY

Exercise 9

1. a) 4764; **b)** 2482; **c)** 5306; **d)** 3847; **e)** 4629; **f)** 3767; **g)** 613; **h)** 2135; **i)** 2799; **j)** 7598; **k)** 3819; **l)** 2081 **2.** Across: **A**—6342; **C**—3304; **D**—5514; **F**—2531; **I**—4205; **J**—1961 Down: **A**—6254; **B**—2435; **D**—5728; **E**—1327; **G**—3041; **H**—7659

Exercise 10

1.

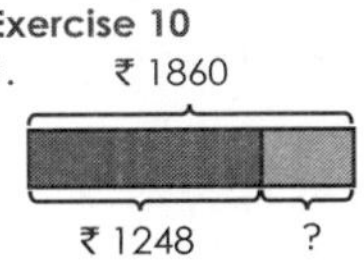

₹ 1860 – ₹ 1248 = ₹ 612

2.

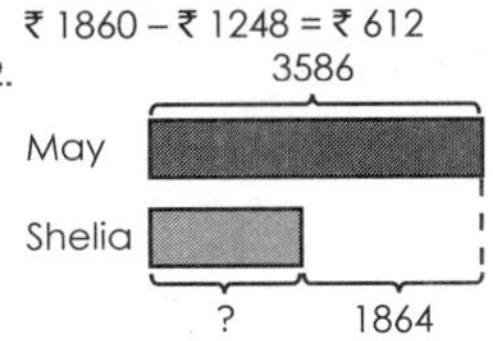

3586 – 1864 = 1722 stamps

3.

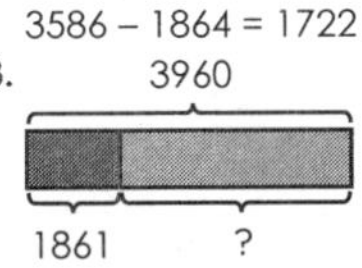

3690 – 1861 = 1829 cards

4.

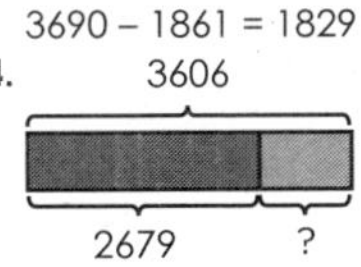

3606 – 2679 = 927 bricks

Exercise 11

1.

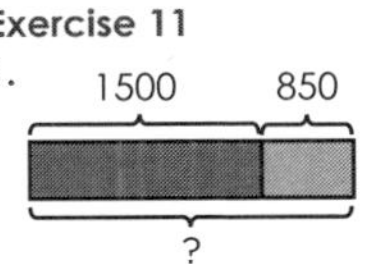

1500 + 850 = 2350 balloons

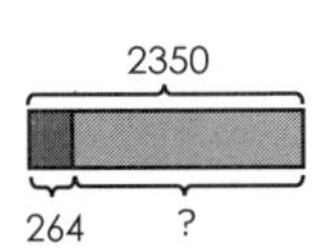

2350 – 264 = 2086 balloons given away

2. 654 + 346 = 1000
Mr Gupta sold 1000 pears this week.
654 + 1000 = 1654
He sold 1654 pears in both weeks.

3.

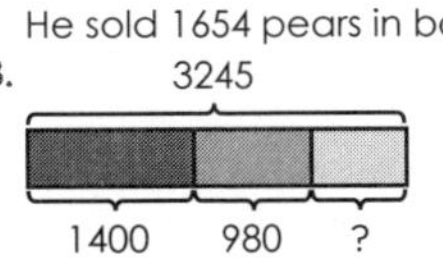

1400 + 980 = 2380 men and women
3245 – 2380 = 865 children

**Note: All unnumbered answers read from left to right.*

 ISBN 978-93-5103-030-0

4.

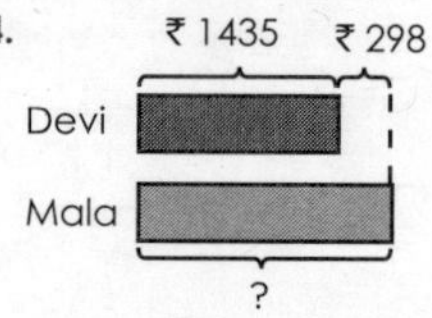

₹ 1435 + ₹ 298 = ₹ 1733
Mala saved ₹ 1733.

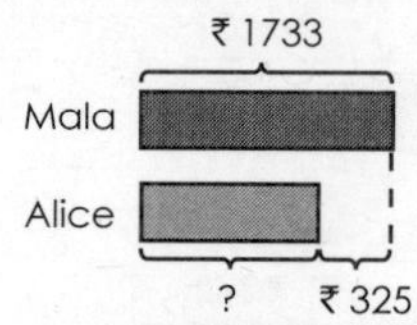

₹ 1733 – ₹ 325 = ₹ 1408
Alice saved ₹ 1408.

5.

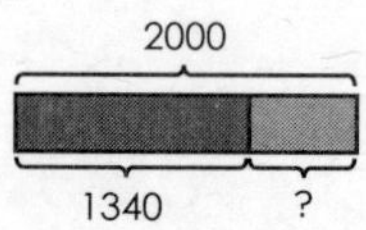

2000 – 1340 = 660 women

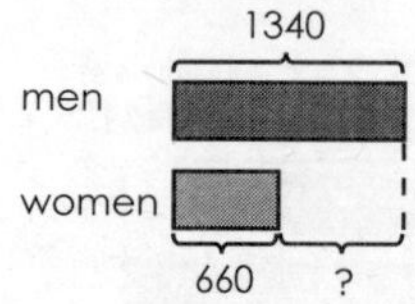

1340 – 660 = 680 more men than women

6.

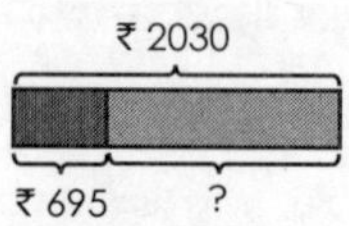

₹ 2030 – ₹ 695 = ₹ 1335

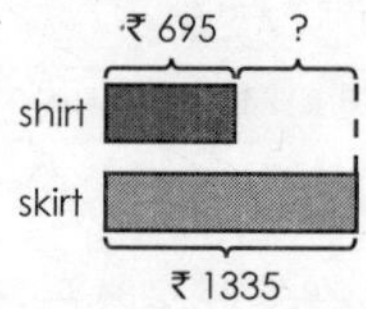

₹ 1335 – ₹ 695 = ₹ 640

Chapter 3

Exercise 1

1. a) 12; **b)** 9; **c)** 6; **d)** 3; **e)** 0 **2. a)** 15; **b)** 0; **c)** 12; **d)** 32; **e)** 0; **f)** 27

Exercise 2

1. a) 12, 120; **b)** 21, 210; **c)** 20, 200; **d)** 18, 1800; **e)** 24, 2400; **f)** 28, 2800; **2. a)**180; **b)** 400; **c)** 1200; **d)** 2700

Exercise 3

1. a) 44; **b)** 46; **c)** 24; **d)** 63; **e)** 39; **f)** 62 **2. a)** 69; **b)** 60; **c)** 84; **d)** 88

Exercise 4

1. 48, 84, 68, 156, 128, 255, 249, 368, 168, 288 **2. a)** 129; **b)** 248; **c)** 355; **d)** 162

Exercise 5

1. a) 51; **b)** 60; **c)** 58; **d)** 80; **e)** 96; **f)** 72 **2. a)** 70; **b)** 76; **c)** 75; **d)** 94

Exercise 6

1. a) 74; **b)** 135; **c)** 116; **d)** 344; **e)** 185; **f)** 115; **g)** 96; **h)** 228; **i)** 195; **j)** 86; **k)** 316; **l)** 490 **2. a)** 104; **b)** 54; **c)** 140; **d)** 144; **e)** 135; **f)** 136; **g)** 130; **h)** 177; **i)** 210; **j)** 280; **k)** 388; **l)** 224

Exercise 7

1. a) 1168; **b)** 1360; **c)** 1805; **d)** 1328; **e)** 1359; **f)** 1776 **2. a)** 1448; **b)** 1173; **c)** 1300; **d)** 1588

Exercise 8

1. 248, 592, 1135, 1024, 906, 1122, 1083, 552, 868 **2.** 465, 1940, 1056, 990, 1000, 1400, 652, 2100, 1120, 3348, 708, 1107

Exercise 9

1. a) 3, 1, 3, 1; **b)** 6, 1, 6, 1; **c)** 8, 1, 8, 1; **d)** 10, 0, 10, 0

Exercise 10

1. 7 R1, 8, 21, 8 R1, 10, 17 R1, 48, 16 R3, 24 R3
2. 60, 94, 88, 32, 56, 50, 74, 16, 18
Ones digit odd numbers: 1, 3, 5, 7, 9
Ones digit even numbers: 0, 2, 4, 6, 8

Exercise 11

1. a) 200, 4, 0, 0, 0, 0, 0; **b)** 150, 2, 10, 10, 0, 0, 0; **c)** 270, 4, 14, 14, 0, 0, 0; **d)** 465, 8, 13, 12, 10, 10, 0; **e)** 440, 8, 8, 8, 0, 0, 0; **f)** 325, 6, 5, 4, 10, 10, 0

Exercise 12

1. a) 41, 1; **b)** 16, 1; **c)** 13, 2; **d)** 32, 0; **e)** 37, 1; **f)** 19, 2; **g)** 26, 2; **h)** 19, 0

Exercise 13

1. a) 236 R1; **b)** 125 R2; **c)** 245; **d)** 239 R2; **e)** 253; **f)** 167
2. 86, 86 R1, 82, 128, 201, 314, 204, 250, 82 R3, HELICOPTER

Exercise 14

1. 3 × 7 = 21 comic books **2.** 20 ÷ 4 = 5 tigers **3.** 8 × 4 = 32 pages after 4 days, 32 + 5 = 37 pages in the book **4.** 36 × 3 = 108 more oranges than apples

5.

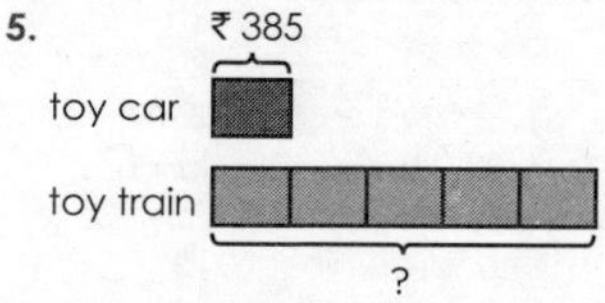

5 × ₹ 385 = ₹ 1925

6.

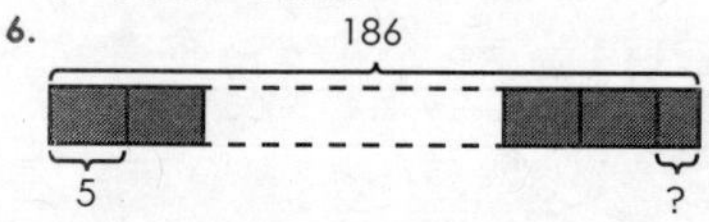

186 ÷ 5 = 37 R1
There were 37 students in Mrs. Rao's class. 1 sticker was left.

7.

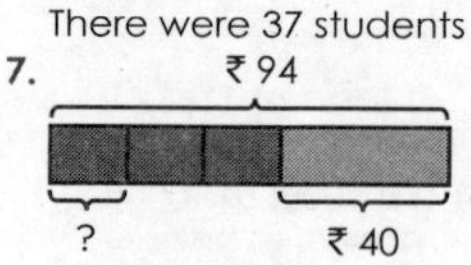

₹ 94 – ₹ 40 = ₹ 54
3 kg of guavas cost ₹ 54.
₹ 54 ÷ 3 = ₹ 18
1 kilogram of guavas cost ₹ 18.

8.

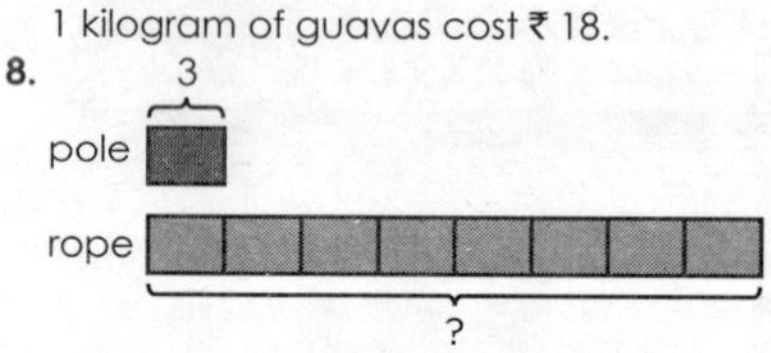

8 × 3 m = 24 m
The length of the rope is 24 metres.

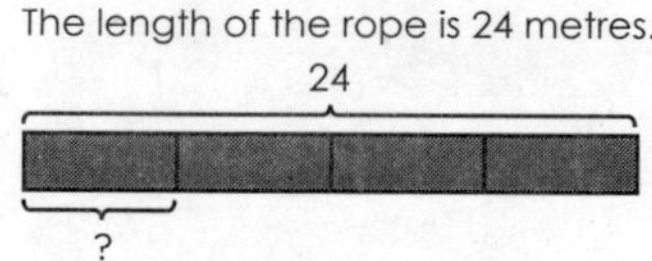

24 m ÷ 4 = 6 m
The length of each piece of rope is 6 metres.

Chapter 4

Exercise 1

1. a) 30, 30; **b)** 36; **c)** 42, 42; **d)** 48, 48; **e)** 54, 54; **f)** 60, 60 **2.** 5 × 6 = 30, 6 × 3 = 18, 2 × 6 = 12, 6 × 8 = 48, 6 × 6 = 36, 9 × 6 = 54, 6 × 4 = 24, 6 × 10 = 60, 7 × 6 = 42

Exercise 2

1. a) 5, 30; **b)** 18, 6; **c)** 42, 42; **d)** 6, 6; **e)** 54, 6; **f)** 6, 60; **g)** 24, 4; **h)** 8, 48; **i)** 0, 0 **2.** Match: **b)** 18 ÷ 6—3; **c)** 60 ÷ 6—10; **d)** 48 ÷ 6—8; **e)** 30 ÷ 6—5; **f)** 54 ÷ 6—9; **g)** 42 ÷ 6—7, PRODUCT

Exercise 3

1. Across: **B**—30; **D**—144; **F**—210; **G**—288 Down: **A**—270; **B**—312; **C**—54; **D**—102; **E**—408 **2.** 258, 450, 588, 1836, 2700, 3444, 4746, 4800, 5538

Exercise 4

1. a) 8 R5; **b)** 12 R3; **c)** 14; **d)** 10 R4; **e)** 8 R1; **f)** 16; **g)** 6 R2; **h)** 9 R5, PENTAGON **2. a)** 15 R2; **b)** 14 R0; **c)** 13 R0; **d)** 133 R2; **e)** 100 R5; **f)** 91 R0; **g)** 82 R4; **h)** 119 R5; **i)** 153 R5

Exercise 5

1. 42, 28, 56, 35, 49, 63, 70, 14, 7

Exercise 6

1. a) 42, 7; **b)** 2, 14; **c)** 7, 8; **d)** 35, 7; **e)** 21, 7; **f)** 63, 9; **g)** 1, 7; **h)** 0, 0; **i)** 7, 49 **2.** Match: **b)** 49 ÷ 7—7; **c)** 28 ÷ 7—4; **d)** 70 ÷ 7—10; **e)** 56 ÷ 7—8; **f)** 21 ÷ 7—3; **g)** 63 ÷ 7—9; **h)** 35 ÷ 7—5, QUOTIENT

Exercise 7

1. 560, 378, 273, 497, 434, 301 **2.** 672, 315, 574, 4900, 2296, 1015, 2821, 4578, 3717, PRAYING MANTIS

Exercise 8

1. a) 11 R3; **b)** 7 R6; **c)** 9 R6; **d)** 6 R1; **e)** 14; **f)** 10 R6; **g)** 12; **h)** 10 R2
2. 13, 19 R2, 65, 133 R1, 110, 114 R5, 88 R3, 102 R2, LADYBIRD

Exercise 9

1. 56, 24, 40, 64, 48, 72, 16, 80, A GOLDFISH

Exercise 10

1. a) 8, 80; **b)** 0, 0; **c)** 3, 3; **d)** 8, 64; **e)** 56, 8; **f)** 1, 8; **g)** 8, 9; **h)** 32, 8; **i)** 6, 48 **2.** Match: 40 ÷ 8—5, 64 ÷ 8—8, 16 ÷ 8—2, 48 ÷ 8—6, 32 ÷ 8—4, 72 ÷ 8—9, 56 ÷ 8—7, 80 ÷ 8—10

 ISBN 978-93-5103-030-0

Exercise 11
1. **b)** 54 × 8—432; **c)** 8 × 50—400; **d)** 8 × 63—504; **e)** 88 × 8—704; **f)** 27 × 8—216; **g)** 8 × 36—288; **h)** 8 × 14—112; **i)** 92 × 8—736, EXCELLENT
2. Across: **A**—368, **D**—464, **F**—1992, **H**—496, **I**—440, **J**—2032
Down: **B**—6424, **C**—5192, **E**—6272, **G**—960
Exercise 12
1. 106 R2, 120 R2, 46 R4, 9 R5, 66, 12, 12 R7, 61, 93 R4, EXERCISE TO KEEP FIT
Exercise 13
1. 45, 90, 36, 18, 63, 54, 81, 72
Exercise 14
1. **a)** 7, 7; **b)** 18, 9; **c)** 9, 27; **d)** 8, 8; **e)** 9, 9; **f)** 54, 54; **g)** 9, 5; **h)** 36, 4
2. Match: 90 ÷ 9—10, 27 ÷ 9—3, 36 ÷ 9—4, 72 ÷ 9—8, 63 ÷ 9—7, 45 ÷ 9—5, 54 ÷ 9—6
Exercise 15
1. 675, 954, 2376, 891, 4707, 5508, 7056, 720, 8523, A JUMBO JET
Exercise 16
1. Match: 80 ÷ 9—8 R8, 99 ÷ 9—11, 90 ÷ 9—10, 59 ÷ 9—6 R5, 25 ÷ 9—2 R7 **2. a)** 103 R2; **b)** 61 R5; **c)** 73; **d)** 42 R3; **e)** 94 R6; **f)** 48 R4; **g)** 23, OSTRICH
Exercise 17
1.
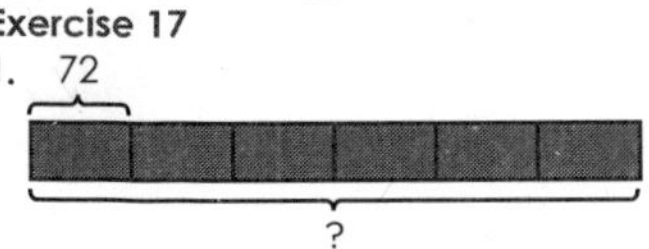

6 × 72 = 432 times
2.
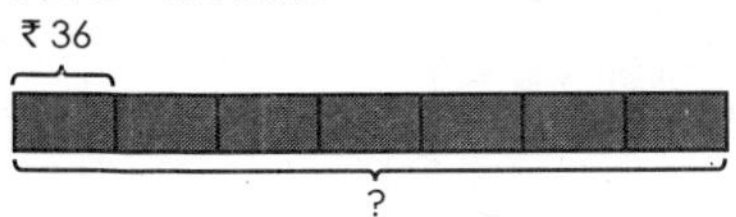

7 × ₹ 36 = ₹ 252
3.
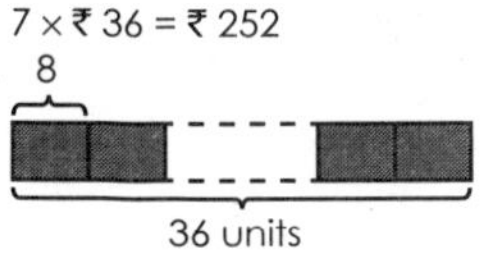

36 × 8 = 288 people
4.
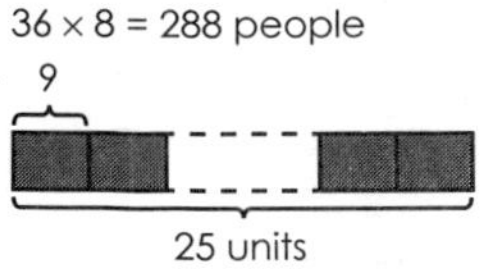

25 × 9 = 225 cans altogether
5.
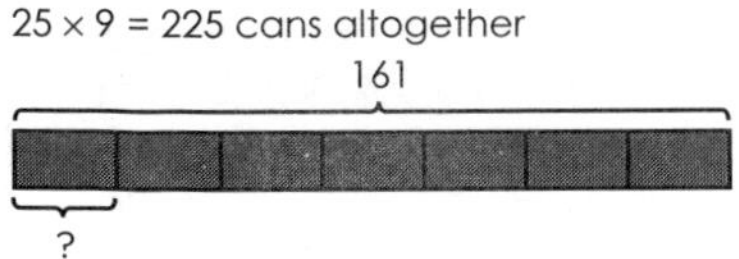

161 ÷ 7 = 23 centimetres
6.
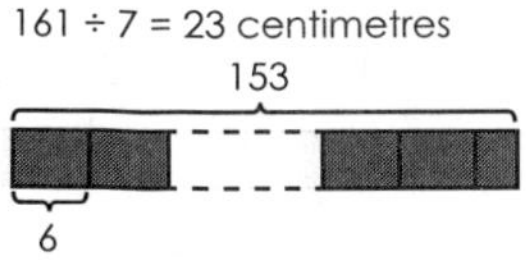

153 ÷ 6 = 25 R3
There were 25 bags.
7.
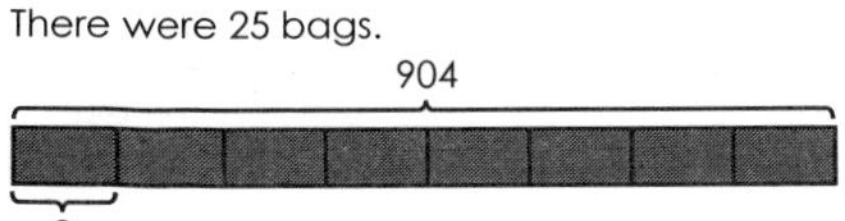

904 ÷ 8 = 113 diaries
8.
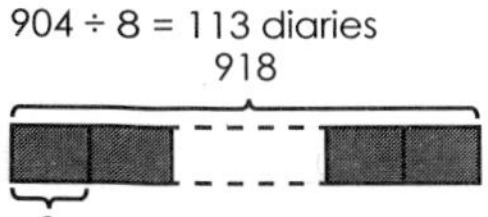

918 ÷ 9 = 102 pieces
Exercise 18
1. 35 × ₹ 6 = ₹ 210
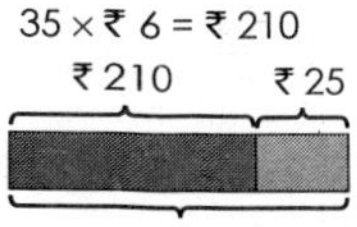

₹ 210 + ₹ 25 = ₹ 235
2.
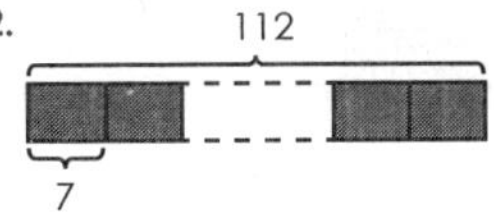

112 ÷ 7 = 16
16 × ₹ 3 = ₹ 48
3.
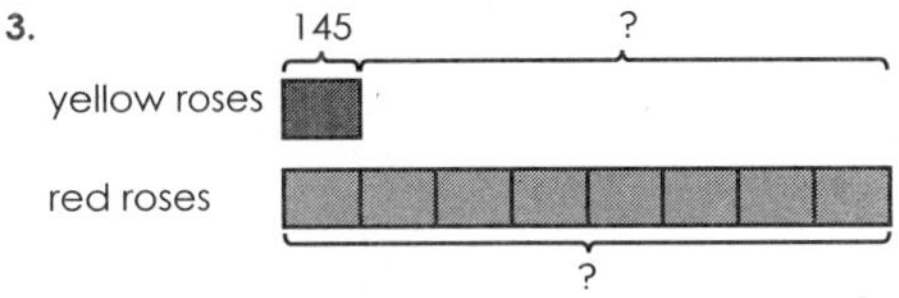

8 × 145 = 1160 red roses
1160 – 145 = 1015 more red roses than yellow roses
4.
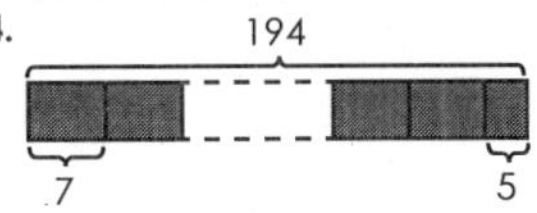

194 – 5 = 189 magazines were not torn
189 ÷ 7 = 27 bundles of magazines.
5.
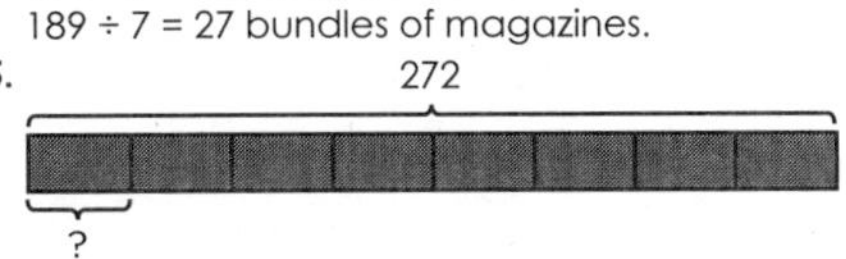

272 ÷ 8 = 34 tickets
34 × ₹ 3 = ₹ 102 collected by each student
6.
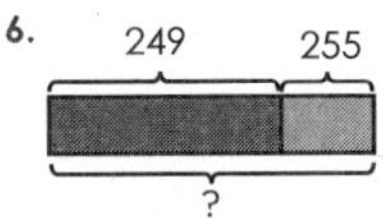

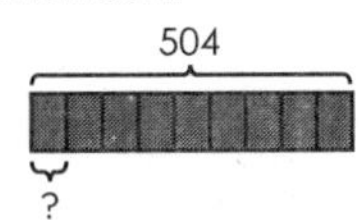

249 + 255 = 504 children altogether

504 ÷ 9 = 56 children in each row

Chapter 5
Exercise 1
2. a) 0.80; **b)** 2.20; **c)** 3.85; **d)** 6.35; **e)** 67.50; **f)** 2205.25
3. a) 28; **b)** 108.30; **c)** 518.50
Exercise 2
1. Match: twenty-three rupees—₹ 23.00, four rupees—₹ 4.00, thirteen rupees and thirty paise—₹ 13.30, twenty paise—₹ 0.20, seven rupees and fifty paise—₹ 7.50, ninety-nine rupees and fifty-five paise—₹ 99.55 **2. a)** ₹ 5; **b)** ₹ 9.75; **c)** ₹ 12.90; **d)** ₹ 154.50 **3. a)** 4, 65; **b)** 0, 70; **c)** 6, 45; **d)** 15, 00; **e)** 354, 90 **4. a)** ₹ 20; **b)** ₹ 47; **c)** ₹ 74. 50; **d)** ₹ 30.45; **e)** ₹ 47.15; **f)** 95 p; **g)** ₹ 40.25; **h)** ₹ 565.75
Exercise 3
1. Match: ₹ 2.70—270 p, ₹ 3.45—345 p, 10 p—₹ 0.10, 35 p—₹ 0.35, 300 p—₹ 3.00 **2. a)** 1; **b)** 2; **c)** 1.25; **d)** 2.40; **e)** 3.60; **f)** 19; **g)** 0.85; **h)** 0.70 **3. a)** 10; **b)** 75; **c)** 250; **d)** 780; **e)** 400; **f)** 345; **g)** 1000; **h)** 2895
Exercise 4
1. **a)** greater, 8, 60, 14.30, 8.60; **b)** 53, 45, 53, 70, 53.70, 53.45; **c)** 278, 50, 278, 25, 279, 65, 279.65, 278.25 **2.** Circle: **a)** ₹ 4.55; **b)** ₹ 15.90; **c)** ₹ 133.40 **3.** Circle: **a)** ₹ 5.00; **b)** ₹ 46.70; **c)** ₹ 371.05 **4.** Circle: **a)** ₹ 61.30; **b)** ₹ 38.35; **c)** ₹ 938.25 **5.** Circle: **a)** ₹ 42.55; **b)** ₹ 85.65; **c)** ₹ 484.85
Exercise 5
1. **a)** 55 p; **b)** 15 p; **c)** 25 p; **d)** 30 p **2.** ₹ 0.30, ₹ 0.25, ₹ 0.35, ₹ 0.15, ₹ 0.45
Exercise 6
1. **a)** 4.85; **b)** 4.45; **c)** 10.05; **d)** 13.70; **e)** 2.55; **f)** 1.90; **g)** 2.85; **h)** 5.40
2. a) 3.45, 3.75, 3.75; **b)** 5.60, 5.85, 5.85; **c)** 5.15, 5.80, 5.80 **3. a)** ₹ 3.60; **b)** ₹ 6.90; **c)** ₹ 4.85; **d)** ₹ 4.90; **e)** ₹ 5.50; **f)** ₹ 8.90
Exercise 7
1. **a)** 1; **b)** 2; **c)** 3; **d)** 5; **e)** 6; **f)** 7 **2. a)** 2.10; **b)** 4.25; **c)** 5.50; **d)** 17.05; **e)** 29.20; **f)** 44.20
Exercise 8
1. **a)** 11.70, 11.95; **b)** 9.85, 10.25; **c)** 34.35, 35.10; **d)** 66.35, 67.20
2. a) 31.55; **b)** 35.10; **c)** 69.15; **d)** 53.40; **e)** 51.45; **f)** 93.20
3. a) 4.80, 4.75; **b)** 8.10, 8.05; **c)** 16.55, 16.50; **d)** 41.30, 41.25
4. a) 16.35; **b)** 28.30; **c)** 40.50; **d)** 30.65; **e)** 46.55; **f)** 60.45
Exercise 9
1. ₹ 3.05, ₹ 5.45, ₹ 3.55, ₹ 8.35, ₹ 8.20, ₹ 9.30, ₹ 6.20, ₹ 6.40, ₹ 9.10, BLUEBERRY
2. ₹ 4.95, ₹ 16.35, ₹ 17.60, ₹ 80.25, ₹ 93.70, ₹ 85.20, ₹ 43.85, ₹ 53.40, ₹ 73.90, TRIANGLES

 ISBN 978-93-5103-030-0

Exercise 10

1.

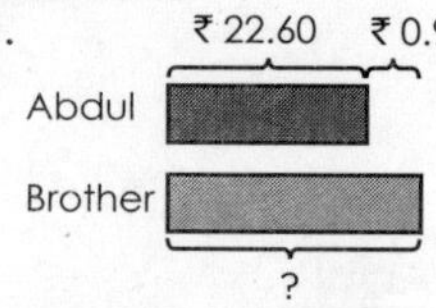

₹ 22.60 + ₹ 0.95 = ₹ 23.55

2.

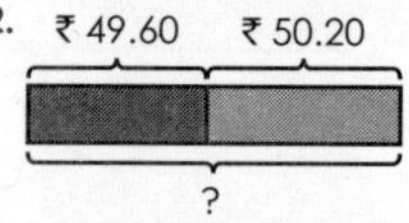

₹ 49.60 + ₹ 50.20 = ₹ 99.80

3.

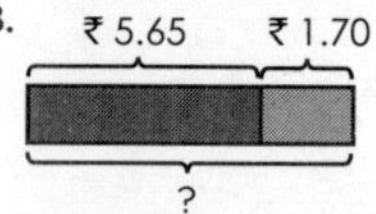

₹ 5.65 + ₹ 1.70 = ₹ 7.35

4.

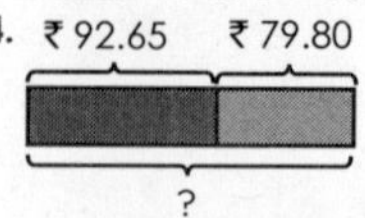

₹ 92.65 + ₹ 79.80 = ₹ 172.45

5.

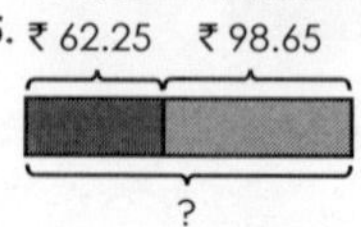

₹ 62.25 + ₹ 98.65 = ₹ 160.90

6.

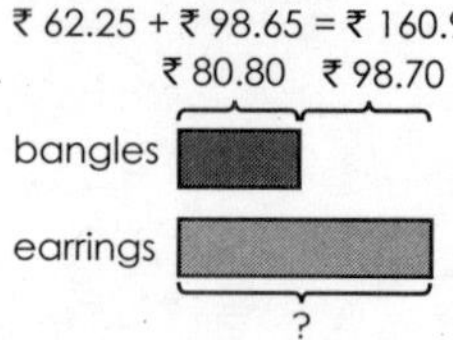

₹ 80.80 + ₹ 98.70 = ₹ 179.50

Exercise 11

1. a) 1.85; **b)** 4.45; **c)** 3.35; **d)** 1.25; **e)** 2.35; **f)** 5.05; **g)** 6; **h)** 9.15
2. a) 4.80, 4.30, 4.30; **b)** 1.75, 1.40, 1.40; **c)** 2.90, 2.25, 2.25 **3. a)** ₹ 3.60; **b)** ₹ 3.25; **c)** ₹ 2.15; **d)** ₹ 4.35; **e)** ₹ 2.45; **f)** ₹ 4.25

Exercise 12

1. a) ₹ 0.80/ 80 p; **b)** ₹ 1.60; **c)** ₹ 7.40; **d)** ₹ 6.90 **2. a)** 50, 3, 3.50; **b)** 75, 7, 7.75; **c)** 5.30; **d)** 6.45; **e)** 8.25

Exercise 13

1. a) 3.20; **b)** 4.30; **c)** 2.45; **d)** 5.25 **2. a)** 80 p; **b)** ₹ 2.05; **c)** ₹ 3.50; **d)** ₹ 12.55; **e)** ₹ 26.90; **f)** ₹ 48.45

Exercise 14

1. a) 2.50, 2.25; **b)** 2.35, 1.55; **c)** 12, 11.40; **d)** 17.05, 16.60 **2. a)** 5.05; **b)** 4.05; **c)** 53.60; **d)** 53.55; **e)** 17.35; **f)** 70.35 **3. a)** 1.20, 1.25; **b)** 16.85, 16.90; **c)** 21.50, 21.55; **d)** 27.35, 27.40 **4. a)** 0.15; **b)** 2.30; **c)** 21.50; **d)** 30.40; **e)** 41.80; **f)** 41.65

Exercise 15

1. ₹ 1.65, ₹ 2.55, ₹ 4.75, ₹ 3.30, ₹ 2.85, ₹ 4.90, ₹ 2.60, ₹ 0.45, ₹ 1.55, CARNATION
2. ₹ 37.20, ₹ 25.70, ₹ 16.45, ₹ 63.45, ₹16.95, ₹ 7.01, ₹ 35.95, ₹ 15.85, ₹ 9.90, TELEPHONE
3. a) 5250, ₹ 52.50; **b)** 2525, ₹ 25.25; **c)** 4540, ₹ 45.40; **d)** 3515, ₹ 35.15

Exercise 16

1.

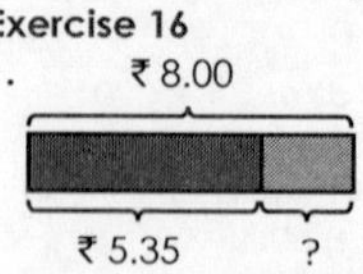

₹ 8.00 – ₹ 5.35 = ₹ 2.65 left

2.

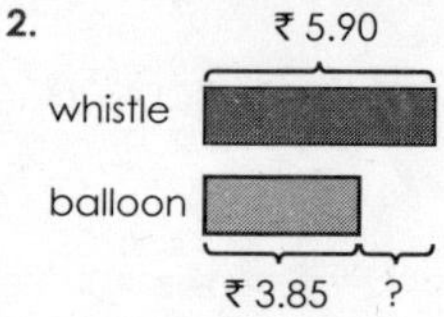

₹ 5.90 – ₹ 3.85 = ₹ 2.05 cheaper

3.

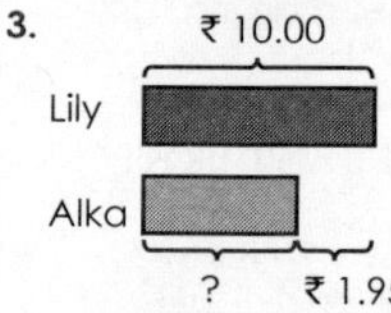

₹ 10.00 – ₹ 1.95 = ₹ 8.05 saved

4.

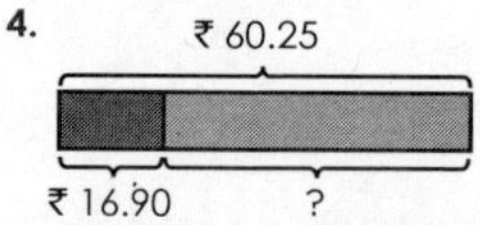

₹ 60.25 – ₹ 16.90 = ₹ 43.35

5.

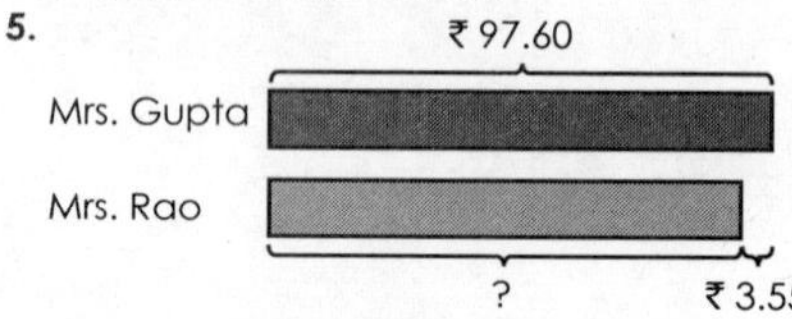

₹ 97.60 – ₹ 3.55 = ₹ 94.05 spent

6.

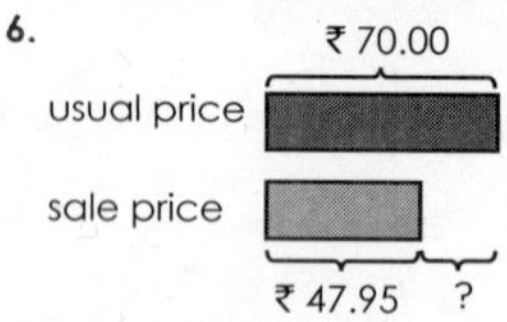

₹ 70.00 – ₹ 47.95 = ₹ 22.05 cheaper

Exercise 17

1.

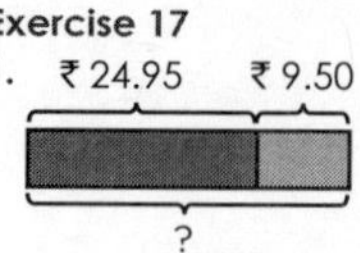

₹ 24.95 + ₹ 9.50 = ₹ 34.45
Maya spent ₹ 34.45 altogether.

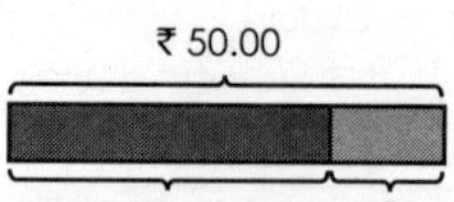

₹ 50.00 – ₹ 34.45 = ₹ 15.55
She received ₹ 15.55 as change.

2.

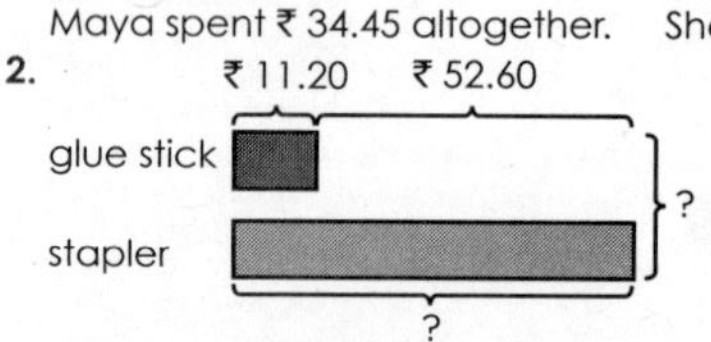

₹ 11.20 + ₹ 52.60 = ₹ 63.80 paid for the stapler
₹ 11.20 + ₹ 63.80 = ₹ 75 spent altogether

3.

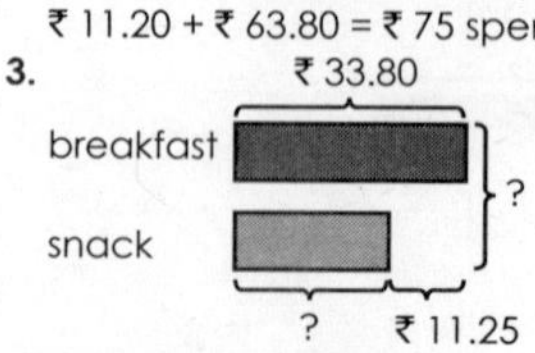

₹ 33.80 – ₹ 11.25 = ₹ 22.55 spent on the snack
₹ 33.80 + ₹ 22.55 = ₹ 56.35 spent altogether
Atul had ₹ 56.35 at first.

4.

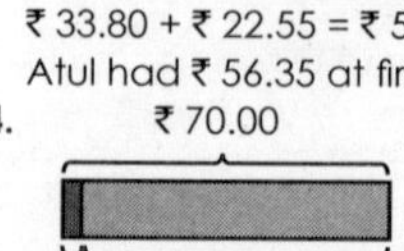

₹ 70.00 – ₹ 2.25 = ₹ 67.75
The pen and notebook cost ₹ 67.75.

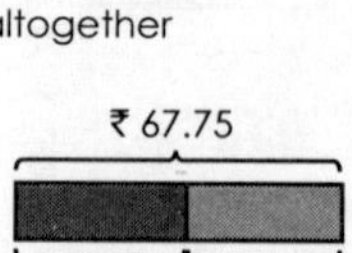

₹ 67.75 – ₹ 37.35 = ₹ 30.40
The pen cost ₹ 30.40.

 ISBN 978-93-5103-030-0

Chapter 6

Exercise 1

1. a) 92; **b)** 83; **c)** 95; **d)** 106 **2. a)** 91; **b)** 57; **c)** 98; **d)** 135; **e)** 106; **f)** 104 **3. a)** 95, 100; **b)** 114, 120 **4. a)** 92; **b)** 70; **c)** 92; **d)** 109

Exercise 2

1. a) 92; **b)** 86; **c)** 130; **d)** 123; **e)** 145; **f)** 140; **g)** 150; **h)** 85 **2. a)** 60; **b)** 100; **c)** 70; **d)** 90; **e)** 100; **f)** 100; **g)** 90; **h)** 100 **3. a)** 105; **b)** 102; **c)** 141; **d)** 166; **e)** 182; **f)** 135; **g)** 190; **h)** 195; **i)** 197; **j)** 198

Exercise 3

1. a) 12; **b)** 5; **c)** 27; **d)** 27 **2. a)** 55; **b)** 29; **c)** 77; **d)** 48 **3. a)** 47, 40, 40; **b)** 63, 59, 59 **4. a)** 18; **b)** 6; **c)** 57; **d)** 19

Exercise 4

1. a) 22; **b)** 13; **c)** 41; **d)** 42; **e)** 23; **f)** 24; **g)** 25; **h)** 26

Exercise 5

1. a) 15, 150; **b)** 20, 200; **c)** 35, 3500; **d)** 24, 2400 **2.** 16, 160, 1600, 21, 210, 2100, 24, 240, 2400, 40, 400, 4000, 36, 360, 3600, 56, 560, 5600
3. a) 8, 80; **b)** 8, 800; **c)** 400; **d)** 120; **e)** 140; **f)** 320; **g)** 200; **h)** 810; **i)** 180; **j)** 140; **k)** 2400; **l)** 4800; **m)** 3600; **n)** 3000; **o)** 2800; **p)** 600; **q)** 1800; **r)** 3500

Exercise 6

1. a) 3, 30; **b)** 2, 20; **c)** 3, 300; **d)** 4, 400 **2.** 3, 30, 300, 4, 40, 400, 5, 50, 500, 3, 30, 300, 4, 40, 400, 3, 30, 300 **3. a)** 5, 50; **b)** 5, 500; **c)** 20; **d)** 80; **e)** 90; **f)** 50; **g)** 60; **h)** 80; **i)** 50; **j)** 70; **k)** 900; **l)** 800; **m)** 500; **n)** 700; **o)** 500; **p)** 600; **q)** 900; **r)** 400

Chapter 7

Exercise 1

1. a) Anil; **b)** Kabir, Arun; **c)** 5; **d)** 20 **2. a)** Paper crocodiles; **b)** Horses; **c)** 28

Exercise 2

1. a) 4; **b)** 2; **c)** 8; **d)** 62 **2. a)** 30; **b)** 15; **c)** Wednesday; **d)** 110

Exercise 3

1. a) 45; **b)** 10; **c)** Raj; **d)** Raj; **e)** 185 **2. a)** 180; **b)** 120; **c)** Ram; **d)** John; **e)** 40 **3. a)** 650; **b)** 150; **c)** Wednesday; **d)** Monday; **e)** 2200

Chapter 8

Exercise 1

1. a) Answers vary. Example: 7, 8, 42; **b)** Answers vary. Example: 4, 4, 80 **2. a)** 200; **b)** 300; **c)** 500; **d)** 900 **3. a)** 4; **b)** 6; **c)** 7; **d)** 8 **4. a)** 150; **b)** 328; **c)** 509 **5. a)** 2, 10; **b)** 2, 75; **c)** 3, 6 **6. a)** Shorter than; **b)** equal to; **c)** longer than **7.** 604 cm, 5 m 114 cm, 6 m 40 cm, 644 cm **8.** 4 m 88 cm, 480 cm, 4 m 18 cm, 408 cm

Exercise 2

1. a) 47; **b)** 15; **c)** 26; **d)** 22; **e)** 3; **f)** 38; **g)** 10; **h)** 35; **i)** 95; **j)** 70 **2. a)** 3, 85; **b)** 4, 70; **c)** 6, 10 **3. a)** 4, 20; **b)** 5, 85; **c)** 7, 68; **d)** 4, 26; **e)** 7, 18 **4. a)** 1, 10; **b)** 2, 59; **c)** 6, 39 **5. a)** 1, 89; **b)** 4, 12; **c)** 3, 85; **d)** 3, 86 **6. a)** 5 m, 9m 16 cm; **b)** 6 m 7 cm, 11 m 88 cm; **c)** 9 m 16 cm, 5 m; **d)** 12 m 47 cm, 6 m 7 cm; **e)** 11 m 88 cm, 12 m 47 cm
Match: **a)** 1 m 45 cm + 3 m 55 cm—8 m 90 cm – 3 m 90 cm;
b) 3 m 68 cm + 2 m 39 cm—10 m 37 cm – 4 m 30 cm;
c) 4 m 4 cm + 5 m 12 cm—10 m 1 cm – 85 cm;
d) 6 m 40 cm + 6 m 7 cm—13 m 50 cm – 1 m 3 cm;
e) 10 m 8 cm + 1 m 80 cm—12 m – 12 cm

Exercise 3

1. a) kilometre; **b)** centimetre; **c)** metre **2. a)** 23; **b)** 90; **c)** 65; **d)** 19; **e)** 6

Exercise 4

1. a) 2000; **b)** 4000; **c)** 5000; **d)** 8000 **2. a)** 3; **b)** 6; **c)** 7; **d)** 9 **3. a)** 1145; **b)** 3050; **c)** 2580; **d)** 1006 **4. a)** 1, 732; **b)** 1, 300; **c)** 3, 260; **d)** 3, 6; **e)** 2, 108 **5. a)** longer than; **b)** longer than; **c)** shorter than **6.** 7 km 900 m, 7100 m, 7090 m, 7 km 10 m **7.** 8 km 5 m, 8050 m, 8 km 500 m, 8555 m

Exercise 5

1. Match: 950 m—50 m, 790 m—210 m, 140 m—860 m, 330 m—670 m, 350 m—650 m, 180 m—820 m, 520 m—480 m, 430 m—570 m **2. a)** 20; **b)** 110; **c)** 210; **d)** 580; **e)** 80; **f)** 120 **3. a)** 1, 850; **b)** 3, 180; **c)** 5, 230 **4. a)** 6, 110; **b)** 7, 970; **c)** 6, 150; **d)** 9, 200 **5. a)** 2, 70; **b)** 3, 940; **c)** 5, 260 **6. a)** 2, 650; **b)** 5, 920; **c)** 3, 750; **d)** 6, 920 **7. a)** 1 km 741 m; **b)** 3 km 865 m; **c)** Library, 2 km 124 m; **d)** 3 km 936 m; **e)** 5 km 601 m

Exercise 6

1. a) centimetres; **b)** kilometres; **c)** millimetres; **d)** metres **2. a)** 40; **b)** 50; **c)** 600; **d)** 700 **3. a)** 1; **b)** 2; **c)** 10; **d)** 30 **4. a)** 15; **b)** 24; **c)** 101 **5. a)** 3, 7; **b)** 9, 9; **c)** 40, 8 **6. a)** as long as; **b)** longer than; **c)** shorter than

Exercise 7

1. a) 1, 6; **b)** 3, 2; **c)** 10, 3 **2. a)** 7, 5; **b)** 8, 2; **c)** 12, 1; **d)** 12, 4 **3. a)** 3, 3; **b)** 9, 9; **c)** 5, 8; **d)** 26, 4

Exercise 8

1. 5 km 500 m + 3 km 5 m = 8 km 505 m altogether

2.

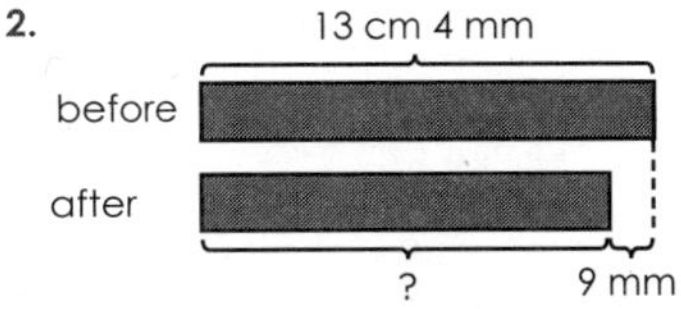

13 cm 4 mm – 9 mm = 12 cm 5 mm

3.

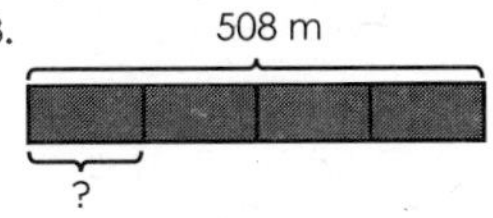

508 m ÷ 4 = 127 m

4.

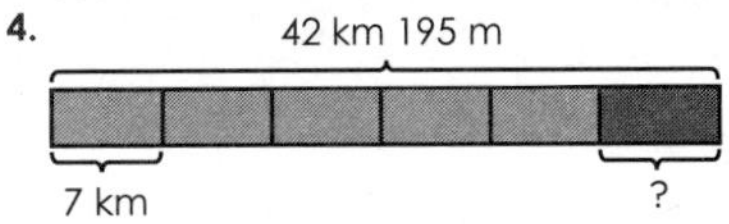

7 km × 5 = 35 km
Radha's friends ran a total distance of 35 kilometres.
42 km 195 m – 35 km = 7 km 195 m
Radha ran a distance of 7 kilometres 195 metres.

5. a) 2 km 1 m + 6 km 210 m = 8 km 211 m
The distance between Rohit's home and Maya's home is 8 km 211 m;
b) 6 km 210 m – 2 km 1 m = 4 km 209 m
The library is 4 km 209 m further away from Maya's home than Rohit's home.

6.

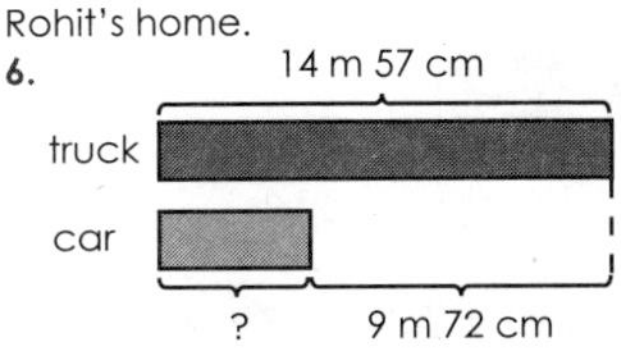

14 m 57 cm – 9 m 72 cm = 4 m 85 cm is the car's length.

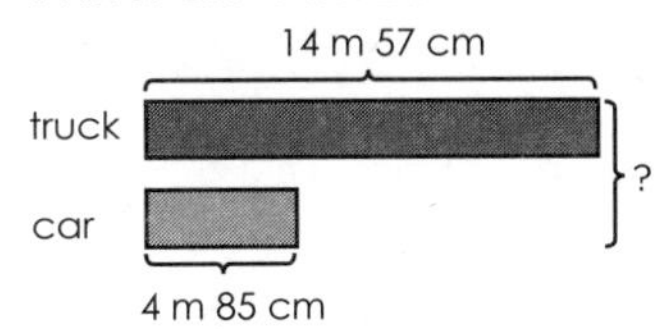

14 m 57 cm + 4 m 85 cm = 19 m 42 cm is the total length

Chapter 9

Exercise 1

1. Answers vary. Example: 1, 1, 340 **2. a)** 2, 500; **b)** 1, 200; **c)** 1, 400; **d)** 2, 500; **e)** 1, 700; **f)** 1, 450

Exercise 2

1. a) 1800; **b)** 6020; **c)** 2300; **d)** 9002; **e)** 4083; **f)** 8015 **2. a)** 1, 280; **b)** 4, 69; **c)** 2, 506; **d)** 5, 108; **e)** 3, 9; **f)** 6, 4 **3.** Match: 9 kg 95 g—9095, 9 kg 905 g—9905 g, 9 kg 59 g—9059 g, 9 kg 590 g—9590 g
4. Heaviest

Exercise 3

1. a) hen, duck; **b)** A, B **2. a)** D; **b)** B; **c)** B; **d)** D; **e)** B, A, C, D

Exercise 4

1. a) 1; **b)** 200; **c)** 550; **d)** 330; **e)** 250; **f)** 610; **g)** 850; **h)** 780 **2. a)** 1, 850; **b)** 3, 250; **c)** 4, 280 **3. a)** 3, 765; **b)** 6, 250; **c)** 6, 55; **d)** 8, 9 **4. a)** 4, 90; **b)** 4, 545; **c)** 6, 635 **5. a)** 1, 156; **b)** 2, 742; **c)** 0, 850; **d)** 6, 736 **6. a)** 430 g; **b)** 430 g – 100 g = 330 g, 330 g **7. a)** 570 g; **b)** 570 g – 250 g = 320 g, 320 g

Exercise 5

1.

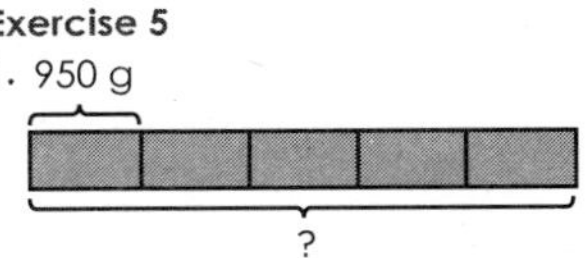

950 g × 5 = 4750 g = 4 kg 750 g

2.

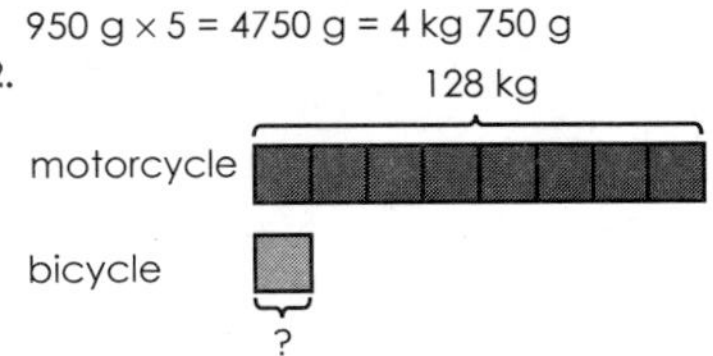

128 kg ÷ 8 = 16 kg

 ISBN 978-93-5103-030-0

3.

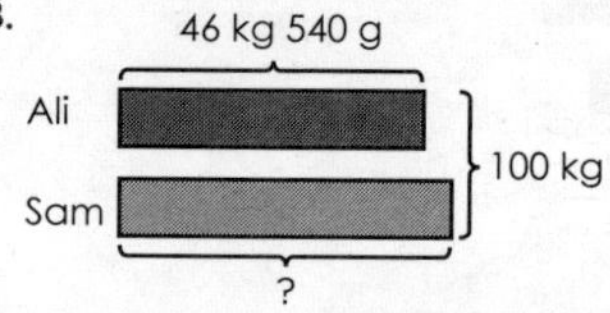

100 kg – 46 kg 540 g = 53 kg 460 g

4. a)

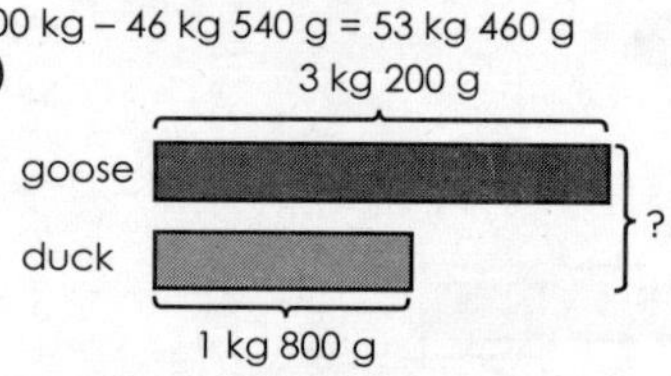

3 kg 200 g + 1 kg 800 g = 5 kg is the total weight

b)

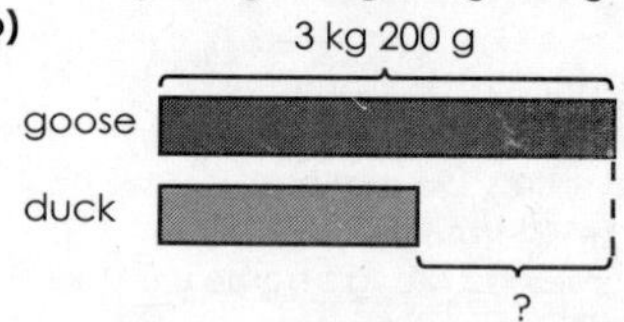

3 kg 200 g – 1 kg 800 g = 1 kg 400 g is the difference

5. a)

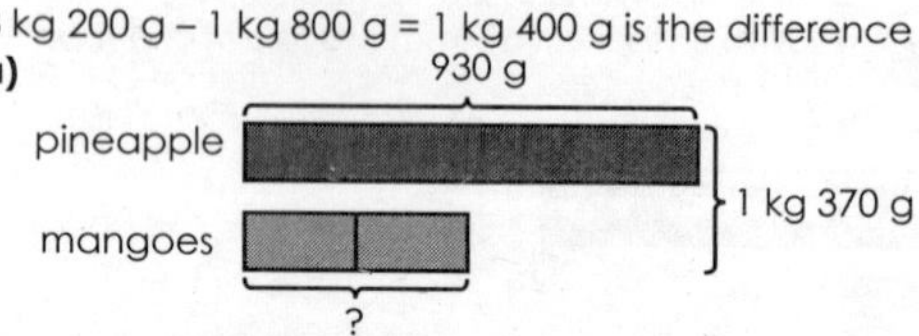

1 kg 370 g – 930 g = 440 g is the weight of two mangoes

b)

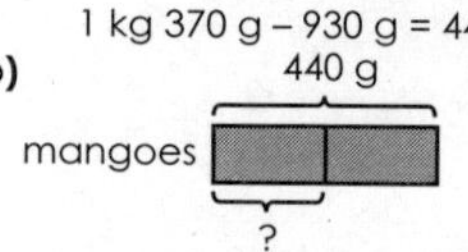

440 g ÷ 2 = 220 g is the weight of one mango

6.

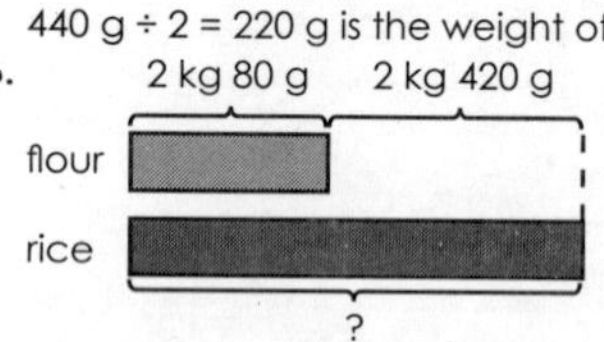

2 kg 80 g + 2 kg 420 g = 4 kg 500 g
The packet of rice weighs 4 kilograms 500 grams.

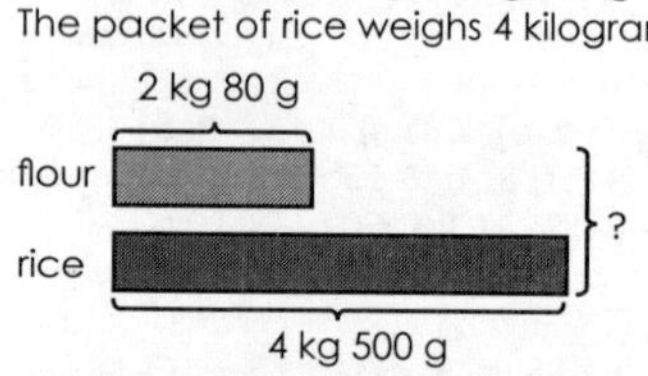

2 kg 80 g + 4 kg 500 g = 6 kg 580 g
The total weight of the packet of flour and the packet of rice is 6 kilograms 580 grams.

7.

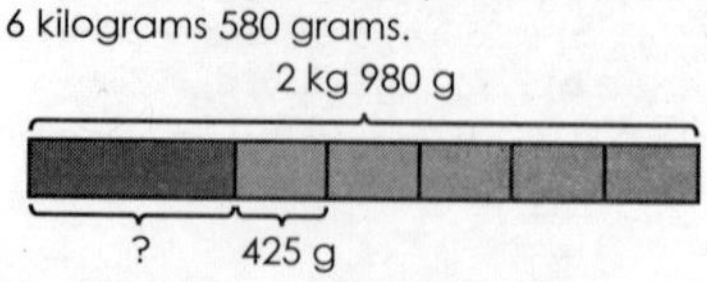

425 g × 5 = 2 kg 125 g
The total weight of the 5 textbooks is 2 kilograms 125 grams.
2 kg 980 g – 2 kg 125 g = 855 g
The weight of the school bag is 855 grams.

8.

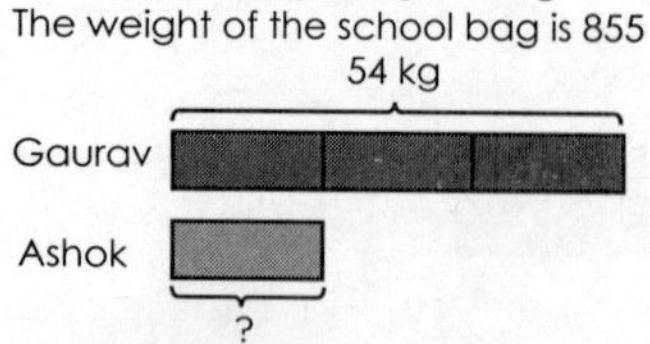

54 kg ÷ 3 = 18 kg
Ashok's weight is 18 kilograms.

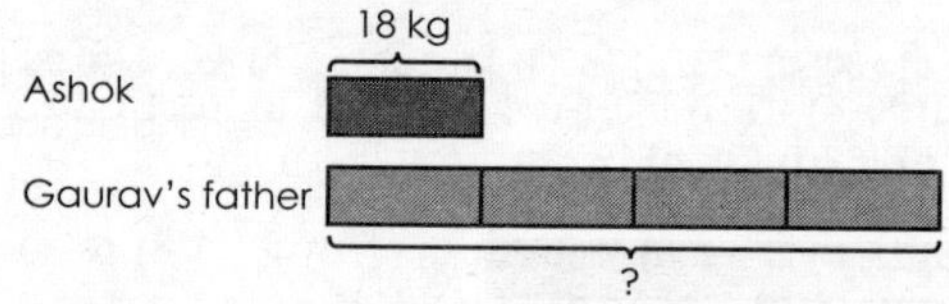

18 kg × 4 = 72 kg
Gaurav's father weight is 72 kilograms.

Chapter 10

Exercise 1

1. A, B **2.** A, B **3. a)** Pot X; **b)** Pot Y **4. a)** 2; **b)** 2; **c)** C; **d)** B

Exercise 2

1. a) A; **b)** B; **c)** A; **d)** B

Exercise 3

1. Circle: **a)** bottle; **b)** bucket **2. a)** Circle: fish tank; Cross: mug; **b)** Circle: water can; Cross: jar **3. a)** 3; **b)** 3 **4. a)** capacity; **b)** capacity; **c)** volume

Exercise 4

1. a) 5; **b)** 2, 5, 2; **c)** 2; **d)** C; **e)** B

Exercise 5

2. Answers vary. Example: 900, 800 **3.** Answers vary. Example: 2, 3

Exercise 6

2. a) 300; **b)** 250; **c)** 350; **d)** 30; **e)** 60; **f)** 80

Exercise 7

1. Match: 1 L 120 ml—1120 ml, 1 L 35 ml—1035 ml, 1 L 350 ml—1350 ml, 2 L 500 ml—2500 ml, 2 L 50 ml—2050 ml **2. a)** 1100; **b)** 1725; **c)** 1640; **d)** 2855; **e)** 2025; **f)** 3005 **3. a)** 1, 300; **b)** 1, 450; **c)** 2, 90; **d)** 2, 105; **e)** 3, 75; **f)** 4, 5 **4. a)** more than; **b)** less than; **c)** equal to; **d)** less than; **e)** less than **5.** 5 L 900 ml, 5800 ml, 5090 ml, 5 L 9 ml

Exercise 8

1. Match: 890 ml—110 ml, 725 ml—275 ml, 495 ml—505 ml, 355 ml—645 ml, 920 ml—80 ml **2. a)** 930; **b)** 450; **c)** 370 **3. a)** 140; **b)** 580; **c)** 250; **d)** 660 **4. a)** 1, 750; **b)** 3, 0; **c)** 4, 150; **d)** 5, 490 **5. a)** 3, 760; **b)** 3, 890; **c)** 5, 70; **d)** 6, 45; **e)** 8, 14 **6. a)** 3, 180; **b)** 4, 40; **c)** 4, 670; **d)** 5, 950 **7. a)** 2, 180; **b)** 1, 64; **c)** 2, 665; **d)** 0, 760; **e)** 5, 921

Exercise 9

1. a) 1, 950; **b)** 4, 50 **2. a)** 2; **b)** 10; **c)** 1, 600

Exercise10

1.

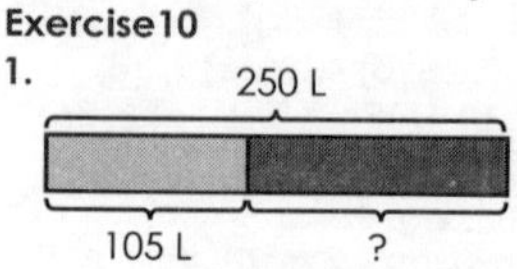

250 L – 105 L = 145 L

2.

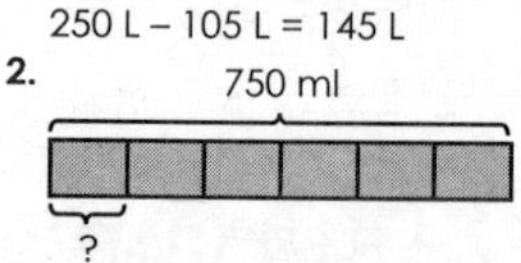

750 ml ÷ 6 = 125 ml

3.

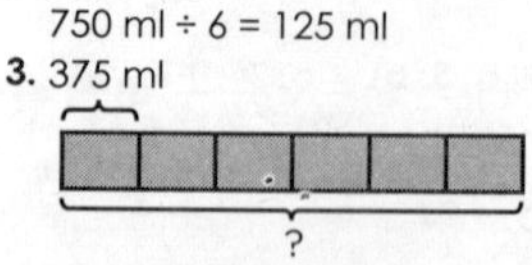

375 ml × 6 = 2250 ml = 2 L 250 ml

4. a)

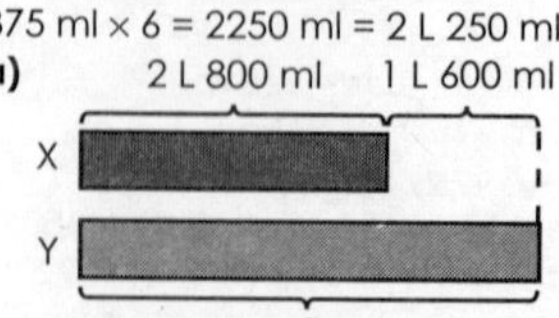

2 L 800 ml + 1 L 600 ml = 4 L 400 ml
Container Y holds 4 litres 400 millilitres of water.

b)

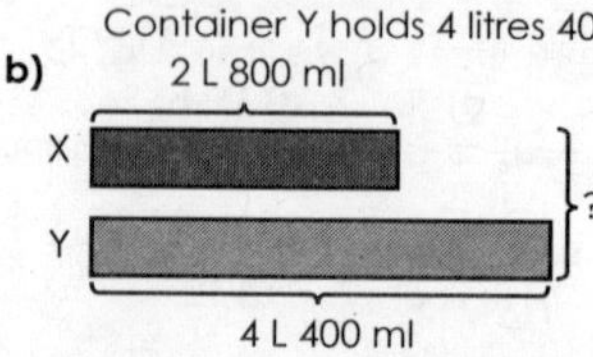

2 L 800 ml + 4 L 400 ml = 7 L 200 ml
The total amount of water in Container X and Container Y is 7 litres 200 millilitres.

 ISBN 978-93-5103-030-0

5.

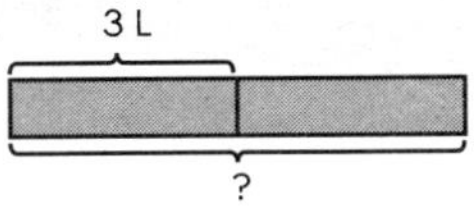

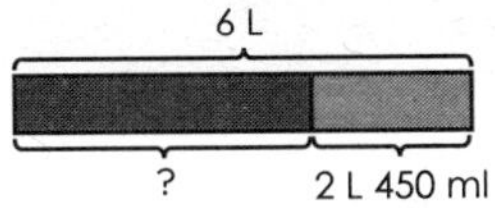

3 L × 2 = 6 L
Gopal bought 6 litres of paint.

6 L − 2 L 450 ml = 3 L 550 ml
Gopal used 3 litres 550 millilitres of paint for painting his house.

6.

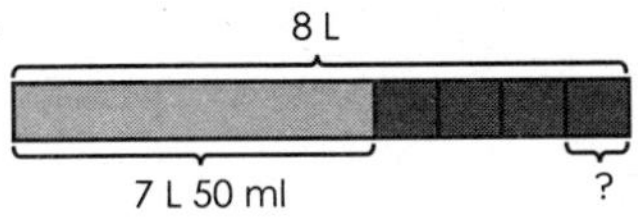

8 L − 7 L 50 ml = 950 ml
950 millilitres of water are needed to fill up the tank completely.
950 ml ÷ 5 = 190 ml
The capacity of each cup is 190 millilitres.

7.

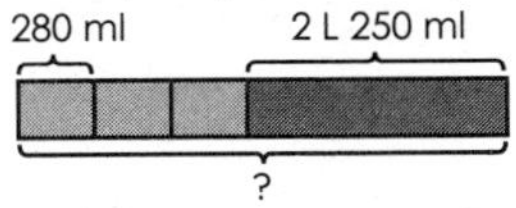

280 ml × 3 = 840 ml
Max and his friends drank a total of 840 millilitres of juice.
2 L 250 ml + 840 ml = 3 L 90 ml
There were 3 litres 90 millilitres of juice in the jug at first.

8.

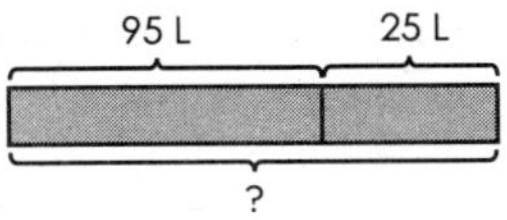

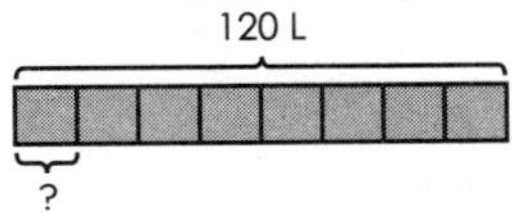

95 L + 25 L = 120 L
120 litres of water were poured into the fish tanks.

120 L ÷ 8 = 15 L
Each fish tank contains 15 litres of water.

Chapter 11

Exercise 1

1. a) 2; **b)** 7; **c)** 11 **2. a)** 8; **b)** 9; **c)** 10 **3. a)** 1; **b)** 3; **c)** 8 **4. a)** 5; **b)** 11; **c)** 7 **5.** Circle: **a)** $\frac{3}{5}$; **b)** $\frac{6}{8}$; **c)** $\frac{5}{6}$; **d)** $\frac{7}{9}$; **e)** $\frac{4}{6}$; **f)** $\frac{6}{7}$

6. Circle: **a)** $\frac{1}{10}$; **b)** $\frac{1}{4}$; **c)** $\frac{4}{7}$; **d)** $\frac{5}{11}$; **e)** $\frac{3}{9}$; **f)** $\frac{2}{10}$ **7.** Circle: **a)** $\frac{3}{7}$; **b)** $\frac{1}{2}$; **c)** $\frac{4}{9}$ **8.** Circle: **a)** $\frac{5}{6}$; **b)** $\frac{4}{5}$; **c)** $\frac{7}{10}$ **9.** $\frac{4}{9}, \frac{1}{2}, \frac{7}{9}$

Exercise 2

1. a) 2; **b)** 3; **c)** 4; **d)** 5 **2. a)** 8; **b)** 12 **3. a)** 12; **b)** 8

4. Match: $\frac{5}{6}$ — $\frac{10}{12}$, $\frac{2}{3}$ — $\frac{6}{9}$, $\frac{5}{10}$ — $\frac{1}{2}$, $\frac{6}{10}$ — $\frac{3}{5}$

Exercise 3

1. a) 6, 12; **b)** 3, 6 **2. a)** $\frac{8}{10}$; **b)** $\frac{8}{12}$ **3.** Circle: $\frac{1}{2}$ — $\frac{2}{4}$, $\frac{4}{5}$ — $\frac{8}{10}$, $\frac{2}{6}$ — $\frac{1}{3}$, $\frac{2}{3}$ — $\frac{4}{6}$, $\frac{1}{4}$ — $\frac{2}{8}$, $\frac{2}{12}$ — $\frac{1}{6}$, $\frac{5}{6}$ — $\frac{10}{12}$, $\frac{3}{5}$ — $\frac{6}{10}$

Exercise 4

1. a) $\frac{2}{4}$; **b)** $\frac{2}{6}$; **c)** $\frac{7}{8}$; **d)** $\frac{1}{2}$; **e)** $\frac{2}{3}$; **f)** $\frac{2}{4}$; **g)** $\frac{2}{3}$ **2. a)** 2; **b)** 3; **c)** 4; **d)** 5

Exercise 5

1. a) $\frac{2}{3}$; **b)** $\frac{3}{4}$ **2. a)** $\frac{1}{2}$; **b)** $\frac{2}{3}$; **c)** $\frac{1}{3}$ **3. a)** $\frac{8}{10}$; **b)** $\frac{2}{5}$; **c)** $\frac{6}{6}, \frac{4}{4}$; **d)** $\frac{3}{4}$; **e)** $\frac{2}{12}$; **f)** $\frac{3}{4}$; **g)** $\frac{5}{10}, \frac{6}{12}$ **4.** Match: **b)** $\frac{4}{12}$ — $\frac{1}{3}$; **c)** $\frac{2}{10}$ — $\frac{1}{5}$; **d)** $\frac{3}{12}$ — $\frac{1}{4}$; **e)** $\frac{4}{8}$ — $\frac{1}{2}$; **f)** $\frac{8}{10}$ — $\frac{4}{5}$; **g)** $\frac{6}{8}$ — $\frac{3}{4}$; **h)** $\frac{10}{12}$ — $\frac{5}{6}$; **i)** $\frac{2}{12}$ — $\frac{1}{6}$; **j)** $\frac{4}{10}$ — $\frac{2}{5}$,
DIVING MASK

Exercise 6

1. Circle: **a)** $\frac{7}{8}$; **b)** $\frac{4}{5}$; **c)** $\frac{2}{3}$; **d)** $\frac{2}{3}$; **e)** $\frac{3}{4}$; **f)** $\frac{11}{12}$

2. Circle: **a)** $\frac{3}{5}$; **b)** $\frac{3}{4}$; **c)** $\frac{5}{12}$; **d)** $\frac{5}{12}$; **e)** $\frac{1}{4}$; **f)** $\frac{3}{4}$

Exercise 7

1. a) $\frac{3}{5}$; **b)** $\frac{7}{8}$; **c)** $\frac{5}{6}$; **d)** $\frac{7}{10}$; **e)** $\frac{3}{4}$; **f)** $\frac{5}{7}$ **2.** 1, $\frac{1}{2}, \frac{2}{3}, \frac{3}{5}, \frac{5}{6}, \frac{5}{7}, \frac{3}{4}, \frac{7}{9}, \frac{9}{10}$, 8

Exercise 8

1. a) $\frac{1}{6} + \frac{4}{6} = \frac{5}{6}$; **b)** $\frac{2}{9} + \frac{6}{9} = \frac{8}{9}$; **c)** $\frac{1}{9} + \frac{3}{9} = \frac{4}{9}$; **d)** $\frac{2}{10} + \frac{1}{10} = \frac{3}{10}$; **e)** $\frac{3}{10} + \frac{2}{10} = \frac{5}{10} = \frac{1}{2}$; **f)** $\frac{1}{8} + \frac{6}{8} = \frac{7}{8}$; **g)** $\frac{3}{8} + \frac{2}{8} = \frac{5}{8}$; **h)** $\frac{1}{12} + \frac{8}{12} = \frac{9}{12} = \frac{3}{4}$; **i)** $\frac{3}{12} + \frac{1}{12} = \frac{4}{12} = \frac{1}{3}$

Exercise 9

1. a) $\frac{3}{5}$; **b)** $\frac{1}{6}$; **c)** $\frac{3}{8}$; **d)** $\frac{3}{10}$; **e)** $\frac{1}{4}$; **f)** $\frac{3}{5}$ **2.** $\frac{1}{3}, \frac{2}{5}, \frac{2}{3}, \frac{5}{8}, \frac{1}{4}, \frac{3}{4}, \frac{3}{5}, \frac{3}{10}, \frac{1}{2}$, 14

Exercise 10

1. 3, 2, $\frac{1}{3}$, $\frac{6}{8} - \frac{5}{8} = \frac{1}{8}$, $\frac{6}{9} - \frac{2}{9} = \frac{4}{9}$, $\frac{9}{12} - \frac{1}{12} = \frac{8}{12} = \frac{2}{3}$, $\frac{4}{10} - \frac{1}{10} = \frac{3}{10}$, $\frac{10}{12} - \frac{5}{12} = \frac{5}{12}$, $\frac{8}{10} - \frac{3}{10} = \frac{5}{10} = \frac{1}{2}$, $\frac{6}{12} - \frac{5}{12} = \frac{1}{12}$, $\frac{7}{12} - \frac{4}{12} = \frac{3}{12} = \frac{1}{4}$,
QUADRILATERAL

Exercise 11

1.

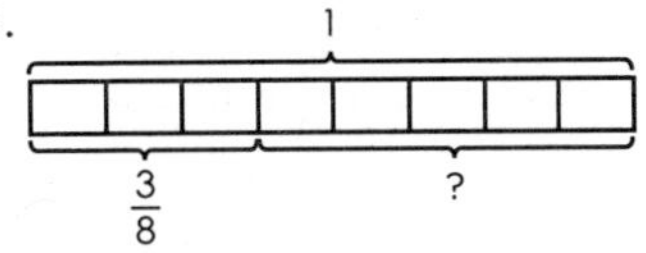

$1 - \frac{3}{8} = \frac{8}{8} - \frac{3}{8} = \frac{5}{8}$ piece of the cloth

2.

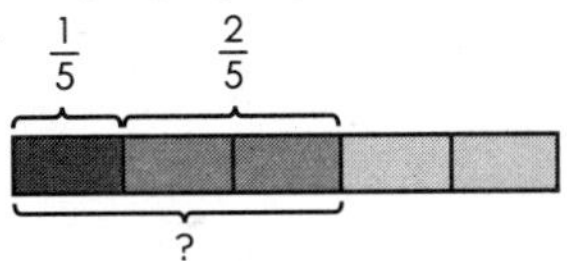

$\frac{1}{5} + \frac{2}{5} = \frac{3}{5}$ of the money

3.

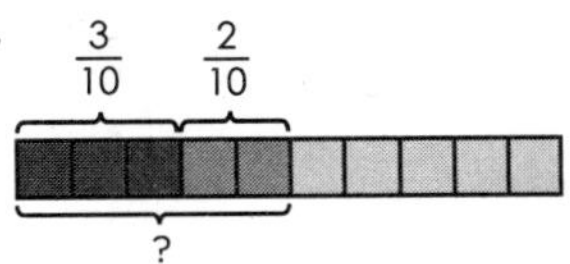

$\frac{1}{5} = \frac{2}{10}$

$\frac{3}{10} + \frac{2}{10} = \frac{5}{10} = \frac{1}{2}$ litre of juice

4.

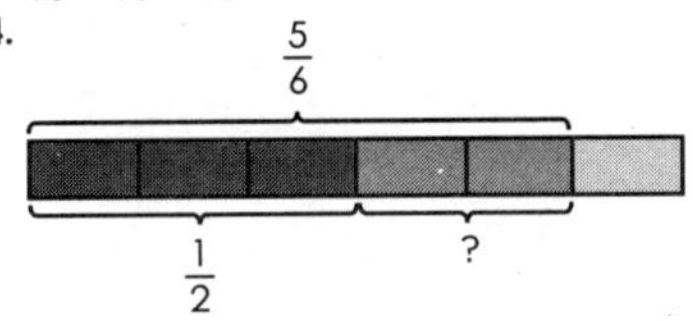

$\frac{1}{2} = \frac{3}{6}$

$\frac{5}{6} - \frac{3}{6} = \frac{2}{6} = \frac{1}{3}$ metre of string left

5.

Akbar

Rita

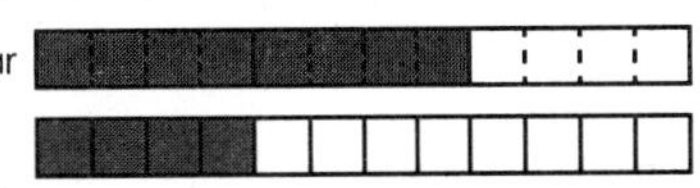

$\frac{2}{3} = \frac{8}{12}$

Akbar used $\frac{8}{12}$ of the roll of ribbon.

Rita used $\frac{4}{12}$ of the roll of ribbon.

$\frac{8}{12} > \frac{4}{12}$

Akbar used more ribbon.

6.

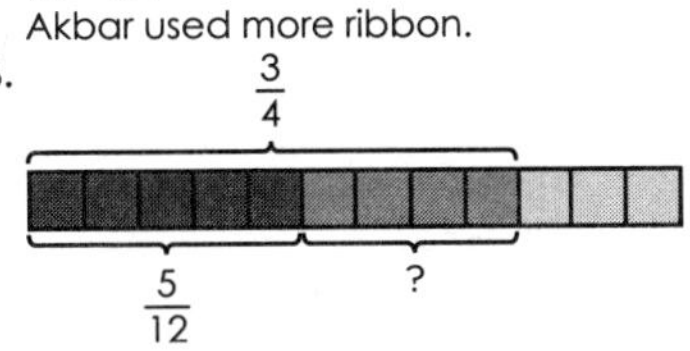

$\frac{3}{4} = \frac{9}{12}$

$\frac{9}{12} - \frac{5}{12} = \frac{4}{12} = \frac{1}{3}$ metre long

Chapter 12

Exercise 1

2. 12:00, noon/ midnight; 4:42, 42 minutes past 4/ 18 minutes to 5; 9:10, 10 minutes past 9; 2:45, 45 minutes past 2/ 15 minutes to 3

Exercise 2

1. a) 5:35, 30, 6:05; **b)** 6:10, 2, 8:10; **c)** 7:25, 3, 10:25 **2. a)** 5:15, 1, 15, 6:30; **b)** 7:40, 8, 00, 3:40; **c)** 2:20, 3, 50, 6:10; **d)** 8:50, 4, 25, 1:15

 ISBN 978-93-5103-030-0

Exercise 3

1. Match: 1 h 30 min—90 min, 2 h—120 min, 2 h 15 min—135 min, 3 h 30 min—210 min **2. a)** 105; **b)** 125, **c)** 1, 25; **d)** 2, 30 **3. a)** 65; **b)** 90; **c)** 145; **d)** 190 **4. a)** 1, 15; **b)** 1, 40; **c)** 2, 20; **d)** 3, 45 **5. a)** Dinesh; **b)** Andy

Exercise 4

1. a) 1, 55; **b)** 2, 25; **c)** 3, 20; **d)** 3, 10 **2. a)** 3, 50; **b)** 2, 50; **c)** 4, 10; **d)** 4, 15; **e)** 5, 10; **f)** 6, 10 **3. a)** 1, 35; **b)** 2, 25; **c)** 1, 15; **d)** 2, 55 **4. a)** 1, 20; **b)** 1, 5; **c)** 1, 15; **d)** 1, 30; **e)** 1, 45; **f)** 2, 55

Exercise 5

1. 1 hour after 7 : 30 p.m. is 8 : 30 p.m.
45 minutes after 8 : 30 p.m. is 9 : 15 p.m.
The movie ended at 9 : 15 p.m.

2. 20 min + 1 h 50 min = 2 h 10 min
Mr. Kumar took 2 hours 10 minutes to catch the first fish.

3. 25 minutes before 7 : 35 p.m. is 7 : 10 p.m.
Jack reached the theatre at 7 : 10 p.m.

4. 20 min + 1 h = 1 h 20 min
Mrs. Roy waited for 1 hour 20 minutes at the airport.

5. 25 minutes after 7 : 35 a.m. is 8 : 00 a.m.
30 minutes after 8 : 00 a.m. is 8 : 30 a.m.
So, 55 minutes after 7 : 35 a.m. is 8 : 30 a.m.
Sam arrived at the museum at 8 : 30 a.m.

6.

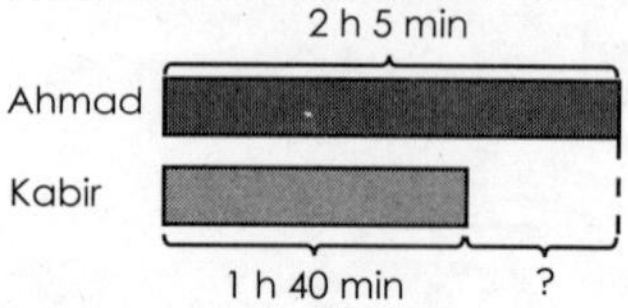

2 h 5 min – 1 h 40 min = 25 min longer

Exercise 6

1. Match: 1 year 6 months—18 months, 2 years—24 months, 1 year 8 months—20 months, 2 years 6 months—30 months, 3 years—36 months, 2 years 2 months—26 months **2. a)** 15; **b)** 29; **c)** 35; **d)** 46 **3. a)** 1, 3; **b)** 2, 1; **c)** 2, 8; **d)** 3, 4

Exercise 7

1. Match: 1 week 3 days—10 days, 2 weeks—14 days, 1 week 6 days—13 days, 2 weeks 2 days—16 days, 2 weeks 6 days—20 days, 3 weeks 1 day—22 days
2. a) 12; **b)** 18; **c)** 24; **d)** 30
3. a) 2, 0; **b)** 3, 4; **c)** 4, 4; **d)** 7, 2

Exercise 8

1. 25 min + 1 h 20 min = 1 h 45 min
Seema spends 1 hour 45 minutes in Mathematics class each day.
1 h 45 min × 2 = 105 min × 2 = 210 min = 3 h 30 min
Seema spends 3 hours 30 minutes in Mathematics class in a week.

2. 1 h 20 min + 4 h 45 min = 6 h 5 min
Rita completed her homework 6 hours 5 minutes after Rob completed his homework.
6 hours after 2 : 30 p.m. is 8 : 30 p.m.
5 minutes after 8 : 30 p.m. is 8 : 35 p.m.
Rita completed her homework at 8 : 35 p.m.

3. 2 hours 5 minutes before 4 : 05 p.m. is 2 : 00 p.m.
Roy reached Karnal at 2 : 00 p.m.
3 hours 15 minutes before 2 : 00 p.m. is 10 : 45 a.m.
So, Roy started driving from Delhi at 10 : 45 a.m.

4. 6 hours after 8 : 20 a.m. is 2 : 20 p.m.
50 minutes after 2 : 20 p.m. is 3 : 10 p.m.
Mohan reached Singapore at 3 : 10 p.m.
1 hour before 5 : 05 p.m. is 4 : 05 p.m.
3 : 10 p.m. (+ 50 min) = 4 : 00 p.m. (+ 5 min) = 4 : 05 p.m.
The stopover was 55 minutes long.

5. 11 years 6 months + 5 years 8 months = 16 years 14 months = 17 years 2 months
Nitin will be 17 years 2 months old.

6.

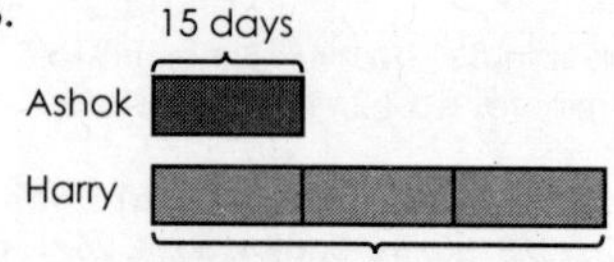

15 days × 3 = 45 days = 42 days + 3 days = 6 weeks 3 days

Chapter 13

Exercise 1

1. a) Point A; **b)** Line BC or CB; **c)** Line segment DE or ED; **d)** Ray FG **2.** Tick: a, d

Exercise 2

1. a) a; **b)** c; **c)** f; **d)** j

Exercise 4

1. B: 5, 5; C: 3, 3; D: 4, 4; E: 6, 6; F: 5, 5

Exercise 5

1. a) acute angle; **b)** right angle; **c)** obtuse angle; **d)** obtuse angle; **e)** right angle

Exercise 6

1. A: 4, 1, 2, 1; B: 4, 1, 2, 1; C: 4 ,0, 4, 0; D: 4, 1, 2, 1; E: 4, 2, 1, 1; F: 5, 2, 3, 0; G: 3, 0, 1, 2; H: 4, 0, 4, 0; I: 4, 1, 2, 1

Chapter 14

Exercise 1

1. b, c, e, f are not perpendicular
a, d are perpendicular
2. a) XZ; **b)** RQ; **c)** HK ⊥ KJ, IJ ⊥ JK; **d)** AB ⊥ BC, BC ⊥ CD, AE ⊥ ED

Exercise 3

1. c, d, f are not parallel
a, b, e are parallel
2. a) QR; **b)** KN || LM, KL || NM; **c)** CD; **d)** XY || WZ, XW || YZ

Chapter 15

Exercise 2

2. a) 8; **b)** 5; **c)** 7; **d)** 11; **e)** 9; **f)** 16

Exercise 3

2. a) 6, 5, 6, 7; **b)** D; **c)** B; **d)** A, C

Exercise 4

1. a) 11, 11, 10, 13; **b)** A, B; **c)** D; **d)** C

Exercise 5

1. a) 9 cm^2; **b)** 7 cm^2; **c)** 5 cm^2; **d)** 10 cm^2; **e)** 8 cm^2; **f)** 9 cm^2

Exercise 6

1. 10, 12, 11, 9, 9, 10
2. a) square metres; **b)** square centimetres; **c)** square centimetres

Exercise 7

1. a) 8 m^2; **b)** 12 m^2; **c)** 5 m^2; **d)** 6 m^2; **e)** 9 m^2; **f)** 8 m^2

 ISBN 978-93-5103-030-0